SOURCES OF UNOFFICIAL UK STATISTICS

Sources of Unofficial UK Statistics

Compiled by

David Mort and Leona Siddall

Warwick Statistics Service
University of Warwick Library

Gower

Published by
Gower Publishing Company Limited,
Gower House,
Croft Road,
Aldershot,
Hants GU11 3HR,
England

Gower Publishing Company,
Old Post Road,
Brookfield,
Vermont 05036,
U.S.A.

British Library Cataloguing in Publication Data
Mort, D.
   Sources of unofficial UK statistics.
   1. Great Britain—Statistical services
   I. Title   II. Siddall, Leona
   314.1'07   HA37.G72

   ISBN 0-566-02620-1

Printed and bound in Great Britain by
Robert Hartnoll (1985) Ltd., Bodmin, Cornwall

Contents

Acknowledgements

The initial research on UK non-official statistics was funded by the British Library Research and Development Department.

We gratefully acknowledge the assistance of all the organisations and individuals who have provided information for the guide and those involved in business information who have offered their advice and comments.

Special thanks go to Heather Cooke and Steve Barber of the University of Warwick Library for their help in the preparation of the guide.

David Mort
Leona Siddall

Warwick Statistics Service is a commercial information service providing statistics and business information to companies and other organisations. The service is based on a comprehensive international collection of statistical and market research data held in the University of Warwick Library, Coventry, UK.

Introduction

Statistical sources play a vital role in the provision of information for business, industry and economic research. Economic analysis, corporate planning, financial planning, forecasting, market research and marketing are just some of the activities where statistics are important. In the United Kingdom, Central Government are the main suppliers of statistical information and these statistics are usually referred to as 'official statistics'. However, there are many other organisations involved in compiling and disseminating statistical information. They include trade associations, professional bodies, local authorities and development corporations, stockbrokers, banks, chambers of commerce, economic research and forecasting organisations, consultants, academic institutions, limited companies, trade unions, employers' federations and commercial publishers. Many of them provide original, more detailed or simply different information which is not available elsewhere, but tracking down these sources can be a costly and time-consuming exercise.

This publication is the first detailed guide to non-official statistics in the United Kingdom. It derives from work undertaken at Warwick Statistics Service between 1983 and 1985 which was initially supported financially by the British Library Research and Development Department. This first edition of the guide gives details of more than 1000 individual titles and services.

Sources Included in the Guide

Over 4000 potential publishing bodies were contacted, of which 635 were identified as publishers of 1059 statistical titles and services.

The basic requirement for inclusion in the guide is that the statistics must be of interest to business and industry. Only statistics produced on a regular basis are included and for a source to be considered as regular it must be produced at least once every six years. One-off surveys or market reports do not qualify.

Only sources issued in and concerning the United Kingdom are included. Material with an international coverage has generally been excluded.

Sources are included even if they have a restricted circulation. In some cases, however, the publishers have asked to be excluded from the guide and we have agreed to their request.

As well as the traditional time series statistics, forecasts, trend surveys and opinion polls are included but data dealing with only one corporate body, such as company annual reports, is excluded.

Most of the items included are clearly statistical publications but there are a number of sources which are essentially non-statistical publications but which contain statistics on a regular basis. Some annual reports, trade journals and periodicals, press releases, directories and yearbooks fall into this category and many of these are included in the guide because of their value as statistical sources.

Sources which cover both the United Kingdom as a whole and particular local areas, such as local authority areas or economic planning regions, are included. However, many local authorities were concerned that they might not be able to cope with the demand generated by the inclusion of their publications in this guide and reluctantly asked us to leave their publications out. Once again, we agreed to this request when made.

Finally, there is no discrimination as to the physical format of the sources included. These range from those in book form to those which consist of only one or two sheets of papers, such as press releases, through to machine-readable data.

The Format of the Guide

Part I of the guide comprises 1059 entries arranged alphabetically by publishing organisation and numbered consecutively. Each entry contains the following information, where available:

Name of the publishing body
Address
Telephone and Telex numbers
Title of source and frequency; date of first issue
General description of contents
Number of tables per issue and source of data (ie own research, other non-official source, central Government)
Proportion of text
Currency of data
Availability of source
Cost per annum
ISSN/ISBN
Further information contact
Comments
Date of initial response to guide questionnaire

The range of information noted above represents the 'ideal' entry. In various instances, however, some of the items are not applicable or it has been impossible to obtain every item. The entries have been based on responses from the publishing bodies themselves and most entries vary slightly from the 'ideal'.

Part II is a general subject index to the sources detailed in Part I. Under each subject entry will be found the relevant source number or numbers.

Part I
The Statistics

1

Originator	ABBEY NATIONAL BUILDING SOCIETY
Title	HOMES : PEOPLE, PLACES, PRICES, quarterly. 1977-
Coverage	Trends in housing market. House prices by age and type of property and region. Also advances and incomes.
Contents & Origin of Statistics	Tables per issue: 18. Own research 90%, Government statistics 10%. Supporting text 50%
Response	1984
Availability	General
Cost	Free
Address	Abbey House, Baker St, London NW1 6XL
Telephone	01 486 5555 ; Telex: 296159
Contact	Nick Cook, Editor

2

Originator	ABERDEEN AND DISTRICT MILK MARKETING BOARD
Title	MILK NEWS, monthly
Coverage	News magazine containing statistics on producers' prices, production and utilisation.
Contents & Origin of Statistics	Tables per issue: 7. Own research 100%. Supporting text 80%
Comments	Publishes 'Key Milk Figures' annually with the other Milk Marketing Boards in Scotland.
Response	1983
Availability	General
Cost	Free
Address	P.O. Box 117, Twin Spires, Bucksburn, Aberdeen AB9 8AH
Telephone	0224 696371
Contact	Above address

3

Originator	ABERDEEN PETROLEUM REPORT
Title	LATEST UK NORTH SEA OIL PRODUCTION, monthly in a weekly journal. 1982-
Coverage	Production figures in barrels per day by North Sea fields.
Contents & Origin of Statistics	Tables per issue: 1. Non official source 100%
Currency	2 weeks

Response	1984
Availability	General
Cost	£225 or £5 for a single issue
ISSN	0263 5054
Address	Aberdeen Petroleum Publishing Ltd, 37 Huntly St, Aberdeen AB1 1TH
Telephone	0224 644725; Telex: 73315
Contact	Ted Strachan, Editor/Publisher

4

Originator	ACCOUNTANCY PERSONNEL LTD
Title	SURVEY OF SALARIES IN ACCOUNTANCY, bi-annual
Coverage	3 sections covering accountancy salaries, merchant and international banking salaries and a general commentary. Information based on surveys carried out in 12 regional centres in England and Wales.
Contents & Origin of Statistics	Tables per issue: 20-25. Own research 100%
Response	1984
Availability	General
Cost	£30
Address	63-65 Moorgate, London EC2R 6BH
Telephone	01 588 2567
Contact	Above address

5

Originator	ADMAP
Title	ADSTATS, approximately 3 times a year in a monthly journal
Coverage	Data on total advertising expenditure, expenditure in selected product categories and by media and type. Most data compiled from Advertising Association surveys.
Contents & Origin of Statistics	Tables per issue: Varies. Non official source 100%
Comments	Also publish a monthly 'Media Race' showing advertising expenditure for the top 30 newspapers and magazines.
Currency	2-3 months
Response	1984
Availability	General
Cost	£75
ISSN	0001 8295
Address	ADMAP Publications Ltd, 44 Earlham St, London WC2H 9LA

Telephone	01 379 6576; Telex: 265906
Contact	Harry Henry, Consultant Editor

6

Originator	ADVERTISING ASSOCIATION
Title	ADVERTISING STATISTICS YEARBOOK, annual
Coverage	General data on advertising industry trends with current figures and long term trend figures.
Contents & Origin of Statistics	Tables per issue: Varies
Currency	Varies
Response	1984
Availability	General
Cost	£15
Address	Abford House, 15 Wilton Rd, London SW1V 1NJ
Telephone	01 828 2771
Contact	Mike Waterson

7

Originator	ADVERTISING ASSOCIATION
Title	FOOD AND DRINK FORECAST, quarterly
Coverage	Sales and expenditure trends and forecasts in 50 food and drink markets.
Contents & Origin of Statistics	Tables per issue: Own research + other non official source 100%
Comments	Previously published by Oyez International Business Communications Ltd.
Availability	General
Cost	£460
Address	Abford House, 15 Wilton Rd, London SW1V 1NJ
Telephone	01 828 2771
Contact	Above address

8

Originator	ADVERTISING ASSOCIATION
Title	FORECAST OF ADVERTISING EXPENDITURE, quarterly
Coverage	Advertising trends over the last 5 years with forecasts for 2 years ahead quarter by quarter.
Response	1984

Availability	General
Cost	£295
Address	Abford House, 15 Wilton Rd, London SW1V 1NJ
Telephone	01 828 2771
Contact	Mike Waterson

9

Originator	ADVERTISING ASSOCIATION
Title	MARKETING POCKET BOOK, annual
Coverage	General compilation of basic marketing data.
Contents & Origin of Statistics	Tables per issue: Varies
Currency	Varies
Response	1984
Availability	General
Cost	£7.50
ISBN	0 902878 36 0
Address	Abford House, 15 Wilton Rd, London SW1V 1NJ
Telephone	01 828 2771
Contact	Mike Waterson

10

Originator	ADVERTISING ASSOCIATION
Title	QUARTERLY REVIEW OF ADVERTISING STATISTICS, quarterly
Coverage	Quarterly data on national advertising and regional newspaper advertising.
Response	1984
Availability	General
Cost	£45
Address	Abford House, 15 Wilton Rd, London SW1V 1NJ
Telephone	01 828 2771
Contact	Mike Waterson

11

Originator	ADVERTISING STANDARDS AUTHORITY LTD
Title	ANNUAL REPORT, annual
Coverage	Gives summary of complaints received by media and type. Number of publications monitored.

Contents & Origin of Statistics	Tables per issue: 7. Own research 100%. Supporting text 90%

Response	1984
Availability	General
Cost	£2.25
Address	Brook House, 2-16 Torrington Place, London, WC1E 7HN
Telephone	01 580 5555; Telex: 27950
Contact	Diana Bird, Press Office

12

Originator	AGB INDEX LTD

Title	INDEX SERVICE, monthly and quarterly
Coverage	A marketing service producing comprehensive reports on all aspects of personal finances and discretionary spending. Monthly data on consumer spending patterns, categories of spending, methods of payment, where the money was spent. Quarterly data on holdings of credit savings, insurance etc. Panel of 10,000 individuals (over 16). Main ITV regions reported separately.

Contents & Origin of Statistics	Tables per issue: Own research 100%

Comments	Can also offer supplementary tailor-made analyses.
Response	1983
Availability	General
Address	Northbridge Rd, Berkhamsted, Herts HP4 1EH
Telephone	04427 3311
Contact	John English, Director

13

Originator	AGRICULTURAL ENGINEERS ASSOCIATION

Title	SELECTED ECONOMIC INDICATORS, fortnightly. 1980-
Coverage	General figures on the agricultural economy.

Contents & Origin of Statistics	Tables per issue: 14pgs. Own research 20%, Other non official source 40%, Government statistics 40%. Supporting text 33%

Response	1984
Availability	Members
Cost	Free
Address	6 Buckingham Gate, London 5W1E 6JU
Telephone	01 828 7973; Telex: 918810
Contact	The Economist

14

Originator	AGRICULTURAL ENGINEERS ASSOCIATION
Title	TRADE ANALYSIS, quarterly. 1983-
Coverage	As indicated by title.
Contents & Origin of Statistics	Tables per issue: 60 pgs. Government statistics 100%.
Currency	5-6 weeks
Response	1984
Availability	Members
Cost	Free
Address	6 Buckingham Gate, London SW1E 6JU
Telephone	01 828 7973; Telex: 918810
Contact	Economist

15

Originator	AGRICULTURAL SUPPLY INDUSTRY
Title	ANALYSIS OF FEED INGREDIENTS, bi-annual in weekly journal. 1977-
Coverage	Analysis of wage of main raw material ingredients in manufactured feeds for cattle, pigs and poultry.
Contents & Origin of Statistics	Tables per issue: 1. Government statistics 100%
Comments	Other regular statistics published - see other entries
Currency	6 months
Response	1984
Availability	General
Cost	£25 or 45p for a single issue
ISSN	0140 4822
Address	Veratbrite Ltd, 53 Beak St, London W1R 3LF
Telephone	01 437 7041; Telex: 28439
Contact	Diane Montague, Editor

16

Originator	AGRICULTURAL SUPPLY INDUSTRY
Title	HARVEST REVIEW, annual supplement in a weekly journal
Coverage	Yield details for varieties of wheat, barley, oilseed rape and details of tonnages sold.

Contents & Origin of Statistics	Tables per issue: 8. Own research + other non official source 85%, Government statistics 15%. Supporting text 20%

Comments	Other regular statistics published - see other entries
Currency	2 months
Response	1984
Availability	General
Cost	£25 or 45p for a single issue
ISSN	0140 4822
Address	Veratbrite Ltd, 53 Beak St, London W1R 3LF
Telephone	01 437 7041; Telex: 28439
Contact	Diane Montague, Editor

17

Originator	AGRICULTURAL SUPPLY INDUSTRY

Title	THIS WEEK'S MARKETS, weekly in a weekly journal. 1971-
Coverage	Prices of materials used for animal feeds.

Contents & Origin of Statistics	Tables per issue: 4. Own research + other non official source 100%

Comments	Other regular statistics published - see other entries
Currency	2 days
Response	1984
Availability	General
Cost	£25 or 45p for a single issue
ISSN	0140 4822
Address	Veratbrite Ltd, 53 Beak St, London W1R 3LF
Telephone	01 437 7041; Telex: 28439
Contact	Diane Montague, Editor

18

Originator	ALUMINIUM FEDERATION LTD

Title	ALUMINIUM STATISTICS PRESS RELEASE, monthly
Coverage	Production, imports and despatches of primary aluminium, secondary aluminium, and wrought and cast products.

Contents & Origin of Statistics	Tables per issue: 1. Own research 100%.

Comments	More detailed statistics available only to members who complete returns.
Currency	4-6 weeks
Response	1984
Availability	General
Cost	Free

Address	Broadway House, Calthorpe Rd, Five Ways, Birmingham B15 1TN.
Telephone	021 455 0311
Contact	Miss E.O. Maltby

19

Originator	AMALGAMATED UNION OF ENGINEERING WORKERS (AUEW/TASS)
Title	ENGINEERING STAFF SALARY CENSUS, annual. 1923-
Coverage	Salary information on six job categories - draughtsmen, tracers, technical clerks, supervisors of production workers, technologists and clerical staff. Salaries are broken down by union branches, age, and salary quartiles. Also contains information on trainees and apprentices and staff in Eire. Sample for the 1984 census based on 40,000 individuals.
Contents & Origin of Statistics	Tables per issue: 74. Own research 100%. Supporting text 5%
Currency	3-4 months
Response	1984
Availability	General
Cost	£50 to non-members
Address	Onslow Hall, Little Green, Richmond, Surrey
Telephone	01 948 2271
Contact	Research Department

20

Originator	ANGLIA BUILDING SOCIETY
Title	HOUSING MARKET, bi-annual
Coverage	Includes house price percentage increases for the year and a house price index for new and re-sold houses for a 6 year period. Data is provided on a regional basis.
Contents & Origin of Statistics	Tables per issue: 3. Own research 100%. Supporting text 90%
Currency	1 month
Response	1983
Availability	General
Cost	Free
Address	Moulton Park, Northampton NN3 1NL
Telephone	0604 495353
Contact	Mrs. E. Cambio, Marketing Department

21

Originator	ARCHITECTS JOURNAL
Title	COST FORECAST, quarterly in a weekly journal. 1976-
Coverage	Trends and short term forecasts for building and tender prices.
Contents & **Origin of** **Statistics**	Tables per issue: 4. Unstated 100%
Currency	1 month
Response	1984
Availability	General
Cost	£36 or 8Op for a single copy
ISSN	0003 8466
Address	The Architectural Press, 9 Queen Anne's Gate, London SW1H 9B7
Telephone	01 222 4333; Telex: 895 3505
Contact	Barrie Evans, Technical Editor

22

Originator	ARTS COUNCIL OF GREAT BRITAIN
Title	ARTS FACTS AND FIGURES, occasional
Coverage	A broad picture of the arts industry including data on audiences, arts spending, employment in the arts, tourism, participation and public expenditure.
Contents & **Origin of** **Statistics**	Tables per issue: 6. Own research + other non official source + government statistics 100%.
Comments	Users requiring more detailed information may discover the sources of the data from the above address
Currency	Varies
Response	1984
Availability	General
Cost	Free
Address	Information Department, 105 Piccadilly, London W1V 0AU
Telephone	01 629 9495
Contact	Above address

23

Originator	ASKHAM BRYAN COLLEGE OF AGRICULTURE AND HORTICULTURE
Title	FARMING IN YORKSHIRE, annual
Coverage	Summary of statistics on the different farming systems in Yorkshire. Financial and physical data on hill farming, sheep farming and arable crop trends.

Contents & Origin of Statistics	Tables per issue: 45. Own research 90%, Other non official source 5%, Government statistics 5%. Supporting text 20%
Comments	Data collected for the Ministry of Agriculture.
Currency	9 months
Response	1984
Availability	General
Cost	£2.50
ISSN	0309 6114
Address	Askham Bryan, York, YO2 3PR
Telephone	0904 702121
Contact	P.G. Green, Head of Management Department

24

Originator	ASSOCIATION OF BRITISH ROOFING FELT MANUFAC-TURERS LTD
Title	QUARTERLY SALES AND EXPORTS, quarterly
Coverage	Sales and export sales of roofing felts and damp-proof courses by member companies.
Response	1984
Availability	Members
Cost	Free
Address	9 Cannon St, London EC4N 5AB
Telephone	01 248 4444
Contact	A.T. Robertson, Secretary

25

Originator	ASSOCIATION OF DISTRICT COUNCILS
Title	OPERATING COSTS OF BUS UNDERTAKINGS, annual. 1976-
Coverage	Municipal passenger transport operating statistics, both financial and traffic details. Based on a survey of members.
Contents & Origin of Statistics	Tables per issue: 26pgs. Own research 100%.
Comments	A short extract of the survey is available on request for 30p (in postage stamps).
Currency	9 months
Response	1984
Availability	District Council Bus Undertakings
Cost	Free
Address	9 Buckingham Gate, London SW1E 6LE
Telephone	01 828 7931
Contact	V.G. Christie, Transport

26

Originator	ASSOCIATION OF ELECTRICAL MACHINERY TRADES
Title	INDUSTRY SURVEY, annual. 1981-
Coverage	Turnover of industrial electrical apparatus repairs, and sales figures, for a limited number of UK companies.
Contents & Origin of Statistics	Tables per issue: 5. Own research 100%
Currency	8 months
Response	1984
Availability	Members contributing to survey
Cost	Free
Address	45 Sheen Lane, London SW14 8AB
Telephone	01 876 4415/6; Telex: 917198
Contact	A.B. Harman, Secretary

27

Originator	ASSOCIATION OF ENGINEERING DISTRIBUTORS
Title	TRADE STATISTICS SURVEY, annual
Coverage	Survey of member firms broken down into 3 categories according to turnover. Covers a 3 year period and gives figures for sales, profits, salaries, stock, transport and holidays. Approximately 63 firms are included.
Contents & Origin of Statistics	Tables per issue: 8pgs. Own research 100%.
Currency	6-12 months
Response	1984
Availability	Members
Cost	£25
Address	Gateway House, 50 High St, Birmingham B4 7SY
Telephone	021 643 6271
Contact	G.K. Edwards, Secretary

28

Originator	ASSOCIATION OF INDEPENDENT RADIO CONTRAC-TORS
Title	SURVEY OF THE RADIO AUDIENCE, 3 times a year. 1977-

Coverage	In 2 volumes, survey of independent local radio audiences conducted on a 'network' basis. Vol 1 has summary for every station, analysed by sex, age and social class, Vol 2 contains full results, showing rate card segment reach, half hour averages and reach and frequency analyses for standard packages.
Contents & Origin of Statistics	Tables per issue: Own research 100%
Comments	Gives information on sampling techniques used. Some radio stations issue data separately for their area from this.
Response	1984
Availability	General
Cost	£103.50 (Vol 2), Free (Vol 1)
Address	Regina House, 259-269 Old Marylebone Rd, London NW1 5RA
Telephone	01 262 6681; Telex: 24543
Contact	Richard Tillett, Marketing Executive

29

Originator	ASSOCIATION OF JUTE SPINNERS AND MANUFAC-TURERS
Title	ANNUAL REPORT, annual
Coverage	Contains a summary of statistics, including yarn and cloth production and trade index of retail prices and number of employees.
Contents & Origin of Statistics	Tables per issue: 3. Own research 50%, Government statistics 40%. Supporting text 40%
Currency	2 months
Response	1984
Availability	Members
Cost	Free
Address	Top Floor, Park Mill, 99 Douglas St, Dundee DD1 5AZ
Telephone	0382 25881
Contact	D.A. Borrie, Director

30

Originator	ASSOCIATION OF MANUFACTURERS OF DOMESTIC ELECTRICAL APPLIANCES (AMDEA)
Title	AMDEA STATISTICAL YEARBOOK, annual
Coverage	Similar data as given in the quarterly reviews (see separate entry) for the year, with 'at a glance' comparisons with the previous year. Also background information on prices, employment, household penetration of appliances etc.
Comments	For certain products AMDEA also provide a fast indicator service by telex.

Response	1984
Availability	General
Cost	£500 + VAT, including quarterly statistics (Free to AMDEA members)
Address	593 Hitchin Rd, Luton LU2 7UN
Telephone	0582 429741; Telex: 825363
Contact	L.T. Williams, Manager

31

Originator	ASSOCIATION OF MANUFACTURERS OF DOMESTIC ELECTRICAL APPLIANCES (AMDEA)
Title	UK DOMESTIC ELECTRICAL APPLIANCE STATISTICS, quarterly
Coverage	Deliveries by U.K. manufacturers, imports by country of origin and imports for various appliances including refrigerators, freezers, washing machines, dryers, cookers, vacuum cleaners, space heaters, electric blankets and medical and other heating pads.
Contents & Origin of Statistics	Tables per issue: 50. Own research 50%, Government statistics 50%.
Comments	For certain products AMDEA also provide a fast indicator service by telex.
Currency	2-5 months
Response	1984
Availability	General
Cost	£500 + VAT, including Statistical Yearbook (Free to AMDEA members)
Address	593 Hitchin Rd, Luton LU2 7UN
Telephone	0582 429741; Telex: 825363
Contact	L.T. Williams, Manager

32

Originator	ASSOCIATION OF MANUFACTURERS OF DOMESTIC ELECTRICAL APPLIANCES (AMDEA)
Title	UK MONTHLY SUMMARIES, monthly
Coverage	Home deliveries by UK manufacturers, export deliveries, total market availability and import penetration and estimated retail sales for 6 product groups - shelf goods, personal care and blankets, refrigeration and home laundry, cookers, floor care and space and water heating.
Comments	For certain products AMDEA also provide a fast indicator service by telex. Data contributors to the above can also receive 'monthly results' tables, often providing more detail than the monthly summaries.
Currency	1 month

Response	1984
Availability	Members and data contributors
Cost	Free to contributing members and £625 per group (maximum £1,250) to contributing non-members
Address	593 Hitchin Rd, Luton LU2 7UN
Telephone	0582 429741; Telex: 825363
Contact	L.T. Williams, Manager

33

Originator	ASSOCIATION OF SHELL BOILERMAKERS
Title	TITLE UNKNOWN, monthly
Coverage	Gives number, sizes, firing, evaporation, production and trade figures
Response	1983
Availability	Members
Cost	Free
Address	P.O. Box No. 498, 12-16 Booth St, Manchester M60 2ED
Telephone	061 236 9721

34

Originator	ASSOCIATION OF YORKSHIRE AND HUMBERSIDE CHAMBERS OF COMMERCE
Title	REGIONAL ECONOMIC SURVEY, quarterly
Coverage	General survey of member companies.
Contents & Origin of Statistics	Tables per issue: Own research 100%. Supporting text 40%
Comments	Issued in the form of a press release.
Response	1984
Availability	Members
Cost	£6.50
Address	2 St Albans Place, Wade Lane, Leeds LS2 8HZ
Telephone	0532 430491; Telex: 55293
Contact	Above address

35

Originator	ATTWOOD STATISTICS LTD
Title	FRESH FOOD MARKETS, monthly and quarterly
Coverage	Monthly report gives % of homes buying food, nationally and by TV areas, with volume and expenditure figures. Quarterly report gives above information plus name and type of retailer, volumes, age of housewife, % of homes with children etc. Panel of 4,OOO housewives used

Contents & **Origin of** **Statistics**	Tables per issue: Varies
Comments	Various other services are available on request
Response	1983
Availability	General
Cost	£10,000 for complete service, from £1,600 for 1 product field
Address	Northbridge Rd, Berkhamsted, Hertfordshire HP4 1EH
Telephone	04427 3311
Contact	Chris Willis

36

Originator	AUDIT BUREAU OF CIRCULATIONS LTD
Title	ABC CIRCULATION REVIEW, bi-annual. 1932-
Coverage	Audited certified average net sales, circulation and distribution data for over 2000 publications. Covers newspapers, magazines and journals.
Contents & **Origin of** **Statistics**	Tables per issue: 40pgs. Own research 100%.
Comments	The data is currently being computerised. British Library holds microfilm of complete results. Access is given to students by appointment.
Currency	3 months
Response	1984
Availability	Members
Cost	Free
Address	13 Wimpole St, London W1M 7AB
Telephone	01 631 1343; Telex: 252476
Contact	Ken Derbyshire, Director

37

Originator	AUTOMATIC VENDING ASSOCIATION OF GREAT BRITAIN
Title	NEWSLETTER, every 2 months
Coverage	Contains statistical information on the automatic vending market.
Response	1983
Availability	Members
Address	50 Eden St, Kingston upon Thames, Surrey KT1 1EE
Telephone	01 549 7311
Contact	W.E.D. Skinner, Director and Chief Executive

38

Originator	BAKER, G.G. AND ASSOCIATES
Title	UK MICROGRAPHIC MARKET, biennial
Coverage	Data on the document microfilming market covering equipment and including a user survey.
Comments	Abridged version of survey available for £20. Also produce 'The COM market in the UK and continent of Europe', biennially
Response	1983
Availability	General
Cost	£175
Address	54 Quarry St, Guildford, Surrey GU1 3UF
Telephone	04868 6653
Contact	Above address

39

Originator	BAKERS REVIEW
Title	COST OF MATERIALS INDEX, monthly in a monthly journal
Coverage	Price changes in bread and flour confectionery.
Contents & Origin of Statistics	Tables per issue: 1. Non official source 100%
Currency	1 month
Response	1984
Availability	General
Address	Turret-Wheatland Ltd, 886 High Rd, Finchley, London N12
Telephone	01 446 2411; Telex: 268207
Contact	C. Lake, Editor

40

Originator	BANK OF ENGLAND
Title	BANK OF ENGLAND QUARTERLY BULLETIN, quarterly
Coverage	Articles and news items plus a statistical annex giving detailed figures on banking, money stock, discount market, reserves, and exchange rates.
Contents & Origin of Statistics	Tables per issue: 20-25. Own research 80%, Government statistics 20%. Supporting text 70%
Comments	Also available on magnetic tape.
Currency	Varies
Response	1984
Availability	General
Cost	£27

ISSN	0005 5166
Address	Threadneedle St, London EC2R 8AH
Telephone	01 601 4030
Contact	Economics Division

41

Originator BAR ASSOCIATION FOR COMMERCE, FINANCE AND INDUSTRY

Title REMUNERATION SURVEY, every 2-3 years
Coverage Survey of members' salaries in all sectors of industry, divided into 5 legal categories. Analysis by age and job and information on fringe benefits.

Contents & Tables per issue: 7. Own research 100%
Origin of
Statistics

Response 1983
Availability General
Cost £25
Address 63 Great Cumberland Place, Bryanston Square, London W1H YLJ
Telephone 01 723 9556
Contact Above address

42

Originator BARCLAYS BANK LTD

Title BARCLAYS REVIEW, quarterly
Coverage Articles and section entitled 'Key Statistics', covering UK financial markets and economy. Also gives international data.

Contents & Tables per issue: c.13. Unstated 100%. Supporting text 50%
Origin of
Statistics

Response 1984
Availability General
Address 54 Lombard St, London EC3P 3AH
Telephone 01 283 8989
Contact Economics Department

43

Originator BARTON PUBLISHERS LTD

Title GRIFFITHS BUILDING PRICE BOOK, annual
Coverage Price guide for pricing medium to smaller contracts, i.e. new to approximately £150,000, alterations and repairs to £225,000.

Contents & Origin of Statistics	Tables per issue: 500. Own research + other non official source 100%
Comments	Edited by Geoffrey Smith and Partners, Chartered Quantity Surveyors
Response	1984
Availability	General
Cost	£25.95
ISSN	0142 713X
Address	Buckland Rd, Yeovil, Somerset BA21 5ET
Telephone	0935 76272
Contact	Above address

44

Originator	BEAMA LTD
Title	BEAMA CONTRACT PRICE ADJUSTMENT CLAUSE AND FORMULAE, monthly. 1970-
Coverage	Labour cost indices, producer price index numbers for electrical machinery nd mechanical plants.
Contents & Origin of Statistics	Tables per issue: Own research 100%
Response	1984
Availability	General
Cost	£70
Address	Leicester House, 8 Leicester St, London WC2H 7BN
Telephone	01 437 0678 ext 250/251; Telex: 263536
Contact	G.J. Morris

45

Originator	BEDFORDSHIRE COUNTY COUNCIL
Title	HOUSE SALES SURVEY, annual
Coverage	Each annual survey covers a particular characteristic of house buyers or sellers. Latest bulletins look at the origin of house buyers and the destinations of house sellers.
Contents & Origin of Statistics	Tables per issue: 12-15. Own research 100%. Supporting text 5%
Comments	Figures compiled by the Council from information supplied by local builders and estate agents.
Response	1984
Availability	General
Cost	Free
Address	County Hall, Cauldwell St, Bedford, Bedfordshire MK42 9AP

21   **46–47**

Telephone	0234 63222
Contact	S.A. Bacon, Assistant Planning Officer

46

Originator	BEDFORDSHIRE COUNTY COUNCIL
Title	POPULATION CHANGE 19--, annual. 1977-
Coverage	Estimates and projections for the county population up to 5 years ahead. Covers composition of the population, number and type of households, economically active numbers, births, deaths and migration.
Contents & Origin of Statistics	Tables per issue: 30. Supporting text 10%
Comments	An additional volume - 'Technical Supplement' explains how the projections were produced and describes the limitations of the data.
Currency	1 year
Response	1984
Availability	General
Cost	£1.50
Address	County Hall, Cauldwell St, Bedford, Bedfordshire MK42 9AP
Telephone	0234 63222
Contact	P.W. Vann, Principal Information Officer, Planning Department

47

Originator	BENN'S HARDWARE AND DIY PRICE LIST
Title	BENN'S HARDWARE AND DIY PRICE LIST, monthly. 1960-
Coverage	Change in market prices of over 1,700 hardware and DIY products.
Contents & Origin of Statistics	Tables per issue: 200 pgs. Own research 100%
Comments	Also a weekly price change supplement included in the 'Hardware Trade Journal'
Currency	Varies
Response	1984
Availability	General
Cost	£35
Address	Benn Publications Ltd, Sovereign Way, Tonbridge, Kent TN9 1RW
Telephone	0732 364422; Telex: 95132
Contact	Mrs. Barbara Shaw, Price List Controller

48

Originator	BERKSHIRE COUNTY COUNCIL
Title	FUTURE POPULATION OF ROYAL COUNTY OF BERK-SHIRE, annual. 1984-
Coverage	Projections of population down to parish level. Population of local government districts given by age and sex.
Contents & Origin of Statistics	Tables per issue: 25. Own research 100%. Supporting text 30%
Currency	6 months
Response	1984
Availability	General
Cost	Free
Address	Shire Hall, Shinfield Park, Reading, Berks RG2 9XD
Telephone	0734 875444, ext 3025
Contact	K. Hawkins, Research and Intelligence Officer

49

Originator	BERKSHIRE COUNTY COUNCIL
Title	POPULATION ESTIMATES, annual. 1984-
Coverage	Population down to parish level by age, sex, components of population change, households and dwellings and economic activity.
Contents & Origin of Statistics	Tables per issue: 20. Own research 100%. Supporting text 30%
Currency	6 months
Response	1984
Availability	General
Cost	Free
Address	Shire Hall, Shinfield Park, Reading, Berks RG2 9XD
Telephone	0734 875444, ext 3025
Contact	K. Hawkins, Research and Intelligence Officer

50

Originator	BICYCLE ASSOCIATION OF GREAT BRITAIN LTD
Title	STATISTICS AND INFORMATION, annual
Coverage	Production, exports, imports and home market deliveries of bicycles from 1967 to date.
Contents & Origin of Statistics	Tables per issue: 1. Unstated 100%

Response	1983
Availability	General
Cost	Free
Address	Starley House, Eaton Rd, Coventry CV1 2FH
Telephone	0203 27427
Contact	Mrs J. Foster, Executive Assistant to Director

51

Originator	BIG FARM WEEKLY
Title	COMMODITIES/THIS WEEK'S PRICES, weekly in a weekly journal
Coverage	Data on main agricultural markets - cereals, livestock, potatoes etc - and supplies including soya, hay and straw. Feed price statistics given on occasional basis
Response	1984
Availability	Controlled circulation to 'big' farmers but available to others on subscription
Cost	Free to 'big' farmers, £25 to others
Address	International Thomson Publishing Ltd, Elm House, 10-16 Elm St, London WC1X 0BP
Telephone	01 253 9355; Telex: 894461
Contact	Robert Bojduniak, Commodities Editor

52

Originator	BIOLOGIST
Title	SALARY SURVEY, every 2 or 3 years in a journal published 5 times a year
Coverage	Salary survey of various categories of membership by sector of employment.
Contents & Origin of Statistics	Tables per issue: Own research 100%
Response	1984
Availability	General
Address	20 Queensberry Place, London SW7 2DZ
Telephone	01 581 8333
Contact	C.J. Kerr

53

Originator	BIRDS EYE WALL'S LTD
Title	BIRDS EYE REVIEW, annual

| Coverage | Review of marketing and consumer trends affecting consumption of frozen foods and a section on British values showing the results of a Gallup poll of 1074 individuals. |

Contents & Origin of Statistics Tables per issue: c.15. Own research 80%, Government statistics 20%. Supporting text 60%

Currency	2-3 months
Response	1983
Availability	General
Cost	Free
Address	Station Avenue, Walton-on-Thames, Surrey KT12 1NT
Telephone	09322 28888
Contact	Above address

54

| Originator | BIRDS EYE WALL'S LTD |

| Title | POCKET MONEY MONITOR, annual. 1975- |
| Coverage | Survey by Gallup of pocket money given to 5-16 year olds in UK. Covers average weekly pocket money by age, region, and sex plus earnings from Saturday jobs and gifts from friends and relatives. Sample of 500 respondents. |

Contents & Origin of Statistics Tables per issue: 12. Own research 100%. Supporting text 30%

Currency	2 months
Response	1983
Availability	General
Cost	Free
Address	Station Avenue, Walton-on-Thames, Surrey KT12 1NT
Telephone	09322 28888
Contact	John Collard/Judy Smith, Telephone 01 631 1008

55

| Originator | BIRDS EYE WALL'S LTD |

| Title | WALLS REPORT, annual |
| Coverage | Review of marketing and consumer trends over the past year affecting the consumption of ice cream. |

Contents & Origin of Statistics Tables per issue: 23. Own research 100%

Currency	3 months
Response	1983
Availability	General

Cost	Free
Address	Station Avenue, Walton-on-Thames, Surrey KT12 1NT
Telephone	09322 28888
Contact	Above address

56

Originator	BIRMINGHAM CHAMBER OF INDUSTRY AND COMMERCE
Title	QUARTERLY ECONOMIC SURVEY, quarterly
Coverage	Survey of member companies covering deliveries and orders, production, stocks, cashflow, labour, investment, confidence and business factors. Number of respondents varies from quarter to quarter.
Contents & Origin of Statistics	Tables per issue: 8. Own research 100%.
Currency	3 weeks
Response	1984
Availability	General
Cost	Free
Address	P.O. Box 360, 75 Harborne Rd, Birmingham B15 3DH
Telephone	021 454 6171
Contact	Miss J. Hollis, Executive Assistant

57

Originator	BIRMINGHAM CITY COUNCIL
Title	ABSTRACT OF BIRMINGHAM STATISTICS, annual
Coverage	Compilation of statistics on the Birmingham area, including details of area and climate, population, births, marriages, deaths, employment and unemployment, industry, transport and communications, housing, health, education, social services, leisure and elections.
Contents & Origin of Statistics	Tables per issue: 170. Own research 45%, Other non official source 10%, Government statistics 45%. Supporting text 10%
Currency	Varies
Response	1984
Availability	General
Cost	£6
ISSN	0305 5213
Address	Central Statistical Office, Council House, Birmingham B1 1BB
Telephone	021 235 2039
Contact	Above address

58

Originator	BIRMINGHAM CITY COUNCIL
Title	ECONOMIC BULLETIN, quarterly
Coverage	General data on economic trends including employment, unemployment, prices, redundancies, industrial strategy and economic initiatives.
Contents & **Origin of** **Statistics**	Tables per issue: 5-10. Own research 20%,Government statistics 80%. Supporting text 70%
Currency	Varies
Response	1984
Availability	General
Cost	Free
Address	Planning Department, P.O. Box 28, 120 Edmund St, Birmingham B3 2RD
Telephone	021 235 4818
Contact	John Scouller

59

Originator	BIS-PEDDER LTD
Title	ANNUAL CENSUS OF UK INSTALLED INFORMATION PROCESSING SYSTEMS, annual. 1973-
Coverage	Computers and electronic office systems, UK installed base and shipments for supplier and model.
Contents & **Origin of** **Statistics**	Tables per issue: 150. Own research 100%. Supporting text 15%
Comments	Special analyses undertaken.
Response	1984
Availability	General
Cost	c. £2600
Address	York House, 199 Westminster Bridge Rd, London SE1 7UT
Telephone	01 633 0866; Telex: 8813024
Contact	Derek Pedder, Managing Director

60

Originator	BLYTH VALLEY BOROUGH COUNCIL
Title	ECONOMIC INFORMATION REPORT, quarterly
Coverage	Includes data on unemployment, labour, trade, national economy and industry land availability in most issues.

Contents & **Origin of** **Statistics**	Tables per issue: 2-5. Own research 50%, Government statistics 50%. Supporting text 80%
Response	1984
Availability	General
Cost	Free
Address	Council Offices, Seaton Delaval, Whitley Bay, Tyne and Wear, NE25 0DX
Telephone	0632 374757
Contact	Mr. W. Tarbit, Planning Department

61

Originator	BOOKSELLER
Title	BOOK PRICE INFLATION, twice-yearly in a weekly journal. 1949-
Coverage	Price trends of new books and new editions based on books published in the 6 month period
Contents & **Origin of** **Statistics**	Tables per issue: 1. Own research 100%. Supporting text 50%
Comments	Other statistics published at regular intervals - see other entries
Currency	2 months
Response	1984
Availability	General
Cost	£35.50p or 55p for a single issue
ISSN	0006 7539
Address	J. Whitaker & Sons Ltd, 12 Dyott St, London WC1A 1DF
Telephone	01 836 8911; Telex: 987117

62

Originator	BOOKSELLER
Title	BOOK PUBLISHERS' OUTPUT, twice-yearly in a weekly journal. 1949-
Coverage	Total numbers and prices of all new books and new editions from publishing companies in the UK with a breakdown by company.
Contents & **Origin of** **Statistics**	Tables per issue: 1. 14pgs. Own research 100%
Comments	Other regular statistics published - see other entries
Currency	2 months
Response	1984
Availability	General
Cost	£40 or 65p for a single issue
ISSN	0006 7539

Address	J. Whitaker & Sons Ltd, 12 Dyott St, London WC1A 1DF
Telephone	01 836 8911; Telex: 987117

63

Originator	BOOKSELLER
Title	BOOKISH PORTFOLIO, approximately every 9 months in a weekly journal. November 1981-
Coverage	Stock market performance of the book publishing manufacturing and distribution sector based on a selection of companies. Total figures and figures on individual companies.
Contents & Origin of Statistics	Tables per issue: 7. Non official source 100%
Comments	Other regular statistics published - see other entries
Currency	2-6 weeks
Response	1984
Availability	General
Cost	£40 or 65p for a single issue
ISSN	0006 7539
Address	J Whitaker & Sons Ltd, 12 Dyott St, London WC1A 1DF
Telephone	01 836 8911; Telex: 987117

64

Originator	BOOKSELLER
Title	BOOKS RECORDED, twice-yearly in a weekly journal
Coverage	Books published from UK companies and recorded in 'British Books in Print' displayed by subject classification and as new books, reprints and new editions, translations and limited editions.
Contents & Origin of Statistics	Tables per issue: 2. Own research 100%. Supporting text 20%
Comments	Other regular statistics published - see other entries
Currency	2-3 weeks
Response	1984
Availability	General
Cost	£40 or 65p for a single issue
ISSN	0006 7539
Address	J. Whitaker & Sons Ltd, 12 Dyott St, London WC1A 1DF
Telephone	01 836 8911; Telex: 987117

65

Originator	BOOKSELLERS ASSOCIATION OF GREAT BRITAIN AND IRELAND
Title	CHARTER GROUP ECONOMIC SURVEY, annual. 1964-
Coverage	Analysis of the economic performance and profitability of the book trade, based on leading bookshops, carried out by Manchester Business School. Sales, profit, and performance by specialisation.
Contents & Origin of Statistics	Tables per issue: 9. Own research 100%. Supporting text 20%
Currency	1 year
Response	1984
Availability	Book trade and General
Cost	£16.50
Address	154 Buckingham Palace Rd, London SW1W 9TZ
Telephone	01 730 8214
Contact	Elizabeth Lamont, Publications Co-ordinator

66

Originator	BORDER TELEVISION
Title	MARKETING FACTS, annual
Coverage	General data on the Borders region including population, households, income and expenditure, retailing, services, agriculture etc.
Contents & Origin of Statistics	Tables per issue: 20-30. Non official source 60%, Government statistics 40%. Supporting text 50%
Currency	Varies
Response	1984
Availability	General
Cost	Free
Address	83 Margaret St, London W1N 7LA
Telephone	01 637 4363
Contact	Kenny Jones, Research Department

67

Originator	BRADFORD CHAMBER OF COMMERCE
Title	ECONOMIC SURVEY, quarterly. 1979-
Coverage	Size of company, main business activity, opinions of future sales/ trade, new orders, capacity, workforce, and investment issued as press release.

Contents & Origin of Statistics	Tables per issue: 11. Own research 100%.
Currency	1 month
Response	1984
Availability	Members
Cost	Free
Address	Commerce House, Cheapside, Bradford BD1 4JZ
Telephone	0274 728166; Telex: 51449
Contact	M.A. Sewell, Commercial Officer

68

Originator	BRADFORD CITY COUNCIL
Title	BRADFORD IN FIGURES, annual
Coverage	Compendium of data on the area, including population, economy, housing, use of land etc.
Contents & Origin of Statistics	Tables per issue: 194. Own research 25%, Government statistics 75%
Response	1984
Availability	General
Cost	£2.50
Address	City Hall, Bradford, West Yorkshire, BD1 1HY
Telephone	0274 752004
Contact	Mr T. Davies, Assistant Policy Officer

69

Originator	BRADFORD CITY COUNCIL
Title	DISTRICT TRENDS, annual
Coverage	Trends and issues currently facing Bradford, eg equal opportunities, politics, economy, environment, health and new technology.
Contents & Origin of Statistics	Tables per issue: c10.
Response	1984
Availability	General
Address	City Hall, Bradford, West Yorkshire BD1 1HY
Telephone	0274 752003
Contact	Mr Shiraz Jiwani, Assistant Policy Officer

70

Originator	BRADWELL, JOHN ASSOCIATES
Title	BEER: SMALL CONTAINERS IMPORTS ANALYSIS SERVICE, quarterly. 1983-
Coverage	Imports of beer made from malt in containers not exceeding 10 litres showing litres and average value per litre by port landed and country of origin and any differences by country of consignment.
Contents & Origin of Statistics	Tables per issue: 8. Own research 40%, Other non official source 20%, Government statistics 40%. Supporting text 33%
Currency	2 months
Response	1984
Availability	General
Cost	£40
Address	21 Great Spilmans, London SE22 8SZ
Telephone	01 693 5692
Contact	J.B. Mayers, Principal

71

Originator	BRADWELL, JOHN ASSOCIATES
Title	SOFT DRINKS IMPORTS ANALYSIS SERVICE, quarterly. 1982-
Coverage	Imports under CCT 22.02 showing litres and average value per litre by port landed and country of origin and any differences by country of consignment. Annual supplement on imports under CCT 21.07, concentrated cordials and fruit squashes.
Contents & Origin of Statistics	Tables per issue: 12. Own research 40%, Other non official source 20%, Government statistics 40%. Supporting text 25%
Currency	2 months
Response	1984
Availability	General
Cost	£55
Address	21 Great Spilmans, London SE22 8SZ
Telephone	01 693 5692
Contact	J.B. Mayers, Principal

72

Originator	BREWERS' SOCIETY
Title	BEER FACTS, annual

Coverage	In the form of an information card, covers production and consumption of beer, employment in the industry, major producers, trade, licensed premises and number of brewers, capital investment and materials. International data.
Contents & Origin of Statistics	Tables per issue: 12. Unstated 100%. Supporting text 15%
Comments	Also issue 'Brewing Review' on an occasional basis which contains some statistics and is available free.
Currency	Varies
Response	1984
Availability	General
Cost	Free
Address	42 Portman Square, London, W1H 0BB
Telephone	01 486 4831
Contact	Kenneth Dunjohn, Head of Public Relations

73

Originator	BREWERS' SOCIETY
Title	UK STATISTICAL HANDBOOK, annual
Coverage	Production and consumption of beer, brewing materials, inter-drink comparisons, prices and incomes, duties, licensing data, drunkenness, structure of the industry. Also contains international data.
Contents & Origin of Statistics	Tables per issue: c77. Own research 10%, Other non official source 10%, Government statistics 80%. Supporting text 10%
Comments	Also issue 'International Statistical Handbook' (£30 in 1981) on an occasional basis.
Currency	Varies
Response	1984
Availability	General
Cost	£14
ISBN	0306 6002
Address	42 Portman Square, London, W1H 0BB
Telephone	01 486 4831
Contact	Christopher Thurman, Statistician

74

Originator	BRICK DEVELOPMENT ASSOCIATION
Title	BRICK DEMAND FORECAST, 3 per year
Coverage	Brick demand forecast for current year plus next two years.

Contents & Origin of Statistics	Tables per issue: 4. Supporting text 25%

Currency Response	3 weeks
Availability	1984
	Members
Address	Woodside House, Winkfield, Windsor, Berks SL4 2DX
Telephone	0344 885651
Contact	Mr M.C. Hayward, Secretary

75

Originator	BRICK DEVELOPMENT ASSOCIATION

Title	DATA ON BRICK USAGE AND DELIVERIES, quarterly. 1969-
Coverage	Analysis of brick deliveries by member firms into construction sectors.

Contents & Origin of Statistics	Tables per issue: 1.

Currency Response	3 months
Availability	1984
	Members
Address	Woodside House, Winkfield, Windsor, Berks SL4 2DX
Telephone	0344 885651
Contact	Mr M.C. Hayward, Secretary

76

Originator	BRISTOL AND WEST BUILDING SOCIETY

Title	FACTUAL BACKGROUND, quarterly. 1969-
Coverage	General data on building societies, personal savings, personal credit (including mortgages) housing and general economic and financial data.

Contents & Origin of Statistics	Tables per issue: 33. Non official source 20%, Government statistics 80%. Supporting text 5%

Currency Response	3 months
Availability	1984
	General
Cost	Free
Address	P.O. Box 27, Broad Quay, Bristol, BS99 7AX.
Telephone	0272 294271; Telex: 44741
Contact	Brian Norris, Research Manager

77

Originator	BRITISH ADHESIVES AND SEALANTS ASSOCIATION
Title	SALES OF SEALANTS - ALL APPLICATIONS AND SALES, HOME AND EXPORT - CERTAIN TYPES, bi-annual
Coverage	Sales in value terms for all types of sealants and sales value and volume for products split by chemical type.
Currency	2-3 months
Response	1984
Availability	Members
Address	2A High St, Hythe, Southampton, SO4 6YW
Telephone	0703 842765
Contact	Dr. P. Bosworth, Secretary

78

Originator	BRITISH AEROSOL MANUFACTURERS' ASSOCIATION
Title	BAMA ANNUAL REPORT, annual
Coverage	Aerosol filling statistics by product category.
Contents & Origin of Statistics	Tables per issue: 2. Own research 100%
Response	1984
Availability	General
Cost	Free
Address	Alembic House, 93 Albert Embankment, London SE1 7TU
Telephone	01 582 1115 ; Telex: 916672
Contact	Miss D. Roe, Public Relations Executive

79

Originator	BRITISH AGGREGATE CONSTRUCTION MATERIALS INDUSTRIES
Title	BACMI MONTHLY STATISTICAL TRENDS, monthly
Coverage	Monthly data compared with previous year. Tonnage of processed store for construction use, of coated materials, cubic metres of ready-mixed concrete and tonnage of sand and gravel.
Contents & Origin of Statistics	Tables per issue: 1. Own research 100%.
Currency	1-2 months
Response	1984
Availability	Members
Cost	Free
Address	25 Lower Belgrave St, London SW1W 0LS

Telephone   01 730 8194
Contact   S. Leslie, Economist

80

Originator	BRITISH AGGREGATE CONSTRUCTION MATERIALS INDUSTRIES
Title	COATED MATERIALS MANUFACTURED AND LAID BY BACMI MEMBERS, quarterly. 1983-
Coverage	Tonnage manufactured and tonnage laid, given by economic planning region. Divided into hot rolled asphalt and all other coated materials.
Contents & Origin of Statistics	Tables per issue: 1. Own research 100%.
Currency	4-5 months
Response	1984
Availability	Members
Cost	Free
Address	25 Lower Belgrave St, London SW1W 0LS
Telephone	01 730 8194
Contact	S. Leslie, Economist

81

Originator	BRITISH AGGREGATE CONSTRUCTION MATERIALS INDUSTRIES
Title	CRUSHED ROCK SOLD BY BACMI MEMBERS, quarterly. 1983-
Coverage	Sales by economic planning region for limestone igneous rock and sandstone and total for crushed rock.
Contents & Origin of Statistics	Tables per issue: 1. Own research 100%.
Currency	7 months
Response	1984
Availability	Members
Cost	Free
Address	25 Lower Belgrave St, London SW1W 0LS
Telephone	01 730 8194
Contact	S. Leslie, Economist

82

Originator	BRITISH AGGREGATE CONSTRUCTION MATERIALS INDUSTRIES
Title	READY-MIXED CONCRETE PRODUCTION BY COUNTY, monthly. 1984-
Coverage	Production given in quantity and number of plants.
Contents & Origin of Statistics	Tables per issue: 1. Own research 100%.
Response	1984
Availability	Members
Cost	Free
Address	25 Lower Belgrave St, London SW1W OLS
Telephone	01 730 8194
Contact	S. Leslie, Economist

83

Originator	BRITISH AGGREGATE CONSTRUCTION MATERIALS INDUSTRIES
Title	READY-MIXED CONCRETE PRODUCTION BY REGION, monthly. 1982-
Coverage	Production by economic planning regions.
Contents & Origin of Statistics	Tables per issue: 1. Own research 100%.
Currency	1-2 months
Response	1984
Availability	Members
Cost	Free
Address	25 Lower Belgrave St, London SW1W OLS
Telephone	01 730 8194
Contact	S. Leslie, Economist

84

Originator	BRITISH AGGREGATE CONSTRUCTION MATERIALS INDUSTRIES
Title	SAND AND GRAVEL SOLD BY BACMI MEMBERS, quarterly. 1983-
Coverage	Sales given by economic planning region.

Contents & Origin of Statistics	Tables per issue: 1. Own research 100%.
Currency	4 months
Response	1984
Availability	Members
Cost	Free
Address	25 Lower Belgrave St, London SW1W OLS
Telephone	01 730 8194
Contact	S. Leslie, Economist

85

Originator	BRITISH AGRICULTURAL AND GARDEN MACHINERY ASSOCIATION
Title	MARKET GUIDE TO USED FARM TRACTORS AND MACHINERY, monthly
Coverage	Current prices and auction prices of used tractors and farm machinery.
Contents & Origin of Statistics	Tables per issue: 144 pgs. Own research 100%.
Currency	1 month
Response	1984
Availability	Members and people in agricultural machinery trade
Cost	£40.50 (£32 to members)
Address	14 Church St, Rickmansworth, Herts WD3 1RQ
Telephone	0923 720241; Telex: 893872
Contact	Norman Stuckey/Linda Palmer, Co-ordinators

86

Originator	BRITISH AGRICULTURAL EXPORT COUNCIL
Title	EXPORTS OF UK AGRICULTURAL INPUTS AND MACHINERY, bi-annual
Coverage	As indicated by title.
Contents & Origin of Statistics	Tables per issue: Government statistics 100%
Response	1984
Availability	Members
Cost	Free
Address	35 Belgrave Sq, London SW1X 8QN

Telephone	01 245 9819
Contact	Clare Parkinson

87

Originator	BRITISH AGROCHEMICALS ASSOCIATION
Title	ANNUAL REPORT AND HANDBOOK, annual
Coverage	Industry sales and employment, pesticide usage in GB and the world market. Also safety.
Contents & Origin of Statistics	Tables per issue: 11. Non official source 10%, Government statistics 30%, Unstated 60%. Supporting text 85%
Response	1984
Availability	General
Cost	Free
Address	Alembic House, 93 Albert Embankment, London SE1 7TU
Telephone	01 735 8471/2; Telex: 916672
Contact	Miss A.H. Buckenham, Secretary

88

Originator	BRITISH AIRPORTS AUTHORITY
Title	BAA ANNUAL REPORT AND ACCOUNTS, annual. 1966-
Coverage	BAA activities throughout the year with statistics throughout. Also separate statistical section giving ten year traffic record by airport,- cargo and passenger movements,runway availability and trade through airports and seaports.Also summary statistics in 'Key statistics' section.
Contents & Origin of Statistics	Tables per issue: 104pgs. Own research 80%, Other non official source 10%, Government statistics 10%. Supporting text 75%
Currency	2-3 months
Response	1984
Availability	General
Cost	Undisclosed
ISBN	0 903460 0 26 0
Address	Head Office, Gatwick Airport, Gatwick, West Sussex RH6 0HZ
Telephone	0293 517755; Telex: 87795
Contact	Mr C. Eldred-Evans, Production Manager

89

Originator	BRITISH ASSOCIATION OF CANNED AND PRESERVED FOOD IMPORTERS AND DISTRIBUTORS
Title	IMPORT STATISTICS, monthly
Coverage	Data on imported preserved foodstuffs by CCT heading.
Response	1983
Availability	Members
Cost	£10 per CCT heading
Address	1 London Bridge Rd, London SE1 9SZ
Telephone	01 403 0141
Contact	W.J. Anzer, Secretary

90

Originator	BRITISH ASSOCIATION OF TOURIST OFFICERS
Title	MEDIA RESPONSE ANALYSIS, annual
Coverage	Analysis of cost per reply to advertisements in various media used by resorts.
Response	1984
Availability	Members
Cost	£5
Address	Moorlands House, Churscombe Rd, Marldon Cross, Paignton, Devon, TQ3 1NA
Telephone	0803 556561
Contact	S.J.F. Lovegrove, Hon. General Secretary

91

Originator	BRITISH BATTERY MAKERS' SOCIETY
Title	UK BATTERY MARKET STATISTICS, monthly and annual
Coverage	General data on the battery market.
Response	1984
Availability	Members
Cost	Free
Address	c/o Chloride Group Ltd, 52 Grosvenor Gardens, London SW1
Telephone	01 730 0866
Contact	J.L. Blasdale, Secretary

92

Originator	BRITISH BRUSH MANUFACTURERS' ASSOCIATION
Title	ANNUAL REPORT, annual
Coverage	Data on sales, imports/exports, production, consumption for different types of brushes, eg household, paint, artists etc.

Contents & Origin of Statistics	Tables per issue: 10. Government statistics 90%-100%. Supporting text 6pgs
Currency	4 months
Response	1984
Availability	Members
Cost	Subscription price not available
Address	6A East St, Epsom, Surrey KT17 1HH
Telephone	03727 27710
Contact	J.A. Snellgrove, Secretary

93

Originator	BRITISH CARPET MANUFACTURERS' ASSOCIATION
Title	ANNUAL REPORT, annual
Coverage	In statistical appendix gives sales by types of construction, trade and fibres used in carpet surface yarns. Market for carpets over 5 years.
Contents & Origin of Statistics	Tables per issue: 5. Government statistics 100%. Supporting text 60%
Currency	6 months
Response	1984
Availability	General
Cost	Free
Address	Royalty House, 4th Floor, 72 Dean St, London W1V 5HB
Telephone	01 734 9853
Contact	Miss M. Smith, Assistant Director

94

Originator	BRITISH CARTON ASSOCIATION
Title	UNTITLED
Coverage	Carton packaging data.
Response	1984
Availability	Members
Address	35 New Bridge St, London EC4V 6BH
Telephone	01 248 5271
Contact	R.R.B. Mackenzie, Director

95

Originator	BRITISH CERAMIC MANUFACTURERS FEDERATION
Title	UNITED KINGDOM EXPORTS OF POTTERY, quarterly

Coverage	Exports of pottery by S.I.T.C. number and country of destination, given in value and quantity over 2 years.
Contents & **Origin of** **Statistics**	Tables per issue: 2. Government statistics 100%.
Currency	2 months
Response	1984
Availability	Members
Cost	Free
Address	Federation House, Stoke-on-Trent ST4 2SA
Telephone	0782 48631
Contact	Mr. N. Nelson

96

Originator	BRITISH CLOTHING INDUSTRY ASSOCIATION
Title	STATISTICAL REPORT ON BRITISH CLOTHING INDUSTRY, annual
Coverage	Clothing production, trade, employment, retail prices, earnings, and consumer expenditure on clothing.
Contents & **Origin of** **Statistics**	Tables per issue: 6. Own research 10%, Government statistics 90%.
Currency	6 months
Response	1984
Availability	General
Cost	Free
Address	Wellington House, 6-9 Upper St. Martin's Lane, London WC2H 9DL
Telephone	01 836 4545
Contact	Neil Pallister, Junior Executive

97

Originator	BRITISH COMPRESSED AIR SOCIETY
Title	UNTITLED, monthly
Coverage	Information collected from member companies and elsewhere is summarised and analysed and results are sent to members.
Response	1984
Availability	Members
Address	8 Leicester St, London WC2H 7BN
Telephone	01 437 0678
Contact	Above address

98

Originator	BRITISH COUNCIL
Title	STATISTICS OF OVERSEAS STUDENTS IN THE UK, annual
Coverage	Data on overseas students by country, educational sector and subject area studied. Figures are given for a 10 year period.
Contents & Origin of Statistics	Tables per issue: 7. Own research 50%, Government statistics 50%
Response	1983
Availability	General
Cost	£5.75
Address	10 Spring Gardens, London SW1A 2BN
Telephone	01 930 8466
Contact	Above address

99

Originator	BRITISH DIRECT MARKETING ASSOCIATION
Title	DIRECT MAIL ORDER RESPONSE IN THE UK, every 2 or 3 years
Coverage	Value of retail trade by mail order houses and selected retail outlets and growth in sales by direct responses and direct mail methods.
Contents & Origin of Statistics	Tables per issue: 5
Response	1984
Availability	Members
Address	1 New Oxford St, London WC1A 1NQ
Telephone	01 242 2254
Contact	Above address

100

Originator	BRITISH DISPOSABLE PRODUCTS ASSOCIATION
Title	UNTITLED, quarterly
Coverage	Sales figures for disposable products.
Response	1983
Availability	Members
Address	35 New Bridge St, London EC4V 6BH
Telephone	01 248 5271
Contact	R.W. Bray, Secretary

101

Originator	BRITISH EDUCATIONAL EQUIPMENT ASSOCIATION
Title	EXPENDITURE ON TEACHING MATERIALS ; SCHOOL-BOOKS, EQUIPMENT AND STATIONERY, bi-annual
Coverage	Expenditure in England and Wales by counties, districts and metropolitan boroughs for 5 years.
Contents & Origin of Statistics	Tables per issue: 5. Non official source 100%. Supporting text 10%
Comments	Sponsored by the Publishers Association.
Response	1984
Availability	General
Cost	Free
Address	Sunley House, 10 Gunthorpe St, London E1 7RN
Telephone	01 247 9320/9326

102

Originator	BRITISH FIBREBOARD PACKAGING ASSOCIATION
Title	ANNUAL PRODUCTION STATISTICS, annual
Coverage	Production by weight and area and the sales invoice value of solid and corrugated fibreboard produced in the UK by BFPA members.
Contents & Origin of Statistics	Tables per issue: 1. Own research 100%.
Response	1984
Availability	Members
Address	Sutherland House, 5/6 Argyll St, London W1V 1AD
Telephone	01 434 3851; Telex: 8953808
Contact	Mr R. Sholem, Secretary

103

Originator	BRITISH FOOTWEAR MANUFACTURERS FEDERATION
Title	FOOTWEAR INDUSTRY STATISTICAL REVIEW, annual. 1969-
Coverage	Structure, materials, production and profitability, employment and earnings, wholesale and retail prices, supplies to the home market and expenditure, retail distribution and overseas trade. Some EEC data.
Contents & Origin of Statistics	Tables per issue: 33. Own research 5%, Government statistics 90%, Unstated 5%. Supporting text 10%

Currency	1 year
Response	1984
Availability	General
Cost	£22
Address	Royalty House, 72 Dean St, London W1V 5HB
Telephone	01 437 5573
Contact	Mrs. E.S. Goodes, Statistics

104

Originator	BRITISH FOOTWEAR MANUFACTURERS FEDERATION
Title	MONTHLY STATISTICS, monthly
Coverage	Short-term economic indicators for the industry eg deliveries, employment, prices, retail sales, trade.
Contents & Origin of Statistics	Tables per issue: 2. Unstated 100%
Comments	'Statistical service' encompasses 3 titles - the above, 'Quarterly Review' and 'Quarterly Statistical Supplement'.
Response	1984
Availability	General
Cost	£30 (only as part of Statistical Service)
Address	Royalty House, 72 Dean St, London W1V 5HB
Telephone	01 437 5573
Contact	Mrs. E.S. Goodes, Statistics

105

Originator	BRITISH FOOTWEAR MANUFACTURERS FEDERATION
Title	QUARTERLY REVIEW, quarterly
Coverage	Covers same areas as 'Monthly Statistics'
Contents & Origin of Statistics	Tables per issue: 18. Unstated 100%
Comments	'Statistical Service' encompasses 3 titles - the above,'Monthly Statistics' and 'Quarterly Statistical Supplement'.
Response	1984
Availability	General
Cost	£30 (only as part of Statistical Service)
Address	Royalty House, 72 Dean St, London W1V 5HB
Telephone	01 437 5573
Contact	Mrs. E.S. Goodes, Statistics

106

Originator	BRITISH FOOTWEAR MANUFACTURERS FEDERATION
Title	QUARTERLY STATISTICAL SUPPLEMENT, quarterly
Coverage	Production, trade and consumption statistics by sectors of the industry.
Contents & Origin of Statistics	Tables per issue: 2. Government statistics 100%
Comments	'Statistical Service' encompasses 3 titles - the above, 'Monthly Statistics' and 'Quarterly Review'.
Response	1984
Availability	General
Cost	Cost (pa):£30 (only as part of Statistical Service)
Address	Royalty House, 72 Dean St, London W1V 5HB
Telephone	01 437 5573
Contact	Mrs. E.S. Goodes, Statistics

107

Originator	BRITISH FRIESIAN CATTLE SOCIETY OF GREAT BRITAIN AND IRELAND
Title	ANNUAL REPORT AND ACCOUNTS, annual
Coverage	Includes number of registrations, sales and transfers, record services, artificial insemination data and breed exports, as well as financial information on the society.
Contents & Origin of Statistics	Tables per issue: 12. Own research 100%
Response	1983
Availability	Members and other relevant organisations
Cost	Free
Address	Scotsbridge House, Rickmansworth, Hertfordshire WD3 3BB
Telephone	0923 774241
Contact	Miss M.R. Lake, Technical Assistant to the Chief Executive

108

Originator	BRITISH FROZEN FOOD FEDERATION
Title	BRITISH FROZEN FOOD FEDERATION YEARBOOK, annual
Coverage	Section on 'frozen food statistics' covering expenditure and general consumption, freezer ownership, markets for ice cream, vegetables, fish and meat, gateaux, retail and catering service trends and future trends in fast foods. Also a section on other countries.

Contents &	Tables per issue: 50. Own research + other non official source 60%,
Origin of	Government statistics 40%
Statistics	

Currency	Varies
Response	1983
Availability	General
Cost	£17.50
Address	Honeypot Lane, Colsterworth, Grantham, Lincolnshire NG33 5LX
Telephone	0476 84414
Contact	P.G. Howell, Secretary-General

109

Originator	BRITISH GAS CORPORATION

Title	FACTS AND FIGURES, annual. 1979-
Coverage	General information on the gas industry plus operating figures for British Gas and figures on the total fuel market.

Contents &	Tables per issue: 4. Own research 100%. Supporting text 50%
Origin of	
Statistics	

Comments	Produced in the form of a 12 sided pocket card.
Currency	3-4 months
Response	1984
Availability	General
Cost	Free
Address	Public Relations Department, 152 Grosvenor Rd, London SW1V 3SL
Telephone	01 821 1444; Telex: 938529
Contact	G.B. Cowen, Publications Officer

110

Originator	BRITISH HARDWARE AND HOUSEWARES MANUFAC-TURERS' ASSOCIATION

Title	STATISTICS SUPPLEMENT, quarterly. 1983-
Coverage	Industry trends, trade, consumers' expenditure, unemployment, and tax and price index.

Contents &	Tables per issue: 4pgs. Own research 10%, Other non official source
Origin of	10%, Government statistics 80%. Supporting text 25%
Statistics	

Currency	2 weeks
Response	1984
Availability	Members
Cost	Free
Address	35 Billing Rd, Northampton NN1 5DD

Telephone   0604 22023
Contact   A.N. Nisbet, General Manager

111

Originator   BRITISH HARDWARE FEDERATION

Title   TODAY'S TRADING TRENDS, monthly. 1981-
Coverage   Sales and gross profit figures for the hardware trade plus data on wages, staff numbers and stock levels.

Contents &   Tables per issue: 1. Own research 100%.
Origin of
Statistics

Currency   1 month
Response   1984
Availability Members
Cost   Free
Address   20 Harborne Rd, Edgbaston, Birmingham B15 3AB
Telephone   021 454 4385; Telex: 338024
Contact   Mr D.H. Rogers, Director

112

Originator   BRITISH HARDWARE FEDERATION

Title   TODAY'S TRADING TRENDS, quarterly. 1982-
Coverage   General statistics based on participants' figures set out in averages covering such things as sales, profits, wages, staff, stock.

Contents &   Tables per issue: 3. Own research 100%. Supporting text 33%
Origin of
Statistics

Comments   Figures appear in the Federation's house journal 'Hardware Today'.
Currency   3-4 months
Response   1984
Availability Primarily Members
Cost   Free
Address   20 Harborne Rd, Edgbaston, Birmingham B15 3AB
Telephone   021 454 4385; Telex: 338024
Contact   Mr D.H. Rogers, Director

113

Originator   BRITISH INDUSTRIAL FASTENERS ASSOCIATION

Title   UK IMPORT STATISTICS, monthly
Coverage   Import figures for 13 main product groups divided by country. Weight and value figures are given.

| Contents & Origin of Statistics | Tables per issue: 13. Government statistics 100% |

Currency	1 month
Response	1983
Availability	Members
Cost	Free
Address	Queens House, Queens Rd, Coventry CV1 3EG
Telephone	0203 22325
Contact	Above address

114

Originator	BRITISH INSTITUTE OF MANAGEMENT
Title	BUSINESS CARS ANNUAL SURVEY, annual
Coverage	A reference tool for car fleet administrators and those responsible for shaping and implementing company car policy. Car practice within 1,000 BIM member companies, outlining trends and showing reactions to changing economic and financial conditions.
Contents & Origin of Statistics	Tables per issue: Own research 100%
Response	1983
Availability	General
Cost	£31.25, £25 to members
Address	Professional Publishing Ltd, Alhambra House, 27-31 Charing Cross Rd, London WC2M 0LR
Telephone	01 930 3951
Contact	Michael Woodmansey

115

Originator	BRITISH INSURANCE ASSOCIATION
Title	BIA MEMBERS STATISTICS, annual. 1980-
Coverage	Members' premium income, underwriting results, investment funds and invisible earnings.
Contents & Origin of Statistics	Tables per issue: 5. Own research 100%. Supporting text 50%
Currency	9 months
Response	1984
Availability	General
Cost	Free
Address	Aldermary House, Queen St, London EC4

Telephone	01 248 4477
Contact	B.D. Hudson, Deputy Manager Statistics

116

Originator	BRITISH INSURANCE ASSOCIATION

Title	INSURANCE FACTS AND FIGURES, annual. 1970-
Coverage	Covers premium income, fire and accident and motor underwriting results, marine aviation and transport, UK premium income and related statistics, life assurance, investments and family expenditure.
Contents & Origin of Statistics	Tables per issue: 25-30. Own research 30%, Other non official source 50%, Government statistics 20%. Supporting text 20%.
Currency	9 months
Response	1984
Availability	General
Cost	Free
ISSN	0308 8308
Address	Aldermary House, Queen St, London EC4
Telephone	01 248 4477
Contact	B.D. Hudson, Deputy Manager, Statistics.

117

Originator	BRITISH INSURANCE ASSOCIATION

Title	INSURANCE PREMIUMS IN THE UK, annual. 1980-
Coverage	Annual update sheets giving data on insurance premiums by type, i.e. fire, marine, motor etc., by registered companies, territories, BIA members and Lloyds.
Contents & Origin of Statistics	Tables per issue: 11. Own research 60%, Other non official source 40%. Supporting text 50%
Currency	15 months
Response	1984
Availability	General
Cost	Free
Address	Aldermary House, Queen St, London EC4
Telephone	01 248 4477
Contact	B.D. Hudson, Deputy Manager, Statistics

118

Originator	BRITISH INSURANCE ASSOCIATION

Title	UK MARKET STATISTICS, annual. 1982-

Coverage	Estimate of the size of the UK insurance market based on 'net retention', i.e. gross premiums received plus reinsurance accepted less reinsurance ceded and retrocessions.
Contents & Origin of Statistics	Tables per issue: 3. Own research 100%. Supporting text 60%
Currency	12-15 months
Response	1984
Availability	General
Cost	Free
Address	Aldermary House, Queen St, London EC4
Telephone	01 248 4477
Contact	B.D. Hudson, Deputy Manager, Statistics

119

Originator	BRITISH INTERNAL COMBUSTION ENGINE MANUFAC-TURERS' ASSOCIATION
Title	UNTITLED
Coverage	Internal combustion engine market data.
Response	1984
Availability	Members
Address	Westmorland House, 127 Regent St, London W1R 7HA
Telephone	01 734 8368/9
Contact	K.H. Higgens, Chief Executive

120

Originator	BRITISH INVISIBLE EXPORTS COUNCIL
Title	ANNUAL REPORT, annual
Coverage	Britain's share of world invisible trade, invisibles in Britain's current account and what the City of London earns abroad.
Contents & Origin of Statistics	Tables per issue: 7. Own research 70%, Government statistics 30%. Supporting text 80%
Comments	Issue 'World invisible trade' annually. Produced a one-off report on 'The overseas earnings of the UK art market'.
Currency	1 year
Response	1984
Availability	General
Cost	Free
Address	14 Austin Friars, London EC2N 2HE
Telephone	01 628 3161 ; Telex: 8953511
Contact	Miss E. Cox, Receptionist

121

Originator	BRITISH INVISIBLE EXPORTS COUNCIL
Title	INFORMATION CARD, bi-annual
Coverage	UK invisible earnings, invisibles in the UK's current account, what the City of London earns overseas and employment.
Contents & Origin of Statistics	Tables per issue: 6. Own research 30%, Government statistics 70%. Supporting text 50%
Currency	Varies
Response	1984
Availability	General
Cost	20p
Address	14 Austin Friars, London EC2N 2HE
Telephone	01 628 3161 ; Telex: 8953511
Contact	Miss E. Cox, Receptionist

122

Originator	BRITISH JOURNAL OF INDUSTRIAL RELATIONS
Title	CHRONICLE - STATISTICAL BACKGROUND TO THE INDUSTRIAL RELATIONS SCENE, 3 times a year in a journal published 3 times a year
Coverage	Data on the labour market, earnings, vacancies, prices, industrial disputes etc.
Contents & Origin of Statistics	Tables per issue: Varies. Government statistics 100%. Supporting text 10%
Comments	Other coments: Published by Basil Blackwell on behalf of the London School of Economics and Political Science.
Currency	Varies
Response	1984
Availability	General
Cost	£19 (institutions), £10 (individuals)
ISSN	0007 1080
Address	Basil Blackwell, 108 Cowley Rd, Oxford OX14 1JF
Telephone	0865 724041
Contact	B.C. Roberts, Editor

123

Originator	BRITISH KNITTING EXPORT COUNCIL
Title	ANNUAL ANALYSIS OF EXPORTS OF UK KNITTED GOODS, annual

Coverage	Breakdown of exports by specific type of article, giving values and quantities.
Contents & Origin of Statistics	Tables per issue: 2. Government statistics 100%.
Response	1983
Availability	Members, and specialists on request
Cost	Free to members and by negotiation to non-members
Address	16/21 Sackville St, London W1X 1DE
Telephone	01 734 6277
Contact	Above address

124

Originator	BRITISH MARKET RESEARCH BUREAU LTD
Title	TARGET GROUP INDEX, annual. October 1968-
Coverage	National product and media survey based on information from 24,000 adults. Breakdowns by social grades and household income. Consists of 34 volumes on different sectors.
Contents & Origin of Statistics	Own research 100%
Comments	Available online from Holborn Research Services, IMS UK Ltd, Telmar Communications Ltd and CACI.
Currency	4 months
Response	1984
Availability	Advertisers and media owners
Cost	£1625 (1 volume), £275 (field), £50 (brand)
Address	Saunders House, 53 The Mall, Ealing, London W5 3TE
Telephone	01 567 3060; Telex: 935526
Contact	Judith Passingham, Information Officer

125

Originator	BRITISH PAPER AND BOARD INDUSTRY FEDERATION
Title	BRITISH PAPER AND BOARD INDUSTRY FACTS, annual
Coverage	Various statistics on the industry, including details of consumption, production, exports, imports, production/capacity ratios, raw materials imports, energy consumption, water usage, manpower, capital expenditure and industry structure.
Contents & Origin of Statistics	Tables per issue: 19. Own research + other non official source 70%, Government statistics 30%
Comments	More detailed statistics available to members
Currency	Varies

Response	1983
Availability	General
Cost	£3 to members, £10 to non-members
Address	Plough Place, Fetter Lane, London EC4A 1AL
Telephone	01 353 5222
Contact	Shirley S. Grey

126

Originator	BRITISH PHONOGRAPHIC INDUSTRY LTD
Title	BPI YEARBOOK, annual
Coverage	Includes statistics on the production of records and tapes plus imports and exports, deliveries, sales, prices, advertising expenditure, hardware ownership, video trends and piracy, and leisure market trends.
Contents & Origin of Statistics	Tables per issue: 45.
Comments	Although usually an annual publication, there were no issues published for 1980 and 1981.
Response	1983
Availability	General
Cost	£6.25p
Address	Roxburghe House, 273/287 Regent St, London W1R 8BN
Telephone	01 629 8642
Contact	June Clark

127

Originator	BRITISH PLASTICS FEDERATION
Title	BUSINESS TRENDS SURVEY, bi-annual. 1975-
Coverage	Survey of sales volume, orders, exports, stock trends, investment, profitability, prices and capacity utilisation.
Contents & Origin of Statistics	Tables per issue: 11. Own research 100%. Supporting text 45%
Currency	1 month
Response	1984
Availability	General
Cost	£40
Address	5 Belgrave Square, London SW1X 8PH
Telephone	01 235 9483; Telex: 8951528
Contact	P. Gerrard, Group Executive

128

Originator	BRITISH PORTS ASSOCIATION
Title	ANNUAL STATISTICAL ABSTRACT OF THE UK PORTS INDUSTRY, annual. (In 2 volumes)
Coverage	Vol 1 relates primarily to mode of transport, Vol 2 emphasises commodity detail. Data given for individual UK ports and trading areas.
Contents & Origin of Statistics	Tables per issue: 356pgs. Government statistics 100%. Supporting text 5%
Response	1984
Availability	General
Cost	£15 (Vol 1), £25 (Vol 2)
Address	Commonwealth House, 1-19 New Oxford St, London WC1A 1DZ
Telephone	01 242 1200; Telex: 295741
Contact	E.P.T. Blake, Office Manager

129

Originator	BRITISH PORTS ASSOCIATION
Title	PORT STATISTICS, annual. 1980-
Coverage	Total traffic by mode of appearance, selected parts by mode of appearance and bulk commodity, container and roll-on traffic and general data on fish, manpower, finance etc.
Contents & Origin of Statistics	Tables per issue: 70. Government statistics 100%. Supporting text 5%
Comments	Published jointly by the Dept. of Transport and the BPA.
Currency	1 year
Response	1984
Availability	General
Cost	£20
ISSN	0263 9149
Address	Commonwealth House, 1-19 New Oxford St, London WC1A 1DZ
Telephone	01 242 1200; Telex: 295741
Contact	E.P.T. Blake, Office Manager

130

Originator	BRITISH PORTS ASSOCIATION
Title	QUARTERLY STATISTICAL ABSTRACT OF THE UK PORTS INDUSTRY, quarterly: 1982-
Coverage	Trade by port, and commodity group, mode, trading area in various combinations.

Contents & Origin of Statistics	Tables per issue: 6. Government statistics 100%. Supporting text 1%
Comments	Data also published as an annual volume 'Annual Statistical Abstract' containing extended detail. Also issue 'Port Statistics Bulletin' on an irregular basis.
Response	1984
Availability	General
Cost	£32.50
ISSN	0264 1070
Address	Commonwealth House, 1-19 New Oxford St, London WC1A 1DZ
Telephone	01 242 1200; Telex 295741
Contact	E.P.T. Blake, Office Manager

131

Originator	BRITISH PRECAST CONCRETE FEDERATION
Title	HARD FACTS ABOUT CONCRETE, biennial
Coverage	Precast concrete, cement and construction data. Some European data also given. 6 years of data.
Contents & Origin of Statistics	Tables per issue: 53. Own research 45%, Other non official source 30%, Government statistics 20%, Unstated 5%. Supporting text 5%
Currency	Varies
Response	1984
Availability	General
Cost	£1
Address	60 Charles St, Leicester LE1 1FB
Telephone	0533 536161
Contact	Mr. J.B. Badiani, Accountant

132

Originator	BRITISH PRINTING INDUSTRIES FEDERATION
Title	ANNUAL REVIEW, annual
Coverage	Contains a statistical section on general trends in the printing industry.
Comments	Produce other surveys for specialised groups amongst members and ad-hoc surveys. Also publish an annual report with a few figures. See also entry headed 'Printing Industries'.
Response	1984
Availability	General
Cost	Free
Address	11 Bedford Row, London WC1R 4DX

Telephone	01 242 6904
Contact	C.J. Sherwood, Industrial Relations Officer

133

Originator	BRITISH PRINTING INDUSTRIES FEDERATION
Title	EMPLOYMENT IN PRINT, annual
Coverage	Manpower data in the printing industry, based on a survey of members.
Contents & Origin of Statistics	Tables per issue: Own research 100%
Comments	Produce other surveys for specialised groups amongst members and ad-hoc surveys. See also entry headed 'Printing Industries'.
Response	1984
Availability	General
Cost	Free to members and academic institutions, £5 to others
Address	11 Bedford Row, London WC1R 4DX
Telephone	01 242 6904
Contact	C.J. Sherwood, Industrial Relations Officer

134

Originator	BRITISH PRINTING INDUSTRIES FEDERATION
Title	SALARY SURVEY, annual
Coverage	Data on salaries of white collar staff in the printing industry based on a survey of members.
Contents & Origin of Statistics	Tables per issue: Own research 100%
Comments	Produce other surveys for specialised groups amongst members, and other ad-hoc surveys. See also entry headed 'Printing Industries'.
Response	1984
Availability	Members
Cost	£35
Address	11 Bedford Row, London WC1R 4DX
Telephone	01 242 6904
Contact	C.J. Sherwood, Industrial Relations Officer

135

Originator	BRITISH PRINTING INDUSTRIES FEDERATION
Title	WAGES SURVEY, annual

Coverage	Details of wages of production workers in printing industry from a survey of members.
Contents & Origin of Statistics	Tables per issue: Own research 100%
Comments	Produce other surveys for specialised groups amongst members and ad-hoc surveys. See also entry headed 'Printing Industries'.
Response	1984
Availability	Members
Cost	Free
Address	11 Bedford Row, London WC1R 4DX
Telephone	01 242 6904
Contact	C.J. Sherwood, Industrial Relations Officer

136

Originator	BRITISH PUMP MANUFACTURERS ASSOCIATION
Title	COST/PRICE INDICES, bi-annual
Coverage	Prices of pumps and valves.
Comments	Published jointly with the British Valve Manufacturers Association.
Response	1983
Availability	Members
Address	37 Castle St, Guildford, Surrey GU1 3UQ
Telephone	0483 37997/8
Contact	T.J. Langhorn, Economist

137

Originator	BRITISH RADIO AND ELECTRONIC EQUIPMENT MANU-FACTURERS' ASSOCIATION
Title	DELIVERIES OF SELECTED VIDEO AND AUDIO PRODUCTS TO THE UK MARKET, quarterly
Coverage	Press release covering deliveries to the trade of television, teletext, video recorders and music centres.
Contents & Origin of Statistics	Tables per issue: 5. Unstated 100%. Supporting text 40%
Comments	Also publish 2 annuals on the market for television receivers and radio receivers respectively - these have been temporarily suspended but the Association are hoping to reinstate them as soon as possible.
Currency	3 months
Response	1984
Availability	General
Cost	Free
Address	Landseer House, 19 Charing Cross Rd, London WC2H OES

Telephone	01 930 3206; Telex: 296215
Contact	Leslie L. Gunde, Economic Services Secretary

138

Originator	BRITISH RAILWAYS BOARD
Title	ANNUAL REPORT, annual
Coverage	Largely financial statistics on the organisation but includes figures on passengers, freight traffic and performance indicators over a 5 year period.
Contents & Origin of Statistics	Tables per issue: 8. Own research 100%
Response	1983
Availability	General
Cost	£3.50
Address	Euston Square, P.O. Box 100, London, NW1 2DZ
Telephone	01 262 3332
Contact	J. Dawson, Press Office

139

Originator	BRITISH READY MIXED CONCRETE ASSOCIATION
Title	CONCRETE FACTS, annual
Coverage	Ready mixed concrete production over a 21 year period. Gives output for members and an estimate of non-members' output.
Contents & Origin of Statistics	Tables per issue: 1. Own research 50%, Government statistics 50%.
Comments	Published on 1 sheet of paper
Response	1983
Availability	General
Cost	Free
Address	Shepperton House, Green Lane, Shepperton, Middlesex TW17 8DN
Telephone	09322 43232
Contact	Above address

140

Originator	BRITISH ROAD FEDERATION
Title	BASIC ROAD STATISTICS, annual. 1934-
Coverage	Roads and road transport, for example traffic, energy, taxation, public expenditure, accidents and some international comparisons.

Contents & Origin of Statistics	Tables per issue: 49. Government statistics 95%, Non official source 5%. Supporting text 3%
Currency	1 year
Response	1984
Availability	General
Cost	£6
ISSN	0309 3638
Address	Cowdray House, 6 Portugal St, London WC2A 2HG
Telephone	01 242 1285
Contact	Andrew Street, Economist

141

Originator	BRITISH ROBOT ASSOCIATION
Title	ROBOT FACTS, annual. 1981-
Coverage	UK robot application analysis and data on the origin of robots installed. Also details of the world robot population.
Contents & Origin of Statistics	Tables per issue: 8.
Comments	Journal 'Industrial Robot' features some statistics from this Association.
Currency	1-2 months
Response	1984
Availability	Members and General
Cost	£14 (free to members)
Address	28-30 High St, Kempston, Bedford MK42 7AJ
Telephone	0234 854477; Telex: 825489
Contact	Alan V. Moutrey, Membership Secretary

142

Originator	BRITISH SECONDARY METALS ASSOCIATION
Title	SURVEY OF MEMBERS, biennial
Coverage	Survey of member companies by employee size, number of sites, investment, turnover, etc.
Contents & Origin of Statistics	Tables per issue: 13. Own research 100%
Comments	Due to economic situation there has been some delay and omissions in producing recent issues.
Response	1983
Availability	General
Cost	Free
Address	40-42 Oxford St, London W1N 9FJ

Telephone   01 580 5228/9
Contact   Above address

143

Originator   BRITISH STEEL CORPORATION

Title   STEEL INDUSTRY STATISTICS, monthly
Coverage   Data on UK steel output for 3 years by month for both the public
             and private sector. Production is also broken down by standard
             regions.

Contents &   Tables per issue: 2. Own research 100%
  Origin of
  Statistics

Comments   Produced in the form of a press release
Currency   1 month
Response   1983
Availability General
Address   9 Albert Embankment, London SE1
Telephone   01 735 7654
Contact   Above address

144

Originator   BRITISH TELECOMMUNICATIONS

Title   STATISTICS, annual
Coverage   Historical data, exchange connections and telephone types. Types of
             exchanges with breakdown of connections capacity. Equipment/line
             plant, telephone calls, telex/telegraph, manpower, motor transport,
             tariffs, finance and growth and development.

Contents &   Tables per issue: 107pgs. Own research 100%. Supporting text 10%
  Origin of
  Statistics

Currency   6-7 months
Response   1984
Availability General
Cost   £10
ISSN   0262 379X
Address   LCS/OPS 1.2.1, Room 201, Leith House, 47-57 Gresham St,
             London EC2V 7JL.
Telephone   01 432 3831; Telex: 883051
Contact   Ron Wilson, OPS 1.2.1

145

Originator	BRITISH TEXTILE CONFEDERATION
Title	ANNUAL REPORT AND REVIEW, annual. 1973-
Coverage	Profile of textile industry, covering value of industry, employment, production, capital expenditure, final consumption and trade.
Contents & Origin of Statistics	Tables per issue: 8. Own research 25%, Government statistics 75%. Supporting text 90%
Currency	3-4 months
Response	1984
Availability	General
Cost	Free
Address	24 Buckingham Gate, London SW1E 6LB
Telephone	01 828 5222 ; Telex: 8814217

146

Originator	BRITISH TEXTILE CONFEDERATION
Title	IMPORT SURVEILLANCE WORKING PARTY REPORT, quarterly. c1977-
Coverage	Textiles and clothing imports by products or product groups and exports by product groups.
Contents & Origin of Statistics	Tables per issue: 17. Government statistics 100%.
Currency	3 months
Response	1984
Availability	General
Cost	£75 (£25 per issue)
Address	24 Buckingham Gate, London SW1E 6LB
Telephone	01 828 5222 ; Telex: 8814217

147

Originator	BRITISH TOURIST AUTHORITY
Title	ANNUAL REPORT, annual
Coverage	Includes general tables on UK tourist trade and overseas visitors.
Contents & Origin of Statistics	Tables per issue: 8. Own research 30%,Government statistics 70%
Response	1984
Availability	General
Cost	£2.25

Address	Queens House, 64 St James's St, London SW1A 1NF
Telephone	01 629 9191
Contact	Research Librarian

148

Originator	BRITISH TOURIST AUTHORITY
Title	BRITISH HOME TOURISM SURVEY, annual
Coverage	Concentrates on travel in Britain by British residents and gives information on holidays, business and conference travel, visits to friends and relatives and overnight tourist trips. Based on a survey of approximately 26,000 adults.
Contents & Origin of Statistics	Tables per issue: 13. Own research 100%
Comments	Detailed survey results available on a monthly basis on application.
Response	1984
Availability	General
Cost	£2.50
Address	Queens House, 64 St James's St, London SW1A 1NF
Telephone	01 629 9191
Contact	Research Librarian

149

Originator	BRITISH TOURIST AUTHORITY
Title	BRITISH NATIONAL TRAVEL SURVEY, annual
Coverage	Data on the level of holiday taking among the British adult population, on the characteristics of holiday takers and on the number and types of holiday taken both abroad and in the UK. The survey is based on a sample of 3,000 adults and the results are analysed in a variety of ways, e.g. by sex, age, income etc.
Contents & Origin of Statistics	Tables per issue: Own research 100%
Comments	Able to add syndicated questions to the survey for a fee.
Response	1984
Availability	General
Cost	£4,250 (4 volumes)
Address	Queens House, 64 St James's St, London SW1A 1NF
Telephone	01 629 9191
Contact	Gillian Gardner-Smith, Research Manager

150

Originator   BRITISH TOURIST AUTHORITY

Title   DIGEST OF TOURIST STATISTICS, every 2 or 3 years
Coverage   Includes extracts from various travel surveys including the British
                    Home Tourism Survey. However, large percentage refer to overseas
                    travel.

Contents &   Tables per issue: 80. Own research + other non official source 60%,
Origin of   Government statistics 40%
Statistics

Currency   Varies
Response   1984
Availability   General
Cost   £10
Address   Queens House, 64 St James's St, London SW1A 1NF
Telephone   01 629 9191
Contact   Research Librarian

151

Originator   BRITISH TOURIST AUTHORITY

Title   SURVEY OF OVERSEAS VISITORS TO LONDON, annual
Coverage   Details of type of visitors, type of visit, type of accommodation,
                    activities, transport and their reactions to the city.

Contents &   Tables per issue: 26. Own research 100%
Origin of
Statistics

Response   1984
Availability   General
Cost   £7.50
Address   Queens House, 64 St James's St, London SW1A 1NF
Telephone   01 629 9191
Contact   Research Librarian

152

Originator   BRITISH TOURIST AUTHORITY

Title   TOURISM INTELLIGENCE QUARTERLY, quarterly
Coverage   Collates and interprets current statistical data and forecasts relating
                    to tourism in the UK. Includes details of overseas visitors, hotel
                    occupancy and tariffs, travel by UK residents and traffic at UK air
                    and seaports.

Contents & Origin of Statistics	Tables per issue: Varies

Response	1984
Availability	General
Cost	£8.50
Address	Queens House, 64 St James's St, London SW1A 1NF
Telephone	01 629 9191
Contact	Research Librarian

153

Originator	BRITISH VALVE MANUFACTURERS ASSOCIATION
Title	BVMA QUARTERLY SALES ANALYSIS, quarterly
Coverage	Sales of member companies.
Comments	Also produce a joint publication with the British Pump Manufacturers Association.
Response	1983
Availability	Members
Address	3 Pannells Court, Chertsey St, Guildford, Surrey GU1 4EU
Telephone	0483 37379
Contact	T.J. Langhorn, Economist

154

Originator	BRITISH VALVE MANUFACTURERS ASSOCIATION
Title	EIF VALVE FORECASTS, bi-annual
Coverage	Forecasts of valve sales.
Comments	Also produce a joint publication with the British Pump Manufacturers Association.
Response	1983
Availability	Members
Address	3 Pannells Court, Chertsey St, Guildford, Surrey GU1 4EU
Telephone	0483 37379
Contact	T.J. Langhorn, Economist

155

Originator	BRITISH WATER AND EFFLUENT TREATMENT PLANT ASSOCIATION
Title	ANNUAL REPORT, annual. 1969-
Coverage	Municipal and industrial water and effluent orders booked by members. Home and export markets.

Contents &	Tables per issue: 2. Own research 100%. Supporting text 95%
Origin of	
Statistics	

Comments	Collect but do not publish sales data.
Response	1984
Availability	Members and some others
Cost	Free
Address	51 Castle St, High Wycombe, Bucks HP13 6RN
Telephone	0494 444603
Contact	D.A. Burroughes, Consultant

156

Originator	BRITISH WATERWAYS BOARD

Title	ANNUAL REPORT AND ACCOUNTS, annual. 1963-
Coverage	Largely concerned with Board's activities and finances but contains some general statistics eg engineering, traffic, staffing.

Contents &	Tables per issue: Varies. Own research 100%. Supporting text 50%
Origin of	
Statistics	

Currency	6 months
Response	1984
Availability	General
Cost	£3.50
ISBN	0 903218 28 3
Address	Melbury House, Melbury Terrace, London NW1 6JX
Telephone	01 262 6711; Telex: 263605
Contact	Paul Higham, Recreation Research and Planning Department. (0923 778231, ext 48)

157

Originator	BRITISH WOOD WORKING FEDERATION

Title	TITLE UNSTATED, 3 issues per year
Coverage	Survey of state of trade based on a cross-section of members.
Response	1983
Availability	Members
Address	82 New Cavendish St, London W1M 8AD
Telephone	01 580 5588
Contact	Peter Shapcott, Director

158

Originator	BRITISH WOODPULP ASSOCIATION

Title	ANNUAL REPORT, annual

Coverage	Contains a 'Statistics Section', including imports of pulp by grade and country of origin, production and consumption of paper and board.
Contents & Origin of Statistics	Tables per issue: 7. Unstated 100%. Supporting text 60%
Currency	4 months
Response	1984
Availability	Members and trade associations
Cost	£20 (free to members)
Address	c/o Graylaw House, Manor Rd, Wallington, Surrey SM6 OER
Telephone	01 669 0911
Contact	Mr. Peter Brown, Secretary

159

Originator	BRITISH WOODPULP ASSOCIATION
Title	STATISTICAL DIGEST, monthly
Coverage	Tonnage imports of wood pulp for paper-making and other purposes.
Contents & Origin of Statistics	Tables per issue: 1. Government statistics 100%.
Currency	6-7 weeks
Response	1984
Availability	Members and trade associations
Cost	£10 (free to members)
Address	c/o Graylaw House, Manor Rd, Wallington, Surrey SM6 0ER
Telephone	01 669 0911
Contact	Mr Peter Brown, Secretary

160

Originator	BRITISH WOOL MARKETING BOARD
Title	ANNUAL REPORT AND ACCOUNTS, annual
Coverage	Mainly details of the organisation and finances of the British Wool Marketing Board but also contains regular statistics on wool production by type of wool produced.
Contents & Origin of Statistics	Tables per issue: 1. Own research 100%. Supporting text 95%
Currency	9 months
Response	1984
Availability	Primarily for Board members and wool producers but usually generally available on request
Cost	Free

Address	Oak Mills, Station Rd, Bradford BD14 6JD
Telephone	0274 882091; Telex: 51406
Contact	Carol P. Wild, Secretary to Economics and Finance Division

161

Originator	BRITISH WOOL MARKETING BOARD
Title	ANNUAL STATISTICS, annual
Coverage	Data on wool production, average clip size, weight of wool taken up, and number of registered producers by UK region.
Contents & Origin of Statistics	Tables per issue: 2. Own research 100%. Supporting text 33%.
Currency	1 month
Response	1984
Availability	Primarily Board members and wool producers but usually generally available on request
Cost	Free
Address	Oak Mills, Station Rd, Bradford BD14 6JD
Telephone	0274 882091; Telex: 51406
Contact	Carol P. Wild, Secretary to Economics and Finance Division

162

Originator	BRITISH WOOL MARKETING BOARD
Title	BASIC DATA, annual
Coverage	Summary information on the sheep population, wool production, prices, registered producers, and the production of mutton and lamb. All figures contained on one sheet of paper.
Contents & Origin of Statistics	Tables per issue: 1. Own research 100%. .
Currency	Latest year
Response	1984
Availability	Primarily Board members and wool producers but usually available generally on request.
Cost	Free
Address	Oak Mills, Station Rd, Bradford BD14 6JD
Telephone	0274 882091; Telex: 51406
Contact	Carol P. Wild, Secretary to Economics and Finance Division

163

Originator	BRMB RADIO
Title	AUDIENCE, annual
Coverage	Gives results of radio diary listening survey (JICRAR), total survey area audience and City of Birmingham audience. Analysis by age, sex, and social class.
Contents & Origin of Statistics	Tables per issue: 3. Own research + other non official source 100%
Response	1983
Availability	General
Cost	Free
Address	P.O. Box 255, Radio House, Aston Rd North, Birmingham B6 4BX
Telephone	021 359 4481/9
Contact	John Panteny, Sales Manager

164

Originator	BRMB RADIO
Title	MARKETING FACTS, every 2-3 years
Coverage	General statistics on the broadcast area such as population, households, living standards etc. and details on shopping trends.
Contents & Origin of Statistics	Tables per issue: 45. Own research + other non official source 73%, Government statistics 27%
Response	1983
Availability	General
Cost	Free
Address	P.O. Box 255, Radio House, Aston Rd North, Birmingham, B6 4BX
Telephone	021 359 4481/9
Contact	John Panteny, Sales Manager

165

Originator	BUCKINGHAMSHIRE COUNTY COUNCIL
Title	RED BOOK OF STATISTICS, annual
Coverage	Financial statistics on the Council plus general data on the county, i.e. population, employment, earnings, housing etc.
Contents & Origin of Statistics	Tables per issue: 23. Own research 50%, Other non official source 50%. Supporting text 5%
Currency	Varies
Response	1983

Availability	General
Cost	Free
ISSN	0140 3508
Address	County Hall, Aylesbury, Buckinghamshire
Telephone	0296 5000
Contact	E.J. Deung, County Treasurer

166

Originator   BUILDER AND MERCHANT

Title   BUILDING TRENDS, monthly in a monthly journal. 1981-

Coverage   Data on building orders and building materials price changes.

Contents & Origin of Statistics   Tables per issue: 4. Own research 75%, Government statistics 25%

Comments   Journal also includes occasional statistical surveys on various building sectors.

Currency	1 week
Response	1984
Availability	General
Cost	£10 or £1 for a single copy
Address	The Builder Group, Builder House, 1-3 Pemberton Row, Fleet St, London EC4P 4HL
Telephone	01 353 2300; Telex: 25212
Contact	Roger Packer, Editor

167

Originator   BUILDING

Title   BUILDING INDICATORS, monthly in a weekly journal

Coverage   Details of new orders, output, activity, mortgage finance, architects' workload, bricks and cement and building index. Usually appears in the second issue each month.

Contents & Origin of Statistics   Tables per issue: 11. Own research 10%, Other non official source 30%, Government statistics 60%

Currency	Varies
Response	1984
Availability	General
Cost	£36 or 60p for a single issue
ISSN	0007 3318
Address	Building (Publishers) Ltd, Builder House, 1-3 Pemberton Row, Red Lion Court, Fleet St, London EC4P 4HL

Telephone	01 353 2300; Telex: 25212
Contact	Jane Roberts, Editorial Librarian

168

Originator	BUILDING
Title	COST FILE, monthly in a weekly journal
Coverage	Costs of individual building materials and products plus costs of external works and plant hire. Usually appears in the first issue each month.
Contents & Origin of Statistics	Tables per issue: Varies. Own research 100%
Currency	2 weeks
Response	1984
Availability	General
Cost	(pa): £36 or 60p for a single issue
ISSN	0007 3318
Address	Building (Publishers) Ltd, Builder House, 1-3 Pemberton Row, Red Lion Court, Fleet St, London EC4P 4HL
Telephone	01 353 2300; Telex: 25212
Contact	Jane Roberts, Editorial Librarian

169

Originator	BUILDING
Title	HOUSING COST INDEX, monthly in a weekly journal. Dec 1973 -
Coverage	Housing cost index covering building, materials, labour costs etc. Usually appears in the first issue each month.
Contents & Origin of Statistics	Tables per issue: 1. Own research 100%
Comments	Overlapped with an earlier index called 'The Cost of Building Index' which covers 1939-1975.
Currency	2 weeks
Response	1984
Availability	General
Cost	£36 or 60p for a single issue
ISSN	0007 3318
Address	Building (Publishers) Ltd, Builder House, 1-3 Pemberton Row, Red Lion Court, Fleet St, London EC4P 4HL
Telephone	01 353 2300; Telex: 25212
Contact	Jane Roberts, Editorial Librarian

170

Originator	BUILDING
Title	JOB TRENDS, monthly in a weekly journal. May 1978 -
Coverage	Index of vacancies by job type, usually appearing in the last issue for each month.
Contents & Origin of Statistics	Tables per issue: 5. Own research + other non official source 100%
Comments	Superseded an earlier index called 'Postscript'
Currency	1 month
Response	1984
Availability	General
Cost	£36 or 60p for a single issue
ISSN	0007 3318
Address	Building (Publishers) Ltd, Builder House, 1-3 Pemberton Row, Red Lion Court, Fleet St, London EC4P 4HL
Telephone	01 353 2300; Telex: 25212
Contact	Jane Roberts, Editorial Librarian

171

Originator	BUILDING
Title	PRICE ADJUSTMENT INDICES, monthly in a weekly journal. Nov 1974 -
Coverage	Price indices for building works and electrical and engineering materials and labour. Usually published in the 4th issue each month.
Contents & Origin of Statistics	Tables per issue: 1. Government statistics 100%
Currency	1 month
Response	1984
Availability	General
Cost	£36 or 60p for a single issue
ISSN	0007 3318
Address	Building (Publishers) Ltd, Builder House, 1-3 Pemberton Row, Red Lion Court, Fleet St, London EC4P 4HL
Telephone	01 353 2300; Telex: 25212
Contact	Jane Roberts, Editorial Librarian

172

Originator	BUILDING EMPLOYERS CONFEDERATION
Title	B.E.C. QUARTERLY CONSTRUCTION REVIEW, quarterly

Coverage	Data on housebuilding, new orders, costs and prices and the construction outlook for the coming year. Also details from the 'State of Trade Enquiry'.
Contents & Origin of Statistics	Tables per issue: 15. Unstated 100%. Supporting text 50%.
Currency	3 months
Response	1984
Availability	General
Cost	Unstated
Address	82 New Cavendish St, London W1M 8AD
Telephone	01 580 5588; Telex: 265763
Contact	Kathleen Dunmore, Construction Economist

173

Originator	BUILDING EMPLOYERS CONFEDERATION
Title	STATE OF TRADE ENQUIRY, quarterly
Coverage	New enquiries for work relative to the previous quarter, volume of work for current year related to previous year and current capacity of operations.
Contents & Origin of Statistics	Tables per issue: 3. Own research 100%. Supporting text 40%
Comments	Published in the form of a news release
Currency	1 month
Response	1984
Availability	General
Cost	Free to media, others through subscription
Address	82 New Cavendish St, London W1M 8AD
Telephone	01 580 5588; Telex: 265763
Contact	Kathleen Dunmore, Construction Economist

174

Originator	BUILDING MANAGEMENT AND MARKETING CONSULTANTS LTD
Title	NATIONAL HOME IMPROVEMENT AND D.I.Y. CONSUMER SURVEY, annual with half-yearly updates. 1981-
Coverage	Details of trends in the home improvement, repairs and maintenance market based on replies of 15,000 households. AGB carry out the survey.
Contents & Origin of Statistics	Tables per issue: Varies. Own research 100%

Currency	1-6 months
Response	1983
Availability	General
Cost	Varies according to the number of sectors, materials taken. Basic package costs £400 with prices up to £1950.
Address	Builder House, 1-3 Pemberton Row, Red Lion Court, Fleet St, London EC4P 4HL
Telephone	01 353 2300
Contact	Mr. D.G. Airey, AGB - see separate entry for AGB for address

175

Originator	BUILDING SERVICES RESEARCH AND INFORMATION ASSOCIATION (BSRIA)
Title	BSRIA STATISTICS BULLETIN, quarterly. 1976-
Coverage	Market review of heating, ventilating, air conditioning, electrical and plumbing services plus forecasts up to 18 months ahead of sales of heating equipment. Also general review of the housebuilding sector and a special profile each month on a particular product.
Contents & Origin of Statistics	Tables per issue: 30-45. Own research 25%, Other non official source 20%, Government statistics 55%. Supporting text 25%
Currency	Varies
Response	1984
Availability	General
Cost	£35
ISSN	0308 6224
Address	Old Bracknell Lane West, Bracknell, Berkshire RG12 4AH
Telephone	0344 426511; Telex: 848288
Contact	Anne King, Statistics and Forecasting Unit

176

Originator	BUILDING SERVICES RESEARCH AND INFORMATION ASSOCIATION (BSRIA)
Title	KEY STATISTICS FOR THE BUILDING SERVICES INDUSTRY, annual. 1979-
Coverage	Summary statistics for the last 4 years on the industry.
Contents & Origin of Statistics	Tables per issue: 8. Unstated 100%.
Comments	Produced in pocket card format.
Currency	15 months
Response	1984
Availability	General
Cost	Free

Address	Old Bracknell Lane West, Bracknell, Berkshire RG12 4AH
Telephone	0344 426511; Telex: 848288
Contact	Anne King, Statistics and Forecasting Unit

177

Originator	BUILDING SOCIETIES ASSOCIATION
Title	BSA BULLETIN, quarterly
Coverage	Data on societies loans, assets, advances, new commitments, mortgages, house prices etc.
Contents & Origin of Statistics	Tables per issue: 18
Comments	Other reports also produced. Title previously called 'Facts and Figures'.
Currency	Varies
Response	1984
Availability	General
Cost	£8
ISSN	0261 6394
Address	3 Savile Row, London W1X 1AF
Telephone	01 437 0655
Contact	Information Department

178

Originator	BURTON UPON TRENT AND DISTRICT CHAMBER OF COMMERCE AND INDUSTRY
Title	ECONOMIC SURVEY, quarterly
Coverage	Trends in manufacturing, labour, cashflow and investment.
Contents & Origin of Statistics	Tables per issue: Own research 100%
Response	1983
Availability	General
Cost	£0.50 per copy, plus p+p
Address	2-3 St Pauls Square, Burton upon Trent, Derbyshire DE14 2EQ
Telephone	0283 63761
Contact	Secretary

179

Originator	BVRLA NEWS
Title	STATISTICAL SURVEY, annual in a journal published 6 times a year
Coverage	Data on the size of the chauffeur drive/private hire, rental and leasing fleets operated by members of the British Vehicle Rental and Leasing Association. 700 members were circulated in 1983 and 598 responded.
Contents & Origin of Statistics	Tables per issue: 8. Own research 100%
Currency	6-8 months
Response	1984
Availability	General
Cost	Free to members, £10 to others
Address	13 St Johns St, Chichester, West Sussex PO19 1UU
Telephone	0243 786782; Telex: 86402
Contact	O.J.H. Dawson, Secretary

180

Originator	C.A.C.I.
Title	ACORN PROFILES, continuous
Coverage	Demographic profiles by geographical and target areas.
Comments	Other computer packages and market analysis packages available, including SITE package.
Response	1984
Availability	General
Cost	On application
Address	289 High Holborn, London WC1V 7HZ
Telephone	01 404 0834
Contact	Above address

181

Originator	CABINET MAKER AND RETAIL FURNISHER
Title	BUSINESS AT A GLANCE, monthly in a weekly journal
Coverage	Furniture retail prices, retail sales, producer prices, orders and deliveries, carpet output and soft furnishing sales.
Contents & Origin of Statistics	Tables per issue: 4. Government statistics 100%
Comments	Other statistics published in different issues - See other entries
Currency	1 month

Response	1984
Availability	General
Cost	£40 or 75p for a single copy
ISSN	007 9278
Address	Benn Publications Ltd, Benn House, Sovereign Way, Tonbridge, Kent TN9 1RW
Telephone	0732 364422; Telex: 95132
Contact	Peter Varley, Marketing Manager

182

Originator	CABINET MAKER AND RETAIL FURNISHER
Title	IMPORT/EXPORT TRENDS IN FURNITURE, quarterly in a weekly journal
Coverage	Imports and exports of furniture by major geographical regions, with commentary.
Contents & Origin of Statistics	Tables per issue: 2. Government statistics 100%
Comments	Other statistics published in other issues - see other entries
Currency	3 months
Response	1984
Availability	General
Cost	£40 or 75p for a single copy
ISSN	007 9278
Address	Benn Publications Ltd, Benn House, Sovereign Way, Tonbridge, Kent TN9 1RW
Telephone	0732 364422; Telex: 95132
Contact	Peter Varley, Marketing Manager

183

Originator	CADBURY SCHWEPPES PLC
Title	CONFECTIONERY MARKET REVIEW, annual
Coverage	Confectionery market, expenditure on and consumption of confectionery, chocolate market - performance by sector, top sellers, advertising.
Contents & Origin of Statistics	Tables per issue: 10. Non official source 100%. Supporting text 30%
Currency	2 months
Response	1984
Availability	General
Cost	Free
Address	Leconfield House, Curzon St, London W1Y 7FB

| Telephone | 01 262 1212; Telex: 338011 |
| Contact | Mary Painter, Group Communications Department |

184

Originator   CAKE AND BISCUIT ALLIANCE LTD

Title   ANNUAL REPORT, annual
Coverage   Statistical section covering biscuit and cake deliveries to the home and export market, imports of biscuits and cakes and ingredients purchased. Figures based on a survey of members.

Contents &   Tables per issue: 6. Own research 100%
Origin of
Statistics

Response   1984
Availability   General
Cost   Free
Address   11 Green St, London W1Y 3RF
Telephone   01 629 8971; Telex: 24738
Contact   Above address

185

Originator   CAKE AND BISCUIT ALLIANCE LTD

Title   CBA FOUR-WEEKLY SUMMARIES, 13 issues per year
Coverage   Despatches of cakes and biscuits.
Response   1984
Availability   Members and General
Cost   Free to members, £75 to others (under review)
Address   11 Green St, London W1Y 3RF
Telephone   01 629 8971; Telex: 24738
Contact   Above address

186

Originator   CAMBRIDGE ECONOMETRICS LTD

Title   ECONOMIC FORECAST REPORTS AND INDUSTRY REPORTS, continuous
Coverage   Forecasts up to the year 2000 for the economy and for 39 industrial sectors with information on employment, output, prices and investment. Subscribers also have 2 free places at an annual seminar.

Contents &   Tables per issue: Varies
Origin of
Statistics

Comments	Information above relates to complete service. Also available are individual subscriptions to the Energy Subscription Service, Industrial Subscription Service and the Project Subscription Service where clients can commission their own work. Services also available on magnetic tape.
Response	1984
Availability	Members
Cost	£8750
Address	P.O. Box 114, 21 St Andrew's St, Cambridge CB2 3RW
Telephone	0223 67524
Contact	Marion Lunan, Administrative Director

187

Originator	CAMBRIDGESHIRE COUNTY COUNCIL
Title	DISTRICT POPULATION FORECASTS, annual
Coverage	Forecasts for county and districts for a 20 year period.·
Contents & Origin of Statistics	Tables per issue: 16. Own research 50%, Government statistics 50%. Supporting text 5%
Currency	3 months
Response	1983
Availability	Mainly internal but available to selected outside users at the Council's discretion
Address	Directorate of Planning and Research, Shire Hall, Castle Hill, Cambridge CB3 0AP
Telephone	0223 317611
Contact	Jean Hardy, Library and Information Service

188

Originator	CAMBRIDGESHIRE COUNTY COUNCIL
Title	HOUSE PRICES IN CAMBRIDGESHIRE, bi-annual
Coverage	Current figures at district and county level and figures for 2 previous years. New property is not included. Also availability of property by type, size and district.
Contents & Origin of Statistics	Tables per issue: 9-10. Own research 100%. Supporting text 45%
Currency	3 months
Response	1983
Availability	General
Address	Shire Hall, Castle Hill, Cambridge CB3 0AP

Telephone	0223 317611
Contact	Jean Hardy, Library and Information Service

189

Originator	CAMPBELL NEILL & CO

Title	SCOTCH WHISKY REVIEW, annual
Coverage	Details of consumption, production, exports, duty, stocks, prices, and profits for the industry. Also provides information on the major brands and individual companies and distilleries.

Contents & Origin of Statistics	Tables per issue: 60. Supporting text 60%

Currency	3 months
Response	1984
Availability	General
Cost	£95
Address	69 St George's Place, Glasgow G2 1JN
Telephone	041 248 6271
Contact	A.S. Gray, Head of Research

190

Originator	CAN MAKERS' INFORMATION SERVICE

Title	THE CAN MAKERS REPORT, biennial. 1981-
Coverage	Sales data for beer.and soft drinks cans plus review of consumer attitudes to drinks packaging.

Contents & Origin of Statistics	Tables per issue: 14. Own research 50%, Other non official source 50%. Supporting text 15%

Comments	Although the document is only produced every 2 years, the latest year's figures are available from the Service. Also produce a regular press release with statistics.
Currency	1-2 years
Response	1984
Availability	General
Cost	Free
Address	3 Beeston Place, London SW1W 0JJ
Telephone	01 629 9621
Contact	Patricia Braun

191

Originator	CAPEL, JAMES AND CO
Title	UK ECONOMIC ASSESSMENT, monthly
Coverage	Forecasts for inflation, PSBR, monetary aggregates, interest rates, balance of payments, sterling, corporate profits, consumer spending, capital investment and unemployment. Forecasts 1-2 years ahead. Also contains special feature articles.
Contents & Origin of Statistics	Tables per issue: 44. Unstated 100%. Supporting text 30%
Comments	Also issue 'International Economic Indicators' monthly,'International Bond and Currency Review' and a wide range of other statistical publications.
Response	1984
Availability	Researchers
Cost	Free
Address	Winchester House, 100 Old Broad St, London EC2N 1BQ
Telephone	01 588 6010; Telex: 888866
Contact	Mrs. J. Seymour-Chalk, Librarian

192

Originator	CAPEL, JAMES AND CO
Title	WEEKLY GILT EDGED DATA SHEET, weekly
Coverage	Interest rates, prices and yields for a variety of stocks, largely Government. Also includes exchange rates, treasury bills, current rates on deposit to local authorities, trade data etc. Gives major international band market comparisons.
Contents & Origin of Statistics	Tables per issue: 2. Unstated 100%.
Response	1984
Availability	Researchers
Cost	Free
Address	Winchester House, 100 Old Broad St, London EC2N 1BQ
Telephone	01 588 6010; Telex: 888866
Contact	Mrs. J. Seymour-Chalk, Librarian

193

Originator	CAPITAL RADIO
Title	CAPITAL MARKETING, annual
Coverage	5 sections covering population, households, consumer expenditure, retailing and marketing services.

Contents & Origin of Statistics	Tables per issue: 27. Own research + other non official source 90%, Government statistics 10%

Currency	Varies
Response	1983
Availability	General
Cost	Free
Address	Euston Tower, London NW1 3DR
Telephone	01 388 6801
Contact	Sales Department

194

Originator	CAR FLEET MANAGEMENT

Title	COST TABLES, six times a year in a journal published six times a year
Coverage	Standing costs and running costs of various company cars.
Contents & Origin of Statistics	Tables per issue: 3. Non official source 100%. Supporting text 20%
Comments	To qualify as a reader a number of cars bought as a tax-offset purchase have to be owned.
Response	1984
Availability	Controlled circulation
Cost	Free
Address	IPC Business Press Ltd, Quadrant House, The Quadrant, Sutton, Surrey
Telephone	01 661 3500; Telex: 892084
Contact	Editor

195

Originator	CARPET AND FLOORCOVERINGS REVIEW

Title	IMPORT STATISTICS, every six weeks in a twice monthly journal
Coverage	Imports of tufted carpets by country.
Contents & Origin of Statistics	Tables per issue: 2. Government statistics 100%
Currency	2 months
Response	1985
Availability	General
Cost	£32 or £1 for a single issue
ISSN	0263 4236
Address	Benn Publications Ltd, Sovereign Way, Tonbridge, Kent TN9 1RW

Telephone	0732 364422; Telex: 95132
Contact	Above address

196

Originator	CARRICK JAMES MARKET RESEARCH

Title	CHILDRENS OMNIBUS SURVEY, monthly
Coverage	Continuous survey of children and teenagers based on a sample of approximately 1,000. Various syndicated and individual subscriber questions asked on behaviour, opinions, spending etc.

Contents & Origin of Statistics	Tables per issue: Varies

Response	1983
Availability	General
Cost	Varies according to range of questions and information required
Address	21 Soho Square, London W1V 5FD
Telephone	01 734 7171/2; Telex: 21879
Contact	J. Perkins

197

Originator	CATERER AND HOTELKEEPER

Title	FOOD PRICES, weekly in a weekly journal
Coverage	Wholesale prices of vegetable, fruit, meat and fish.

Contents & Origin of Statistics	Tables per issue: 1. Own research 100%. Supporting text 10%

Currency	1 Week
Response	1985
Availability	General
Cost	£50 or 75p for a single issue
ISSN	0008 7777
Address	Business Press International Ltd, Quadrant House, The Quadrant, Sutton, Surrey SM2 5AS
Telephone	01 661 3500; Te;ex: 892084
Contact	Above address

198

Originator	CEMENT ADMIXTURES ASSOCIATION

Title	STATISTICAL RETURN, bi-annual
Coverage	Sales by volume and value of cement treated for a variety of types of admixture.

Contents & Origin of Statistics	Tables per issue: 1.

Currency	3 months
Response	1984
Availability	Members
Address	2A High St, Hythe, Southampton SO4 6YW
Telephone	0703 842765
Contact	Dr P. Bosworth, Secretary

199

Originator	CEMENT AND CONCRETE ASSOCIATION
Title	CEMENT - CHANNEL OF SALE MONTHLY FIGURES, monthly. 1978-
Coverage	Deliveries of Portland cement by type of customer in each county, DoE region and nationally.
Contents & Origin of Statistics	Tables per issue: 1. Own research 100%.
Currency	Less than a month
Response	1984
Availability	Limited
Cost	Free
Address	Wexham Springs, Wexham, nr Slough, SL3 6PL
Telephone	02816 2727 ; Telex: 848352
Contact	D.A. Weston, Market Development

200

Originator	CEMENT AND CONCRETE ASSOCIATION
Title	CEMENT - CHANNEL OF SALE QUARTERLY FIGURES, quarterly. 1973-
Coverage	Deliveries of Portland cement by type of customer in each DoE region and nationally.
Contents & Origin of Statistics	Tables per issue: 1. Own research 100%.
Comments	Part is republished by the DoE as table 18 in 'Monthly statistics of building materials and components'.
Currency	1 month
Response	1984
Availability	Limited
Cost	Free
Address	Wexham Springs, Wexham, nr Slough SL3 6PL

Telephone	02816 2727 ; Telex: 848352
Contact	D.A. Weston, Market Development

201

Originator	CEMENT AND CONCRETE ASSOCIATION
Title	CEMENT - FINAL DESTINATION FIGURES, annual. 1978-
Coverage	Final destination of Portland cement deliveries by construction site type and by DoE region.
Contents & Origin of Statistics	Tables per issue: 1. Own research 70%, Other non official source 30%.
Comments	Series temporarily discontinued but may recommence in early 1986.
Response	1984
Availability	Limited
Cost	Free
Address	Wexham Springs, Wexham, nr Slough SL3 6PL
Telephone	02816 2727 ; Telex: 848352
Contact	D.A. Weston, Marketing Development

202

Originator	CEMENT AND CONCRETE ASSOCIATION
Title	CEMENT - SITE DESTINATION FIGURES, quarterly. 1977-
Coverage	Deliveries of Portland cement direct to construction sites by site type in each DoE region and nationally.
Contents & Origin of Statistics	Tables per issue: 1. Own research 100%.
Currency	1 month
Response	1984
Availability	Limited
Cost	Free
Address	Wexham Springs, Wexham, nr Slough SL3 6PL
Telephone	02816 2727 ; Telex: 848352
Contact	D.A. Weston, Market Development

203

Originator	CENTRAL ELECTRICITY GENERATING BOARD
Title	CEGB STATISTICAL YEARBOOK, annual. 1964-
Coverage	Financial results, operations, and plant, power stations and transmission.

Contents & Origin of Statistics	Tables per issue: 20. Own research 100%. Supporting text 10%

Currency	4-5 months
Response	1984
Availability	General
Cost	Free
ISBN	0902543 76 8
Address	Sudbury House, 15 Newgate St, London EC1A 7AY
Telephone	01 248 1202
Contact	D.F. Grace, Publicity Office

204

Originator	CENTRAL INDEPENDENT TELEVISION

Title	CENTRAL GROCERY MANUAL, annual
Coverage	Analysis of turnover by grocery outlets, penetration of shoppers and their expenditure within outlets by socio-demographic groups, number of named grocery multiple outlet branches in the region.

Contents & Origin of Statistics	Tables per issue: 33. Own research 50%, Other non official source 50%. Supporting text 5%

Currency	Varies
Response	1983
Availability	General
Address	35-38 Portman Square, London W1A 2HZ
Telephone	01 262 8040; Telex: 24337
Contact	Janet Eathorne, Research Supervisor

205

Originator	CENTRAL INDEPENDENT TELEVISION

Title	CENTRAL MARKETING MANUAL, biennial
Coverage	Range of figures on population, communications, living standards, retailing, leisure, holidays, finance, agriculture, motoring etc.

Contents & Origin of Statistics	Tables per issue: 55. Non official source 80%, Government statistics 20%. Supporting text 10%

Currency	Varies
Response	1983
Availability	General
Cost	Free
Address	35-38 Portman Square, London W1A 2HZ

Telephone	01 262 8040; Telex: 24337
Contact	Janet Eathorne, Research Supervisor

206

Originator	CENTRAL SERVICES UNIT (FOR CAREERS AND APPOINTMENTS SERVICES)
Title	CSU STATISTICAL QUARTERLY, quarterly
Coverage	University and polytechnic graduates employment, analysed by discipline, type of employer and work.
Contents & Origin of Statistics	Tables per issue: 9. Own research + other non official source 100%
Comments	See other entries for other statistical publications in 'Statistical Package'
Response	1984
Availability	General
Cost	£75, as part of a statistical package
Address	Crawford House, Precinct Centre, Manchester M13 9EP
Telephone	061 273 4233
Contact	Steve Pickman

207

Originator	CENTRAL SERVICES UNIT (FOR CAREERS AND APPOINTMENTS SERVICES)
Title	THE OUTPUT OF UK UNIVERSITIES BY INSTITUTION AND DISCIPLINE, annual
Coverage	Data on all disciplines except medicine, dentistry and veterinary science. Further divided according to domicile and sex, with figures for individual universities.
Contents & Origin of Statistics	Tables per issue: 36. Non official source 100%
Response	1984
Availability	General
Cost	£5
Address	Crawford House, Precinct Centre, Manchester M13 9EP
Telephone	061 273 4233
Contact	Steve Pickman

208

Originator	CENTRAL SERVICES UNIT (FOR CAREERS AND APPOINTMENTS SERVICES)
Title	POLYTECHNIC FIRST DEGREE AND HIGHER DIPLOMA STUDENTS, annual
Coverage	Details of first destinations, by fields of study type of employer and type of work. Comparative figures for preceding years and longer trends.
Contents & Origin of Statistics	Tables per issue: 12. Non official source 100%
Comments	Prepared by Working Party of Polytechnic Careers Advisers with the co-operation of the Secretariat of the Committee of Directors of Polytechnics. More detailed breakdown available.
Response	1984
Availability	General
Cost	£1.50
Address	Crawford House, Precinct Centre, Manchester M13 9EP
Telephone	061 273 4233
Contact	Steve Pickman

209

Originator	CENTRAL SERVICES UNIT (FOR CAREERS AND APPOINTMENTS SERVICES)
Title	THE SUPPLY OF UNVERSITY GRADUATES: TRENDS AND PREDICTIONS, annual
Coverage	Output of university first degree graduates over a 6 year period and the output of specific disciplines within 3 main interest groups - engineering, science and administration and business trends. Supply of university graduates available for employment.
Contents & Origin of Statistics	Tables per issue: Own research + other non official source 100%
Response	1984
Availability	General
Address	Crawford House, Precinct Centre, Manchester M13 9EP
Telephone	061 273 4233
Contact	Steve Pickman

210

Originator	CENTRAL SERVICES UNIT (FOR CAREERS AND APPOINTMENTS SERVICES)
Title	UNIVERSITY GRADUATES: SUMMARY OF FIRST DESTINATION AND EMPLOYMENT, annual
Coverage	Supply of graduates and those entering employment by employer, type of work and fields of study. Comparative figures for preceding years and longer trends.
Contents & Origin of Statistics	Tables per issue: 19. Non official source 100%
Comments	Produced in conjunction with the Association of Graduates Careers Advisory Services (AGCAS) and summarises UGC's 'First destination of university graduates' published later.More breakdown available.
Response	1984
Availability	General
Cost	£1.50
Address	Crawford House, Precinct Centre, Manchester M13 9EP
Telephone	061 273 4233
Contact	Steve Pickman

211

Originator	CENTRE FOR LIBRARY AND INFORMATION MANAGEMENT
Title	AVERAGE PRICES OF BRITISH ACADEMIC BOOKS, bi-annual. 1974-
Coverage	Average prices (1974=100) broken down by Dewey subject divisions, type of binding and distribution of prices.
Contents & Origin of Statistics	Tables per issue: 6. Non official source 100%. Supporting text 20%
Currency	3 months
Response	1984
Availability	General
Cost	£15
ISSN	0261 0302
Address	Dept of Library and Information Studies, Loughborough University Loughborough, LE11 3TU
Telephone	0509 213176
Contact	Lorraine Wood, Research Assistant

212

Originator   CHAMBERS AND PARTNERS

Title   LAWYERS IN INDUSTRY SALARY SURVEY, annual
Coverage   Survey of approximately 183 lawyers in finance, commerce and industry. Three job categories are included - legal assistant, legal adviser, senior legal adviser. Includes average salary by job and age, salary increases since 1974 and use of company cars.

Contents &   Tables per issue: 4. Own research 100%
Origin of
Statistics

Response   1983
Availability   'Bona fide' researchers on request
Cost   Free
Address   74 Long Lane, London EC1A 9ET
Telephone   01 606 9371
Contact   Above address

213

Originator   CHAMBERS COX & CO

Title   SNAP - A 19.. REVIEW OF UK PHOTOGRAPHY, annual. 1981-
Coverage   Market information on the industry including camera sales, household penetration, lens sales, film sales, photographic paper sales, consumer spending by area, retail outlets, video market etc.

Contents &   Tables per issue: 20. Own research 60%, Other non official source
Origin of   35%, Government statistics 5%. Supporting text 65%
Statistics

Currency   6 months
Response   1984
Availability   General
Cost   £30
Address   7/8 Rathbone Place, London W1P 1DE
Telephone   01 631 5414; Telex: 266606
Contact   Victoria Crawshaw

214

Originator   CHART ANALYSIS LTD

Title   COMMODITIES, weekly. 1972-
Coverage   Trends and prices in the UK and USA futures markets. Covers 33 different commodities in the food, grain, livestock and meat, industrial softs, metals and money sectors.

Contents & Origin of Statistics	Tables per issue: 72. Own research 100%. Supporting text 5%
Comments	All data presented in graph form. Also publish 'International Currency and Financial Futures' weekly report.
Currency	1 day
Response	1984
Availability	General
Cost	£350
Address	37-39 St Andrews Hill, London EC4V 5DD
Telephone	01 248 6581; Telex: 883356
Contact	Anne Whitby, Director

215

Originator	CHART ANALYSIS LTD
Title	UK POINT AND FIGURE LIBRARY, weekly/monthly. 1972-
Coverage	Charts of the UK stock market covering group indices, share prices by sector and by company. Also F.T. share indices.
Contents & Origin of Statistics	Tables per issue: 102. Non official source 100%. Supporting text 5%.
Comments	All data printed in graph form. Also publish 'International Currency and Financial Futures' weekly report.
Currency	Varies
Response	1984
Availability	General
Cost	£700 for weekly service, £300 for monthly service
Address	37-39 St Andrews Hill, London EC4V 5DD
Telephone	01 248 6581; Telex: 883356
Contact	Anne Whitby, Director

216

Originator	CHARTERED INSTITUTE OF BUILDING
Title	SURVEY OF STUDENT NUMBERS, annual. 1967-
Coverage	Number of students on building courses at technicians level and above with a regional breakdown.
Contents & Origin of Statistics	Tables per issue: 4. Own research 100%. Supporting text 25%
Currency	2 months
Response	1984
Availability	General
Cost	Free
Address	Englemere, Kings Ride, Ascot, Berkshire SL5 8BJ

Telephone   0990 23355
Contact   Mrs J.S. Pritchard, Education Officer

217

Originator   CHARTERED INSTITUTE OF PUBLIC FINANCE AND
               ACCOUNTANCY (CIPFA)

Title   ADMINISTRATION OF JUSTICE - ESTIMATES, annual
Coverage   Estimated expenditure and income figures for both Magistrates and
               Coroners courts per thousand population.

Contents &   Tables per issue: Own research 100%
  Origin of
  Statistics

Comments   SIS Computer database available for direct enquiries and access by
               remote terminal, commission of statistical analysis and production
               of tapes, discs etc.
Response   1984
Availability   General
Cost   £11 (Total subscription to all publications available)
Address   2/3 Robert St, London WC2N 6BH
Telephone   01 930 3456
Contact   CIPFA Statistical Information Service

218

Originator   CHARTERED INSTITUTE OF PUBLIC FINANCE AND
               ACCOUNTANCY (CIPFA)

Title   AIRPORTS STATISTICS - ACTUALS, annual
Coverage   An analysis of the revenue accounts and balance sheets of local
               authority airports plus a range of non-financial information.

Contents &   Tables per issue: 9. Own research 100%
  Origin of
  Statistics

Comments   SIS database available for direct enquiries, access by remote terminal
               link, commission of statistical analysis and production of tapes, discs
               etc.
Response   1984
Availability   General
Cost   £11 (Total subscription to all publications available)
Address   2/3 Robert St, London WC2N 6BH
Telephone   01 930 3456
Contact   CIPFA Statistical Information Service

219

Originator	CHARTERED INSTITUTE OF PUBLIC FINANCE AND ACCOUNTANCY (CIPFA)
Title	BLOCK GRANT STATISTICS, annual
Coverage	Total expenditure for each local authority and the parameters necessary to calculate Block Grant in the current financial and calculated entitlements to such grants.
Comments	SIS Computer database available for direct enquiries and access by remote terminal, commission of statistical analysis and production of tapes, discs etc.
Response	1984
Availability	General
Cost	£15 (Total subscription to all publications available)
Address	2/3 Robert St, London WC2N 6BH
Telephone	01 930 3456
Contact	CIPFA Statistical Information Service

220

Originator	CHARTERED INSTITUTE OF PUBLIC FINANCE AND ACCOUNTANCY (CIPFA)
Title	CAPITAL EXPENDITURE AND DEBT FINANCING STATISTICS, annual
Coverage	Analysis of capital expenditure, capital receipts and debt statistics by individual local authorities in England, Wales, Scotland and Northern Ireland.
Contents & Origin of Statistics	Tables per issue: 18. Own research 100%. Supporting text 5%
Comments	Previously published as 'Return of Outstanding Debt'. SIS computer database also available for direct enquiries, analysis via remote terminals, statistical analysis and production of tapes, discs etc.
Currency	6 months
Response	1984
Availability	General
Cost	£19 (Total subscription to all publications available)
ISSN	0263 2985
Address	2/3 Robert St, London WC2N 6BH
Telephone	01 930 3456
Contact	CIPFA Statistical Information Service

221

Originator	CHARTERED INSTITUTE OF PUBLIC FINANCE AND ACCOUNTANCY (CIPFA)
Title	CEMETRIES AND CREMATORIA - ACTUALS, annual
Coverage	Expenditure, income, fees and non-financial data.
Contents & Origin of Statistics	Tables per issue: Own research 100%
Comments	SIS database available for direct enquiries, access by remote terminal, commission of statistical analysis, production of tapes, discs etc.
Response	1984
Availability	General
Cost	£15 (Total subscription to all publications available)
Address	2/3 Robert St, London WC2N 6BH
Telephone	01 930 3456
Contact	CIPFA Statistical Information Service

222

Originator	CHARTERED INSTITUTE OF PUBLIC FINANCE AND ACCOUNTANCY (CIPFA)
Title	EDUCATION STATISTICS - ACTUALS, annual. 1970-
Coverage	Non-financial data on pupil, school and teacher numbers and financial data split by type of school and local authority areas. Unit costs per pupil and totals for schools, teachers and pupils are also given.
Contents & Origin of Statistics	Tables per issue: 29pgs. 15. Government statistics 100%. Supporting text 2%
Comments	SIS database available for direct enquiries, access by remote terminal, commission of statistical analysis, and production of discs, tapes etc. 'Estimates' publication on above topic also produced at £11.
Currency	15 months
Response	1984
Availability	General
Cost	£15 (Total subscription to all publications available)
ISSN	0309 5614
Address	2/3 Robert St, London WC2N 6BH
Telephone	01 930 3456
Contact	CIPFA Statistical Information Service

223

Originator	CHARTERED INSTITUTE OF PUBLIC FINANCE AND ACCOUNTANCY (CIPFA)
Title	EDUCATION UNIT COSTS HANDBOOK, annual
Coverage	Institutional costs, pupil and student support, capital costs, salary costs, pupil teacher ratios, recurrent expenditure and university costs.
Contents & Origin of Statistics	Tables per issue: Government statistics 100%
Comments	SIS Computer database available for direct enquiries and remote access by terminal, commission of statistical analysis and production of discs, tapes etc.
Response	1984
Availability	General
Cost	£9
Address	2/3 Robert St, London WC2N 6BH
Telephone	01 930 3456
Contact	CIPFA Statistical Information Service

224

Originator	CHARTERED INSTITUTE OF PUBLIC FINANCE AND ACCOUNTANCY (CIPFA)
Title	ENVIRONMENTAL HEALTH - ACTUALS, annual
Coverage	Environmental health data by individual local authority area.
Contents & Origin of Statistics	Tables per issue: Own research 100%
Comments	SIS Computer database available for direct enquiries and access by remote terminal, commission of statistical analysis and production of tapes, discs etc.
Response	1984
Availability	General
Cost	£15 (Total subscription to all publications available)
Address	2/3 Robert St, London WC2N 6BH
Telephone	01 930 3456
Contact	CIPFA Statistical Information Service

225

Originator	CHARTERED INSTITUTE OF PUBLIC FINANCE AND ACCOUNTANCY (CIPFA)
Title	FINANCE AND GENERAL STATISTICS, annual. 1976-

Coverage	Summary information on local authority expenditure and income and data for each local authority in England and Wales, based on estimates, plus estimated expenditure and income per head of the population.
Contents & Origin of Statistics	Tables per issue: 100pgs. 30. Own research 100%. Supporting text 5%
Comments	SIS computer database available for direct enquiries, access by remote terminal, commission of statistical analysis and production of tapes, discs etc.
Currency	3 months
Response	1984
Availability	General
Cost	£19 (Total subscription to all publications available)
ISSN	0263 2276
Address	2/3 Robert St, London WC2N 6BH
Telephone	01 930 3456
Contact	CIPFA Statistical Information Service

226

Originator	CHARTERED INSTITUTE OF PUBLIC FINANCE AND ACCOUNTANCY (CIPFA)
Title	FIRE SERVICE STATISTICS - ACTUALS, annual
Coverage	Summary data on expenditure and income and similar figures for each local authority and per thousand population. In addition, figures are given for fire stations, training, applications, return of calls, inspections and manpower.
Contents & Origin of Statistics	Tables per issue: 23pgs. 9. Own research 100%. Supporting text 5%
Comments	SIS computer database available for direct enquiries, access by remote terminal, commission of statistical analysis and production of floppy discs, tapes, etc. 'Estimates' publication on above topic also produced at £11.
Currency	6 months
Response	1984
Availability	General
Cost	£11 (Total subscription to all publications available)
ISSN	0309 622X
Address	2/3 Robert St, London WC2N 6BH
Telephone	01 930 3456
Contact	CIPFA Statistical Information Service

227

Originator	CHARTERED INSTITUTE OF PUBLIC FINANCE AND ACCOUNTANCY (CIPFA)
Title	HIGHWAYS AND TRANSPORTATION STATISTICS - ACTUALS, annual
Coverage	The final outturn figures are shown for highways and transportation expenditure by county councils in England and Wales.
Contents & Origin of Statistics	Tables per issue: Own research 100%
Comments	SIS database available for direct enquiries, access by remote terminal, commission of statistical data and production of tapes, discs etc. 'Estimates' publication on above topic also produced at £15.
Response	1984
Availability	General
Cost	£11 (Total subscription to all publications available)
Address	2/3 Robert St, London WC2N 6BH
Telephone	01 930 3456
Contact	CIPFA Statistical Information Service

228

Originator	CHARTERED INSTITUTE OF PUBLIC FINANCE AND ACCOUNTANCY (CIPFA)
Title	HOMELESSNESS STATISTICS - ACTUALS, annual
Coverage	A financial survey of the operation of the Housing (Homeless Persons) Act 1977.
Comments	SIS Computer database available for direct enquiries and access by remote terminal, commission of statistical analysis, and production of tapes, discs etc.
Response	1984
Availability	General
Cost	£11 (Total subscription to all publications available)
Address	2/3 Robert St, London WC2N 6BH
Telephone	01 930 3456
Contact	CIPFA Statistical Information Service

229

Originator	CHARTERED INSTITUTE OF PUBLIC FINANCE AND ACCOUNTANCY (CIPFA)
Title	HOUSING MANAGEMENT AND MAINTENANCE STATISTICS - ACTUALS, annual

Coverage   Analysis of expenditure on housing maintenance and supervision and management plus unit costs per dwelling for each housing authority in England and Wales. Also given is comparative information on number of dwellings, rent collection procedures and decorating cycles.

Contents &   Tables per issue: 25. Own research 100%. Supporting text 2%
   Origin of
   Statistics

Comments   SIS database available for direct enquiries, access by remote terminal, commission of statistical analysis and production of tapes, discs etc. 'Housing Statistics - Estimates' also produced at £15.

Response   1984
Availability   General
Cost   £15 (Total subscription to all publications available)
Address   2/3 Robert St, London WC2N 6BH
Telephone   01 930 3456
Contact   CIPFA Statistical Information Service

230

Originator   CHARTERED INSTITUTE OF PUBLIC FINANCE AND ACCOUNTANCY (CIPFA)

Title   HOUSING RENTS, annual
Coverage   Analysis of housing stock by age and type, average weekly net unrebated rents and rebates and allowances for housing authorities in England and Wales. Summary tables give the split over Economic Planning Regions.

Contents &   Tables per issue: 30. Own research 100%
   Origin of
   Statistics

Comments   SIS database available for direct enquiries, access by remote terminal, commission of statistical analysis and production of tapes, discs etc.

Response   1984
Availability   General
Cost   £15 (Total subscription to all publications available)
Address   2/3 Robert St, London WC2N 6BH
Telephone   01 930 3456
Contact   CIPFA Statistical Information Service

231

Originator   CHARTERED INSTITUTE OF PUBLIC FINANCE AND ACCOUNTANCY (CIPFA)

Title   HOUSING REVENUE ACCOUNT STATISTICS - ACTUALS, annual. 1950-

Coverage	The final outturn figures of Housing Revenue Account income and expenditure are shown in total and for each housing authority in England and Wales. In addition, details are given of rents, rent arrears, number of dwellings, average rates of loan interest and details on the sale of council houses.
Contents & Origin of Statistics	Tables per issue: 35pgs. 8. Own research + government statistics 100%. Supporting text 2%
Comments	SIS computer database available for direct enquiries, access by remote terminal, commission of statistical analysis and production of tapes, discs etc.
Currency	9 months
Response	1984
Availability	General
Cost	£15 (Total subscription to all publications available)
ISSN	0260 4078
Address	2/3 Robert St, London WC2N 6BH
Telephone	01 930 3456
Contact	CIPFA Statistical Information Service

232

Originator	CHARTERED INSTITUTE OF PUBLIC FINANCE AND ACCOUNTANCY (CIPFA)
Title	LEISURE AND RECREATION - ESTIMATES, annual
Coverage	Estimated expenditure and income on sports and recreation, cultural and other facilities.
Contents & Origin of Statistics	Tables per issue: Own research 100%
Comments	SIS Computer database available for direct enquiries and access by remote terminal, commission of statistical analysis and production of tapes, discs etc.
Response	1984
Availability	General
Cost	£15 (Total subscription to all publications available)
Address	2/3 Robert St, London WC2N 6BH
Telephone	01 930 3456
Contact	CIPFA Statistical Information Service

233

Originator	CHARTERED INSTITUTE OF PUBLIC FINANCE AND ACCOUNTANCY (CIPFA)
Title	LEISURE CHARGES - ESTIMATES, annual

Coverage	Sample survey of charges for leisure centre facilities, swimming pools and outdoor sports. Drawn from a sample of 150 authorities.
Contents & Origin of Statistics	Tables per issue: Own research 100%
Comments	SIS Computer database available for direct enquiries and access by remote terminal, commission of statistical analysis and production of tapes, discs etc.
Response	1984
Availability	General
Cost	£11 (Total subscription to all publications available)
Address	2/3 Robert St, London WC2N 6BH
Telephone	01 930 3456
Contact	CIPFA Statistical Information Service

234

Originator	CHARTERED INSTITUTE OF PUBLIC FINANCE AND ACCOUNTANCY (CIPFA)
Title	LEISURE USAGE - ACTUALS, annual
Coverage	Sample survey of the use made of leisure centre facilities, swimming pools and outdoor sports based on a sample of 150 authorities.
Contents & Origin of Statistics	Tables per issue: Own research 100%
Comments	SIS Computer database available for direct enquiries and access by remote terminal, commission of statistical analysis and production of tapes, discs etc.
Response	1984
Availability	General
Cost	£11 (Total subscription to all publications available)
Address	2/3 Robert St, London WC2N 6BH
Telephone	01 930 3456
Contact	CIPFA Statistical Information Service

235

Originator	CHARTERED INSTITUTE OF PUBLIC FINANCE AND ACCOUNTANCY (CIPFA)
Title	LOCAL GOVERNMENT COMPARATIVE STATISTICS, annual
Coverage	Statistical indicators for all the major local authority services.
Contents & Origin of Statistics	Tables per issue: 30. Own research + other non official source 100%

Comments	SIS computer database available for data enquiries, access by remote terminal, commission of statistical analysis and production of tapes, discs etc.
Currency	Varies
Response	1984
Availability	General
Cost	£19 (Total subscription to all publications available)
Address	2/3 Robert St, London WC2N 6BH
Telephone	01 930 3456
Contact	CIPFA Statistical Information Service

236

Originator	CHARTERED INSTITUTE OF PUBLIC FINANCE AND ACCOUNTANCY (CIPFA)
Title	LOCAL GOVERNMENT TRENDS, annual. 1973-
Coverage	General data for all local authorities in aggregate on various local authority sectors such as education, environmental health, housing, leisure, social services, transportation and industrial development. There are also general figures on population, employment and earnings, the political framework and total local authority expenditure.
Contents & Origin of Statistics	Tables per issue: 85. Own research 20%, Other non official source 10%, Government statistics 70%. Supporting text 12%
Comments	SIS computer database available for direct enquiries, analysis by remote terminal, commission of statistical work and production of discs, tapes.
Currency	Varies
Response	1984
Availability	General
Cost	£19 (Total subscription to all publications available)
ISSN	0307 0441
Address	2/3 Robert St, London WC2N 6BH
Telephone	01 930 3456
Contact	CIPFA Statistical Information Service

237

Originator	CHARTERED INSTITUTE OF PUBLIC FINANCE AND ACCOUNTANCY (CIPFA)
Title	NON-TEACHING HOSPITAL STATISTICS - ACTUALS, annual
Coverage	Sample survey of the revenue consequences of capital schemes.
Comments	SIS Computer database available for direct enquiries and access by remote terminal, commission of statistical analysis and production of tapes, discs etc.
Response	1984

Availability	General
Cost	£10 (Total subscription to all publications available)
Address	2/3 Robert St, London WC2N 6BH
Telephone	01 930 3456
Contact	CIPFA Statistical Information Service

238

Originator	CHARTERED INSTITUTE OF PUBLIC FINANCE AND ACCOUNTANCY (CIPFA)
Title	PERSONAL SOCIAL SERVICES STATISTICS - ACTUALS, annual
Coverage	Analysis of residential, day and community care provision giving gross and net expenditure and the number of clients by local authority area. Expenditure on field work, administration and joint financing is also shown and other information includes a breakdown of the total population by age groups.
Contents & Origin of Statistics	Tables per issue: 15. Own research 100%
Comments	SIS database available for direct enquiries, access by remote terminal, commission of statistical analysis and production of tapes, discs etc. 'Estimates' publication also produced
Response	1984
Availability	General
Cost	£15 (Total subscription to all publications available)
Address	2/3 Robert St, London WC2N 6BH
Telephone	01 930 3456
Contact	CIPFA Statistical Information Service

239

Originator	CHARTERED INSTITUTE OF PUBLIC FINANCE AND ACCOUNTANCY (CIPFA)
Title	PLANNING AND DEVELOPMENT - ACTUALS, annual
Coverage	Capital and revenue expenditure on the planning and development functions in summary and by individual local authority.
Contents & Origin of Statistics	Tables per issue: 20. Own research 100%
Comments	SIS database available for direct enquiries, access by remote terminal, commission of statistical analysis and production of tapes, discs on above topic at £15.
Response	1984
Availability	General
Cost	£13 (Total subscription to all publications available)

Address	2/3 Robert St, London WC2N 6BH
Telephone	01 930 3456
Contact	CIPFA Statistical Information Service

240

Originator	CHARTERED INSTITUTE OF PUBLIC FINANCE AND ACCOUNTANCY (CIPFA)
Title	POLICE STATISTICS - ACTUALS, annual
Coverage	The final outturn figures are shown for expenditure and income and manpower in total for all police forces and by individual police force and regional crime squad. Also gives names and addresses of chief constables and treasurers of police forces.
Contents & Origin of Statistics	Tables per issue: 24pgs. 9. Own research 100%. Supporting text 2%
Comments	SIS computer database available for direct enquiries and access by remote terminal, commission of statistical analysis and production of tapes, discs etc. 'Estimates' publication also
Currency	6 months
Response	1984
Availability	General
Cost	£11 (Total subscription to all publications available)
ISSN	0144 9915
Address	2/3 Robert St, London WC2N 6BH
Telephone	01 930 3456
Contact	CIPFA Statistical Information Service

241

Originator	CHARTERED INSTITUTE OF PUBLIC FINANCE AND ACCOUNTANCY (CIPFA)
Title	PROBATION - ACTUALS, annual
Coverage	Expenditure and income in the probation service per thousand population aged 15-29 and manpower for the service in England and Wales.
Comments	SIS Computer database available for direct enquiries and access by remote terminal, commission of statistical analysis and production of tapes, discs etc. Estimates also published at £11.
Response	1984
Availability	General
Cost	£11 (Total subscription to all publications available)
Address	2/3 Robert St, London WC2N 6BH
Telephone	01 930 3456
Contact	CIPFA Statistical Information Service

242

Originator	CHARTERED INSTITUTE OF PUBLIC FINANCE AND ACCOUNTANCY (CIPFA)
Title	PUBLIC LIBRARY STATISTICS - ACTUALS, annual. 1962-
Coverage	The final outturn figures for expenditure and income, manpower, agency services, books and other stocks and service points are given in total and for each library service in Great Britain and Northern Ireland. Summary tables are included for annual issues and inter-library loans.
Contents & Origin of Statistics	Tables per issue: 27pgs. 14. Own research 100%.
Comments	SIS Computer database available for direct enquiries, access by remote terminal, commission of statistical analysis and production of tapes, discs etc. produced on above topic at £11.
Currency	6 months
Response	1984
Availability	General
Cost	£14 (Total subscription to all publications available)
ISSN	0309 6629
Address	2/3 Robert St, London WC2N 6BH
Telephone	01 930 3456
Contact	CIPFA Statistical Information Service

243

Originator	CHARTERED INSTITUTE OF PUBLIC FINANCE AND ACCOUNTANCY (CIPFA)
Title	RATE COLLECTION STATISTICS - ACTUALS, annual. 1950-
Coverage	Data on rateable values and rate collection in total and by individual districts and boroughs in England and Wales. Includes details of rate income, arrears, costs and methods of collection, staff involved, number of hereditaments and rateable value by category.
Contents & Origin of Statistics	Tables per issue: 63pgs. 9. Own research 100%
Comments	SIS Computer database available for direct enquiries, remote terminal access, commission of statistical analysis and production of discs, tapes etc.
Currency	12 months
Response	1984
Availability	General
Cost	£19 (Total subscription to all publications available)
ISSN	0260 5546
Address	2/3 Robert St, London WC2N 6BH

Telephone	01 930 3456
Contact	CIPFA Statistical Information Service

244

Originator	CHARTERED INSTITUTE OF PUBLIC FINANCE AND ACCOUNTANCY (CIPFA)
Title	SCHOOL MEALS - ACTUALS, annual
Coverage	Data on meals served for all LEAs in England and the number of free meals served and the charges made to paying pupils.
Comments	SIS Computer database available for direct enquiries and access by remote terminal, commission of statistical analysis and production of tapes, discs etc.
Response	1984
Availability	General
Cost	£9
Address	2/3 Robert St, London WC2N 6BH
Telephone	01 930 3456
Contact	CIPFA Statistical Information Service

245

Originator	CHARTERED INSTITUTE OF PUBLIC FINANCE AND ACCOUNTANCY (CIPFA)
Title	TEACHING HOSPITAL STATISTICS - ACTUALS, annual
Coverage	Operating costs of teaching hospitals in England and Wales.
Contents & Origin of Statistics	Tables per issue: Own research 100%
Comments	SIS Computer database available for direct enquiries and access by remote terminal, commission of statistical analysis and production of discs, tapes etc.
Response	1984
Availability	General
Cost	£15 (Total subscription to all publications available)
Address	2/3 Robert St, London WC2N 6BH
Telephone	01 930 3456
Contact	CIPFA Statistical Information Service

246

Originator	CHARTERED INSTITUTE OF PUBLIC FINANCE AND ACCOUNTANCY (CIPFA)
Title	WASTE COLLECTION - ACTUALS, annual

Coverage	Data on waste collection including income and expenditure, staff numbers, charges, quantities collected and methods and frequency of collection. Summary information and by local authority area.
Contents & Origin of Statistics	Tables per issue: 59pgs. 30. Own research 100%
Comments	SIS database available for direct enquiries, access by remote terminal, commission of statistical analysis and production of tapes, discs etc.
Response	1984
Availability	General
Cost	£15 (Total subscription to all publications available)
ISSN	0260 7603
Address	2/3 Robert St, London WC2N 6BH
Telephone	01 930 3456
Contact	CIPFA Statistical Information Service

247

Originator	CHARTERED INSTITUTE OF PUBLIC FINANCE AND ACCOUNTANCY (CIPFA)
Title	WASTE DISPOSAL - ACTUALS, annual
Coverage	Data on revenue income and expenditure, capital expenditure and financing, methods of treatment, waste arising and reclaimed waste by tonnage, vehicle disposals, manpower and unit costs in summary and by local authority area.
Contents & Origin of Statistics	Tables per issue: 14. Own research 100%
Comments	SIS database available for direct enquiries, access by remote terminal, commission of statistical analysis and production of tapes, discs etc. 'Estimates' publication also produced on above topic at £11.
Response	1984
Availability	General
Cost	£11 (Total subscription to all publications available)
ISSN	0140 0150
Address	2/3 Robert St, London WC2N 6BH
Telephone	01 930 3456
Contact	CIPFA Statistical Information Service

248

Originator	CHARTERED INSTITUTE OF PUBLIC FINANCE AND ACCOUNTANCY (CIPFA)
Title	WATER SERVICES CHARGES, annual

Coverage	Analysis of charges for regional water authorities and water companies.
Contents & Origin of Statistics	Tables per issue: Own research 100%
Comments	SIS Computer database available for direct enquiries and access by remote terminal, commission of statistical analysis and production of tapes, discs etc. The above publication is not part of the Statistical Information Service.
Response	1984
Availability	General
Cost	£10
Address	2/3 Robert St, London WC2N 6BH
Telephone	01 930 3456
Contact	CIPFA Statistical Information Service

249

Originator	CHARTERED QUANTITY SURVEYOR
Title	QUARTERLY BUILDING PRICES AND BUILDING COSTS AND QUARTERLY TENDER LEVELS AND BUILDING COSTS, quarterly in a monthly journal. January 1980-
Coverage	Building industry prices, costs and tender levels.
Contents & Origin of Statistics	Tables per issue: Varies. Non official source 50%, Government statistics 50%
Comments	Non-official statistics supplied by the Building Cost Information Service of the Royal Institution of Chartered Surveyors
Currency	1-2 months
Response	1984
Availability	General
Cost	£19 or £1.50 for a single issue
ISSN	0142 5196
Address	RICS Journals Ltd, P.O. Box 87, 1-3 Pemberton Row, Red Lion Court, Fleet St, London EC4P 4HL
Telephone	01 353 2300; Telex: 252121
Contact	The Editor

250

Originator	CHARTERHOUSE J ROTHSCHILD
Title	BUSINESS FORECAST, quarterly
Coverage	Forecasts up to 1 year ahead for major economic variables plus summary of forecasts from other organisations.

Contents & Origin of Statistics	Tables per issue: 7. Own research 60%, Government statistics 40%. Supporting text 55%
Response	1983
Availability	General
Cost	Free
Address	65 Holborn Viaduct, London EC1A 2DR
Telephone	01 248 4000
Contact	Communications Department

251

Originator	CHEMICAL INDUSTRIES ASSOCIATION LTD
Title	ECONOMICS BULLETIN, quarterly
Coverage	Economic situation in the UK chemical industry.
Contents & Origin of Statistics	Tables per issue: 8
Comments	In one issue per year there is an 'Investment Intentions Survey'
Currency	3 months
Response	1983
Availability	General
Cost	£30
Address	Alembic House, 93 Albert Embankment, London SE1 7TS
Telephone	01 735 3001
Contact	~~Jane Singleton~~, Information Officer *Peter Carter*

252

Originator	CHEMICAL INDUSTRIES ASSOCIATION LTD
Title	UK CHEMICAL INDUSTRY FACTS, monthly
Coverage	Includes industry sales, growth rate, output, capital investment, trade, costs, employees, etc.
Contents & Origin of Statistics	Tables per issue: 15. Own research 25%, Government statistics 75%
Response	1983
Availability	General
Cost	Free
Address	Alembic House, 93 Albert Embankment, London SE1 7TU
Telephone	01 735 3001
Contact	~~Jane Singleton~~, Information Officer

Peter Carter

253

Originator	CHEMIST AND DRUGGIST PRICE LIST
Title	CHEMISTS' PRICES, monthly in a monthly journal. 1960-
Coverage	Prices of products sold by chemists.
Contents & Origin of Statistics	Tables per issue: Own research 100%
Currency	1 month
Response	1983
Availability	General
Address	Benn Publictions Ltd, Tonbridge, Kent TN9 1RW
Telephone	0732 364422
Contact	Above address

254

Originator	CHESHIRE COUNTY COUNCIL
Title	CHESHIRE CURRENT FACTS AND FIGURES, monthly. April 1977-
Coverage	General data on Cheshire including population trends, economy, elections, education, social services, housing, transport, environment, countryside and recreation etc. Each monthly update covers a particular topic.
Contents & Origin of Statistics	Tables per issue: Varies
Comments	Produced in the form of loose-leaf sheets (binder provided).
Currency	Varies
Response	1984
Availability	General
Cost	£5
Address	Research and Intelligence Section, County Treasury, County Hall, Chester CH1 1SG
Telephone	0244 602409
Contact	G.W. Smith, Head of Research and Intelligence

255

Originator	CHESHIRE COUNTY COUNCIL
Title	CHESHIRE POPULATION REPORT, annual. 1978-
Coverage	Population statistics by district and by district small area, by age and sex. Forecasts of population up to 13 years ahead.

Contents & Origin of Statistics	Tables per issue: 96pgs. Supporting text 30%
Comments	Details of the methodology and assumptions are available in a separate volume on request.
Currency	Varies
Response	1984
Availability	General
Cost	£8
ISBN	0 906767 33 4
Address	County Planning Department, Commerce House, Hunter St, Chester
Telephone	0244 603120
Contact	P.G. Thomas, Principal Planning Officer

256

Originator	CHESHIRE COUNTY COUNCIL
Title	CHESHIRE UNEMPLOYMENT BULLETIN, quarterly. July 1981-
Coverage	General data on unemployment by age, sex and long-term unemployment. Details of vacancies and redundancies and comparisons with other counties.
Contents & Origin of Statistics	Tables per issue: 15. Own research 5%, Government statistics 95%. Supporting text 35%
Currency	2-3 months
Response	1984
Availability	General
Cost	Free
Address	Planning Department, Commerce House, Hunter St, Chester CH1 1SN
Telephone	0244 603120
Contact	A.K. de Longa, Planning Officer

257

Originator	CINEMA ADVERTISING ASSOCIATION LTD
Title	COVERAGE AND FREQUENCY PROGRAM, annual
Coverage	In 2 parts: national information by age, sex, marital status and social grades; data relating to special market areas such as ITV areas and metropolitan counties. Average coverage and frequency for any number of weeks from 1 to 52.
Contents & Origin of Statistics	Tables per issue: 50 pgs. Own research 100%. Supporting text 5%
Response	1984

Availability	General
Cost	Free
Address	127 Wardour St, London W1V 4AD
Telephone	01 439 9531
Contact	Bob Wittenbach, Secretary

258

Originator	CINEMA ADVERTISING ASSOCIATION LTD
Title	MASTER LIST OF CINEMAS, annual
Coverage	List of cinemas arranged in alphabetical order by county and their advertising rates. Number of screens by ITV area and rates for a week on all screens by metropolitan county and countries.
Contents & Origin of Statistics	Tables per issue: 69 pgs. Own research 100%.
Response	1984
Availability	General
Cost	Free
Address	127 Wardour St, London W1V 4AD
Telephone	01 439 9531
Contact	Bob Wittenbach, Secretary

259

Originator	CIVIL AVIATION AUTHORITY
Title	UK AIRLINES, monthly, 1983-
Coverage	Operating and traffic statistics for UK airlines by domestic and international services and by types of operations.
Contents & Origin of Statistics	Tables per issue: 35. Own research 100%.
Comments	Previously published in 'CAA Monthly Statistics', 1973-1982
Currency	1 month
Response	1984
Availability	General
Cost	£25
ISSN	0265 0266
Address	Greville House, 37 Gratton Rd, Cheltenham, Gloucestershire, GL50 2BN
Telephone	0242 35151
Contact	Above address

260

Originator	CIVIL AVIATION AUTHORITY
Title	UK AIRPORTS, monthly. 1983-
Coverage	Monthly statements of movements, passengers, and cargo at UK airport.
Contents & Origin of Statistics	Tables per issue: 15. Own research 100%.
Comments	Formerly published, from 1973-1982, in two series known as 'CAA Monthly and Annual Statistics.'
Currency	1 month
Response	1984
Availability	General
Cost	£25
ISSN	0265 0258
Address	Greville House, 37 Gratton Rd, Cheltenham, Gloucestershire GL50 2BN
Telephone	0242 35151
Contact	Above address

261

Originator	CIVIL AVIATION AUTHORTIY
Title	UK AIRPORTS, annual. 1983-
Coverage	UK airports movements, passengers and cargo statistics.
Contents & Origin of Statistics	Tables per issue: 18. Own research 100%.
Comments	Formerly published from 1973-1982, in two series known as 'CAA Monthly and Annual Statistics'.
Currency	3-4 months
Response	1984
Availability	General
Cost	£25
ISBN	0 86039 211 2
Address	Greville House, 37 Gratton Rd, Cheltenham, Gloucestershire, GL50 2BN
Telephone	Telephone 0242 35151
Contact	Above address

262

Originator	CLEVELAND COUNTY COUNCIL
Title	CLEVELAND STATISTICS IN BRIEF, annual. 1974-

Coverage	Regional and national data on population, housing, rates and manpower. County service statistics and expenditure.
Contents & Origin of Statistics	Tables per issue: 4. Own research 25%, Other non official source 25%, Government statistics 50%. Supporting text 15%
Comments	1981 'Census in brief' produced as a one-off in similar form i.e. pocket card.
Currency	Varies
Response	1984
Availability	General
Cost	Free (£5 per 100)
Address	Research and Intelligence Unit, 6th Floor, Rede House, Corporation Rd,Middlesbrough, Cleveland TS1 1LY
Telephone	0642 248155, Ext. 2384
Contact	Gill Rollings, Statistician

263

Originator	CLWYD COUNTY COUNCIL
Title	ABSTRACT OF STATISTICS, annual
Coverage	Districts, elections, population, economy, finance, personnel, education, social services, transport, protection of the public, housing, agriculture and cultural activities.
Contents & Origin of Statistics	Tables per issue: 88. Own research 55%, Other non official source 5%, Government statistics 35%, Unstated 5%. Supporting text 5%
Currency	Varies
Response	1984
Availability	General
Cost	£3
Address	Shire Hall, Mold, Clwyd CH7 6NB
Telephone	0352 2121; Telex: 61454
Contact	P.R. Burrows, Policy Development Assistant

264

Originator	CO-OPERATIVE UNION LTD
Title	CO-OPERATIVE STATISTICS, annual
Coverage	Retail distribution by individual co-operative society and other information on co-operative wholesaling, banking and insurance activities.
Contents & Origin of Statistics	Tables per issue: c80-90. Own research 98%, Government statistics 2%. Supporting text 50%
Currency	6 months
Response	1984

Availability	General
Cost	£12.50 (plus p+p)
Address	Holyoake House, Hanover St, Manchester M60 0AS
Telephone	061 832 4300
Contact	G.V.J. Pratt, Economic and Research Officer

265

Originator	CO-OPERATIVE UNION LTD
Title	ECONOMIC PROSPECTS, annual
Coverage	Covers recent developments in the UK economy and the world economy, economic forecasts for the UK up to 36 months ahead and population forecasts up to 2000 plus.
Contents & Origin of Statistics	Tables per issue: Varies
Currency	6 months
Response	1984
Availability	General
Cost	£10.50 (plus p+p)
Address	Holyoake House, Hanover St, Manchester M60 0AS
Telephone	061 832 4300
Contact	G.V.J. Pratt, Economic and Research Department

266

Originator	COCKS WILLIAMSON ASSOCIATES LTD
Title	BAROMETER, bi-annual
Coverage	Study involving 400-450 interviews with 8-14 year olds to elicit behaviour, lifestyle and attitudes.
Contents & Origin of Statistics	Tables per issue: Own research 100%. Supporting text 50%
Response	1983
Availability	Clients
Address	90-92 Islington High St, London N1
Contact	Michael Williamson

267

Originator	COCOA CHOCOLATE AND CONFECTIONERY ALLIANCE
Title	ANNUAL REPORT, annual

Coverage	Includes general statistics on the industry such as sales by manufacturers, home trade despatches, labour employed, exports, imports, ingredients purchased etc.
Contents & Origin of Statistics	Tables per issue: 13. Own research 50%, Other non official source 5%, Government statistics 45%. Supporting text 80%
Response	1984
Availability	General
Cost	On application
Address	11 Green St, London W1Y 3RF
Telephone	01 629 8971; Telex: 24738
Contact	Above address

268

Originator	COCOA CHOCOLATE AND CONFECTIONERY ALLIANCE
Title	CCCA FOUR-WEEKLY SUMMARIES, 13 issues per year
Coverage	Despatches of chocolate and sugar confectionery.
Contents & Origin of Statistics	Tables per issue: Own research 100%
Currency	1-3 months
Response	1984
Availability	Members and General
Cost	Free to members, £150 to others (under review)
Address	11 Green St, London W1Y 3RF
Telephone	01 629 8971; Telex: 24738

269

Originator	COMMERCIAL MOTOR
Title	TABLES OF OPERATING COSTS, annually as a separate item from the journal
Coverage	Standing and running costs for a wide range of vehicles.
Contents & Origin of Statistics	Tables per issue: 9. Own research 100%
Response	1984
Availability	General
Cost	£3.50
Address	IPC Transport Press Ltd, Quadrant House, The Quadrant, Sutton, Surrey SM2 5AS

Telephone   01 661 3500; Telex: 892084
Contact   Above address

270

Originator   COMMITTEE OF DIRECTORS OF POLYTECHNICS

Title   FIRST DESTINATIONS OF POLYTECHNIC STUDENTS, annual. 1976-
Coverage   First destinations of those obtaining first degrees and higher diplomas by full-time and sandwich study, analysed by employer category and type of work.

Contents &   Tables per issue: 24. Supporting text 4%
Origin of
Statistics

Currency   7 months
Response   1984
Availability General
Cost   £6.70
Address   309 Regent St, London W1R 7PE
Telephone   01 637 9939
Contact   R.P. Blows, Administrative Assistant

271

Originator   COMMITTEE OF DIRECTORS OF POLYTECHNICS

Title   POLYTECHNICS ENROLMENT SURVEY, annual. 1974-
Coverage   Enrolments to advanced courses at polytechnics (30 polytechnics), analysed by level, subject and mode of study.

Contents &   Tables per issue: 10. Supporting text 16%
Origin of
Statistics

Comments   Published in the form of a press release.
Currency   3-4 months
Response   1984
Availability General
Cost   Free
Address   309 Regent St, London W1R 7PE
Telephone   01 637 9939
Contact   R.P. Blows, Administrative Assistant

272

Originator   COMMITTEE OF LONDON CLEARING BANKERS

Title   ABSTRACT OF BANKING STATISTICS, annual. 1984-

Coverage	Data on London and Scottish clearing banks, eg. accounts, infra-structure. Clearing and credit card statistics.
Contents & Origin of Statistics	Tables per issue: 52. Own research 100%. Supporting text 15%
Comments	Section of notes and definitions.
Currency	4 months
Response	1984
Availability	General
Cost	Free
Address	10 Lombard St, London EC3V 9AP
Telephone	01 283 8866
Contact	Mr. A.N. Grayson, Head of Statistical Unit

273

Originator	COMMITTEE OF LONDON CLEARING BANKERS
Title	ANALYSIS OF ADVANCES TO UK RESIDENTS BY THE LONDON CLEARING BANKS' GROUPS, quarterly. 1974-
Coverage	Advances in sterling and foreign currencies by offices of the London Clearing Banks by industrial sector.
Contents & Origin of Statistics	Tables per issue: 1. Own research 100%. Supporting text 5%
Comments	There was a major break in the analysis headings in November 1983 and there have been minor changes in coverage of a number of other dates.
Currency	1 month
Response	1984
Availability	General
Cost	Free
Address	10 Lombard St, London EC3V 9AP
Telephone	01 283 8866
Contact	Mr. A.N. Grayson, Head of Statistical Unit

274

Originator	COMMITTEE OF LONDON CLEARING BANKERS
Title	ANNUAL SUMMARY OF CLEARING STATISTICS, annual. 1949-
Coverage	Turnover of inter-bank clearings through Bankers' Clearing House and Bankers' Automated Clearings Services - Credit and debit.
Contents & Origin of Statistics	Tables per issue: 1. Own research 100%.

Comments	The Bankers' Clearing House has published statistics of the clearings since 1873.
Currency	1 month
Response	1984
Availability	General
Cost	Free
Address	10 Lombard St, London EC3V 9AP
Telephone	01 283 8866
Contact	Mr. A.N. Grayson, Head of Statical Unit

275

Originator	COMMITTEE OF LONDON CLEARING BANKERS
Title	BALANCES OF THE LONDON CLEARING BANKS GROUPS, monthly. 1973-
Coverage	Liabilities and assets of offices of London Clearing Banks in aggregate form and as individual groups.
Contents & Origin of Statistics	Tables per issue: 3. Own research 100%. Supporting text 5%
Comments	Major break in the statistics in June 1975 and there have been minor changes in coverage at a number of other dates.
Currency	1 month
Response	1984
Availability	General
Cost	Free
Address	10 Lombard St, London EC3V 9AP
Telephone	01 283 8866
Contact	Mr. A.N. Grayson, Head of Statistical Unit

276

Originator	COMMITTEE OF LONDON CLEARING BANKERS
Title	CLEARING STATISTICS, monthly. 1950-
Coverage	Inter-bank clearings through bankers' clearing house and bankers automated clearing statistics by value of clearings and number of items.
Contents & Origin of Statistics	Tables per issue: 1. Own research 100%.
Comments	The Bankers' Clearing House has published statistics of clearings since 1873.
Response	1984
Availability	General
Cost	Free

Address	10 Lombard St, London EC3V 9AP
Telephone	01 283 8866
Contact	Mr. A.N. Grayson, Head of Statistical Unit.

277

Originator	COMMITTEE OF SCOTTISH CLEARING BANKERS
Title	ANALYSIS OF ADVANCES TO UK RESIDENTS BY THE SCOTTISH CLEARING BANKS' GROUPS, quarterly
Coverage	Covers advances in both sterling and foreign currencies by sector - manufacturing, financiaal, services and persons.
Contents & Origin of Statistics	Tables per issue: 1. Own research 100%
Response	1983
Availability	General
Cost	Free
Address	19 Rutland Square, Edinburgh EH1 2DD
Telephone	031 229 1326
Contact	J.C. Sutherland, Secretary

278

Originator	COMMITTEE OF SCOTTISH CLEARING BANKERS
Title	BALANCES OF THE SCOTTISH CLEARING BANKS' GROUPS, monthly
Coverage	Covers the business of the offices of the Scottish clearing banks and their subsidiaries. Gives their liabilities and assets, divided into sterling deposits and foreign currency deposits.
Contents & Origin of Statistics	Tables per issue: 2. Own research 100%
Response	1983
Availability	General
Cost	Free
Address	19 Rutland Square, Edinburgh EH1 2DD
Telephone	031 229 1326
Contact	J.C. Sutherland, Secretary

279

Originator	COMPANY CAR
Title	FLEET COST TABLES, monthly in a monthly journal. 1981-

Coverage	Standing, running and total operating costs of petrol and diesel car fleets.
Contents & Origin of Statistics	Tables per issue: 3. Own research 100%
Comments	The tables are computed by the Mercedes-Benz Fleet Information Service using data supplied by fleet operators, leasing companies etc.
Currency	1 month
Response	1984
Availability	General
Cost	£16
Address	Business Press International, Quadrant House, The Quadrant, Sutton, Surrey SM2 5AS
Telephone	01 661 3732; Telex: 892084
Contact	J. Blauth, Editor

280

Originator	COMPUTER ECONOMICS LTD
Title	COMPUTER STAFF SALARY SURVEY, bi-annual. 1968-
Coverage	The survey covers 41 job descriptions, analysed by location, experience, age, areas of responsibility, level of technology and fringe benefits.
Contents & Origin of Statistics	Tables per issue: 190. Own research 100%. Supporting text 15%
Currency	6 weeks
Response	1984
Availability	Participants only
Cost	£179-435
Address	Survey House, 51 Portland Rd, Kingston-upon-Thames, Surrey KT1 2SH
Telephone	01 549 8726
Contact	Peter Stevens, Director

281

Originator	COMPUTER WEEKLY
Title	ANNUAL SURVEY OF DATA PROCESSING USERS, annual in a weekly journal
Coverage	A random sample of 10,000 journal subscribers to gather information on systems used, and their operation, such as type of industry, principal applications, source of applications programs, programming language used and future acquisition plans. Results of the survey appear in 2 or 3 issues at the beginning of each year.

Contents & **Origin of** **Statistics**	Tables per issue: Varies. Own research 100%
Comments	Survey undertaken in association with Datapro. Datapro publish the detailed survey report separately.
Currency	3-4 months
Response	1984
Availability	Controlled circulation
Cost	Free
ISSN	0010 4787
Address	Electrical-Electronic Press, Quadrant House, The Quadrant, Sutton, Surrey SM2 5AS
Telephone	01 661 3122; Telex: 892084
Contact	David Craver, Editor

282

Originator	COMPUTER WEEKLY
Title	DP EXPENDITURE AND VERTICAL MARKET SURVEY, ANNUAL IN A WEEKLY JOURNAL
Coverage	Presents global view of expenditure at approximately 38,000 computer sites in the UK and reviews trends in individual sectors. Results of the surveys appear in various issues throughout the year.
Contents & **Origin of** **Statistics**	Tables per issue: Varies. Own research 100%
Comments	Survey undertaken in association with International Data Corporation.
Currency	Varies
Response	1984
Availability	Controlled circulation
Cost	Free
ISSN	0010 4787
Address	Electrical-Electronic Press, Quadrant House, The Quadrant, Sutton, Surrey SM2 5AS
Telephone	01 661 3122; Telex: 892084
Contact	David Craver, Editor

283

Originator	COMPUTING
Title	USER EXPENDITURE TRENDS IN UK DP, quarterly in a weekly journal
Coverage	9 user sectors are polled every quarter on the trends in hardware software and budgets. An extended annual survey gives absolute levels of expenditure on the above areas.

Contents & Origin of Statistics	Tables per issue: 9. Own research 100%
Currency	1 month
Response	1985
Availability	General
Cost	£32 or 90p for a single issue
Address	VNU Business Publications, 55 Frith St, London W1A 2H9
Telephone	01 439 4242; Telex: 23918
Contact	R. Sharpe, Editor

284

Originator	COMPUTING PUBLICATIONS LTD
Title	COMPUTER USER'S YEARBOOK, annual, 1969-
Coverage	General guide to the computer industry but includes an annual salary survey covering 21 job categories by size and location of installation. Also one-page summary of computer industry statistics.
Contents & Origin of Statistics	Tables per issue: 95. Own research 99%. Government statistics 1%. Supporting text 90%.
Currency	5 months
Response	1984
Availability	General
Cost	£ 57.25, plus £ 2.50 p+p.
ISBN	0 902908 19 7
Address	Evelyn House, 62 Oxford St, London W1A 2HG
Telephone	01 323 3211
Contact	B.I. Hypher, Editor

285

Originator	CONFEDERATION OF BRITISH INDUSTRY (CBI)
Title	ECONOMIC SITUATION REPORT, monthly
Coverage	General economic summary plus general results of the quarterly industrial trends survey, general results of the distributive trades survey, regional reports and comparative data for other European countries. There is a general economic forecast up to 6 months ahead and a comparison of the major forecasts. 4 issues per year only contain results of the latest economic trends inquiry.
Contents & Origin of Statistics	Tables per issue: 50. Own research 49%,Other non official source 2%,Government statistics 49%
Currency	Varies
Response	1984
Availability	General

Cost	£95 for CBI members, £140 to others
ISSN	0142 6419
Address	103 New Oxford St, London WC1A 1DU
Telephone	01 379 7400; Telex: 21332
Contact	Economic Trends Department

286

Originator	CONFEDERATION OF BRITISH INDUSTRY (CBI)
Title	INDUSTRIAL TRENDS SURVEY, quarterly. 1958-
Coverage	Trends for 44 individual industry groups for orders, stocks, output, capital expenditure, exports, costs, labour etc. for the last 4 months and the next 4 months. Based on a survey of approximately 1700 companies.
Contents & Origin of Statistics	Tables per issue: 74. Own research 100%
Comments	An abbreviated monthly inquiry is carried out between the quarterly surveys and is also available on request.
Response	1984
Availability	General
Cost	£95 to CBI members, £150 to others
ISSN	0142 6435
Address	103 New Oxford St, London WC1A 1DU
Telephone	01 379 7400; Telex: 21332
Contact	Economic Trends Department

287

Originator	CONFEDERATION OF BRITISH INDUSTRY (CBI)
Title	SURVEY OF THE DISTRIBUTIVE TRADES, monthly. July 1983-
Coverage	In 8 issues a year a short review of the trade is given covering volume of sales, orders and stocks. Each quarter a large survey is conducted with additional questions on employment, investment, prices, business expenditure etc. Based on a survey of distributive units in 22 individual sectors.
Contents & Origin of Statistics	Tables per issue: Own research 100%
Response	1984
Availability	General
Cost	£125 for CBI members, £175 to others
Address	103 New Oxford St, London WC1A 1DU

| Telephone | 01 379 7400; Telex: 21332 |
| Contact | Economic Trends Department |

288

Originator	CONSTRUCTION NEWS
Title	CONSTRUCTION INDICES, monthly in a weekly journal
Coverage	Cost indices for work and materials in building works, civil engineering and specialist engineering.
Contents & Origin of Statistics	Tables per issue: 3. Government statistics 100%
Comments	Also publish an annual statistical review of the top 200 companies in the industry
Currency	1 week
Response	1984
Availability	General
Cost	£35 or 45p for a single issue
Address	International Thomson Publishing Ltd, Elm House, 10-16 Elm St, London WC1X 0BP
Telephone	01 278 2345, Telex: 21746
Contact	J.D. Allen, Editor-in-Chief

289

Originator	CONSTRUCTION PLANT-HIRE ASSOCIATION
Title	CPA ACTIVITY AND HIRE RATE STUDIES, quarterly. 1979-
Coverage	Activity levels as a % and hire rate averages and ranges for a selection of popular plant types
Contents & Origin of Statistics	Tables per issue: 9. Own research 100%. Supporting text 30%
Currency	2 weeks
Response	1984
Availability	Participating members
Cost	Free
Address	28, Eccleston St, London SW1W 9PY
Telephone	01 730 7117
Contact	J.A. Smith, Assistant Director

290

Originator	CONSTRUCTION PLANT-HIRE ASSOCIATION
Title	CPA COST STUDIES, bi-annual. 1977-

Coverage	Costs versus cost trends in hired plant.
Contents & Origin of Statistics	Tables per issue: 10. Own research 100%. Supporting text 10%
Comments	Previously known as Contractors' Plant Association. Summary data on Prestel and as press release.
Currency	2 months
Response	1984
Availability	Members
Cost	Free
Address	28, Eccleston St, London SW1W 9PY
Telephone	01 730 7117
Contact	J.A. Smith, Assistant Director

291

Originator	CONTAINERISATION INTERNATIONAL RESEARCH
Title	UK UNITISED TRADE STATISTICS, annual. 1983-
Coverage	Detailed structure of UK containerised ro-ro trade. Statistics relate to loaded container and trailer trade between individual UK seaports and overseas trade areas. Also data on rail ferry and non-unitised trade, and unitised penetration for individual commodities.
Contents & Origin of Statistics	Tables per issue: 120
Comments	This publication serves as an introduction to the even more extensive Cirstat computer data bank. Analyses of Cirstat data are tailored to clients' individual needs.
Response	1984
Availability	General
Cost	£85
Address	National Magazine House, 72 Broadwick St, London W1V 2BP
Telephone	01 831 6979; Telex: 263879
Contact	Raymond H. Fenyoe, Head of Research

292

Originator	CONTRACT JOURNAL
Title	DATAFILE - MARKET INDICATORS, monthly in a weekly journal
Coverage	Data on the value of construction contracts received in the UK by type of contract, eg type of construction planned. Latest month given plus a month-by-month total for the current year.

Contents &	Tables per issue: 7. Own research 100%. Supporting text 20%
Origin of	
Statistics	
Comments	More detailed data and analysis is available on a regular basis at a cost of £10 per year
Currency	1-2 months
Response	1985
Availability	General
Cost	£49
Address	Business Press International Ltd, Oakfield House, 35 Perrymount Rd, Haywards Heath, West Sussex RH16 3DH
Telephone	0444 459188; Telex: 946564
Contact	George Battley, Assistant Editor

293

Originator	COOPERS AND LYBRAND ASSOCIATES (NI) LTD.
Title	NORTHERN IRELAND ECONOMY : CURRENT SITUATION AND PROSPECTS, bi-annual. 1980-
Coverage	Review of labour market, business conditions, prices and public expenditure, economic background. Appendices on labour market.
Contents &	Tables per issue: 40-45. Own research 10%, Other non official source
Origin of	10%, Government statistics 80%. Supporting text 65%
Statistics	
Currency	4-6 weeks
Response	1984
Availability	General
Cost	£40
Address	Fanum House, 108 Great Victoria St, Belfast BT2 7AX
Telephone	0232 245454
Contact	Arthur Luke, Director

294

Originator	COPPER DEVELOPMENT ASSOCIATION
Title	ALUMINIUM BRONZE PRODUCTION STATISTICS, quarterly. 1979-
Coverage	Production of aluminium bronze alloys by user industry and product form.
Contents &	Tables per issue: 2. Own research 100%.
Origin of	
Statistics	
Currency	3 months
Response	1984
Availability	Members
Cost	Free

Address	Orchard House, Mutton Lane, Potters Bar, Herts EN6 3AP
Telephone	0707 50711; Telex: 27711
Contact	Mrs Rogers, Information Department

295

Originator	CORNWALL COUNTY COUNCIL
Title	BASIC PLANNING STATISTICS, issued at irregular intervals. 1970s-
Coverage	Series of loose leaf sheets on population, employment, incomes, housing, electorate, tourism and transport for Cornwall and its districts.
Contents & Origin of Statistics	Tables per issue: Varies. Own research 10%, Government statistics 90%.
Currency	Varies
Response	1984
Availability	General
Cost	Free
Address	County Planning Department, County Hall, Truro, Cornwall TR1 3BB
Telephone	0872 74282, ext 63
Contact	P.W. Mitchell, Information and Research Section

296

Originator	COSMETIC, TOILETRY AND PERFUMERY ASSOCIATION LTD
Title	HAIR PREPARATIONS SURVEY, bi-annual
Coverage	Statistics on hair colourants, bleaches and dyes.
Contents & Origin of Statistics	Tables per issue: 1. Own research 100%
Response	1983
Availability	Members
Cost	Free
Address	35 Dover St, London W1X 3RA
Telephone	01 491 8891
Contact	R. McCulloch, Secretary

297

Originator	COST ENGINEER
Title	COST INDICES, 6 times a year in a journal published 6 times a year
Coverage	Costs of erected chemical process plants in the UK.
Contents & Origin of Statistics	Tables per issue: 1. Government statistics 100%
Currency	4 months
Response	1984
Availability	General
Cost	£10
Address	Association of Cost Engineers, 26 Chapel St, Sandbach, Cheshire CW11 9DS
Telephone	09367 4798
Contact	Gordon H. Gilbert

298

Originator	COUNCIL FOR NATIONAL ACADEMIC AWARDS (CNAA)
Title	ANNUAL REPORT, annual. 1964-
Coverage	Data on enrolments, awards made and research, by type of course and subject.
Contents & Origin of Statistics	Tables per issue: 19. Own research 100%. Supporting text 60%
Response	1984
Availability	General
Cost	Free
Address	344/354 Grays Inn Rd, London WC1X 8BP
Telephone	01 278 4411,ext 227
Contact	R.J. Hunt, Assistant Secretary

299

Originator	COUNCIL OF THE STOCK EXCHANGE
Title	STOCK EXCHANGE FACT BOOK, quarterly. 1979-
Coverage	Financial data of the Stock Exchange, for example, sector turnover, new issues, shares traded etc.
Contents & Origin of Statistics	Tables per issue: 21. Unstated 100%. Supporting text 5%
Response	1984

Availability	General
Cost	£15 (£35 for Full Service)
ISSN	0143 229X
Address	The Stock Exchange Fact Service, The Stock Exchange, London EC2N 1HP
Telephone	01 588 2355, ext 8767
Contact	Miss D.A. Steer, Administrator, Fact Service

300

Originator	COUNCIL OF THE STOCK EXCHANGE
Title	STOCK EXCHANGE FACT SHEET, monthly
Coverage	Serves as a back up to the Fact Book. Information on new companies, share issues, the USM market and shares traded.
Contents & Origin of Statistics	Tables per issue: 9. Unstated 100%. Supporting text 5%
Response	1984
Availability	General
Cost	£8 (£35 for Full Service)
ISSN	0265 1513
Address	The Stock Exchange Fact Service, The Stock Exchange, London EC2N 1HP
Telephone	01 588 2355, ext 8767
Contact	Miss D.A. Steer, Administrator, Fact Service

301

Originator	COUNCIL OF THE STOCK EXCHANGE
Title	STOCK EXCHANGE SURVEY OF SHARE OWNERSHIP, annual
Coverage	Survey of ordinary share ownership - sample of 222 companies. Analysis in 17 categories.
Contents & Origin of Statistics	Tables per issue: 10. Own research 100%. Supporting text 50%
Response	1984
Availability	General
Cost	£ 7 (£35 For Full Service)
ISSN	0265 5748
Address	The Stock Exchange Fact Service, The Stock Exchange, London EC2N 1HP
Telephone	01 588 2355, ext 8767
Contact	Miss D.A. Steer, Administrator, Fact Service

302

Originator	COUNTY COUNCILS GAZETTE
Title	VARIOUS TITLES, monthly
Coverage	Every month statistics are published on a particular topic, e.g. waste disposal, capital expenditure, rate precept returns, national parks etc.
Contents & Origin of Statistics	Tables per issue: Varies. Non official source 90%, Government statistics 10%
Currency	Varies
Response	1984
Availability	General
Cost	£6.60 or 55p for a single issue
Address	Association of County Councils, Eaton House, 66A Eaton Square, London SW1W 9BH
Telephone	01 235 1200
Contact	Above address

303

Originator	COVENTRY CITY COUNCIL
Title	ECONOMIC MONITOR, quarterly. 1975-
Coverage	Review of trends in the local economy covering job market, industrial trends and the business climate. Special feature article in each issue.
Contents & Origin of Statistics	Tables per issue: 25-30. Non official source 30%, Government statistics 70%. Supporting text 50%
Currency	2-3 months
Response	1984
Availability	General
Cost	Free
ISBN	0263 9394
Address	Economic Unit, Treasurer's Dept., Council House, Coventry
Telephone	0203 25555
Contact	D. Hamilton, Economic Research Officer

304

Originator	CREMATION SOCIETY OF GREAT BRITAIN
Title	DIRECTORY OF CREMATORIA, annual. 1979/80-
Coverage	Progress of cremation over the last 100 years. Facts and figures section with numbers of crematoria, cremation comparisons between areas of UK, cremations carried out by county and fees charged.

Contents & Origin of Statistics	Tables per issue: 10. Own research 100%. Supporting text 90%
Response	1984
Availability	General
Cost	£11
ISSN	0143 3164
Address	Woodcut House, Ashford Rd, Hollingbourne, Maidstone, Kent ME17 1XH
Telephone	0622 38034/37877
Contact	Mr R. N. Arber, Secretary

305

Originator	CROUDACE CONSTRUCTION
Title	CONSTRUCTION INDUSTRY FORECAST, bi-annual
Coverage	Output forecasts for the construction industry over a 2-3 year period. Gives own forecast, together with those of BMP, NEDO and Savory Milln. Covers starts and orders for public and private housing, private industrial and commercial construction, repair and maintenance. Also summary profile of orders at constant prices, and output.
Contents & Origin of Statistics	Tables per issue: 10. Own research + other non official source 90%, Government statistics 10%
Response	1983
Availability	General
Cost	Negotiable
Address	Croudace House, Caterham, Surrey CR3 6XQ
Telephone	0883 46464
Contact	D.S. Bean, Commercial Director

306

Originator	CUMBERNAULD DEVELOPMENT CORPORATION
Title	CUMBERNAULD - THE FACTS AND THE FIGURES, annual
Coverage	Gives data on population, housing, industry, industrial floorspace, employment, finance, leisure, education, commerce.
Contents & Origin of Statistics	Tables per issue: 10. Unstated 100%
Response	1983
Availability	General
Cost	Free
Address	Corporation Offices, Cumbernauld House, Cumbernauld, Glasgow

Telephone   023 67 21155
Contact   Planning Research Department

307

Originator   CUMBERNAULD DEVELOPMENT CORPORATION

Title   STATISTICAL TRENDS, annual
Coverage   Contains sections on demography, housing, employment, industry, commerce, social and community facilities, recreation. Also contains a number of maps and diagrams.

Contents &   Tables per issue: 47. Own research + other non official source 60%,
Origin of   Unstated 40%
Statistics

Response   1983
Availability General
Cost   £1 for 1981
Address   Corporation Offices, Cumbernauld House, Cumbernauld, Glasgow
Telephone   023 67 21155
Contact   Planning Research Department

308

Originator   CUMBRIA COUNTY COUNCIL

Title   CUMBRIA IN FIGURES, annual. 1975-
Coverage   Basic data on population, housing, labour market, agriculture, environment, transport, social services, finance, education, and council representation. Some comparisons with national figures.

Contents &   Tables per issue: 11. Own research 50%, Government statistics 50%.
Origin of
Statistics

Comments   Produced in card format.
Currency   6 months
Response   1984
Availability General
Cost   Free
Address   Couunty Planning Department, County Offices, Kendal, Cumbria, LA9 4RQ
Telephone   0539 21000
Contact   P.W. Robinson, Group Leader.

309

Originator   CUMBRIA COUNTY COUNCIL

Title   MONITOR, monthly. 1980-

Coverage	Statistics and review of trends in unemployment, redundancies, vacancies etc, by district, plus reports of developments proposed and closures.
Contents & Origin of Statistics	Tables per issue: 4. Government statistics 100%. Supporting text 30%
Currency	1-2 weeks
Response	1984
Availability	Mainly internal circulation but available generally on subscription
Cost	£5
Address	County Planning Department, County Offices, Kendal, Cumbria LA9 4JA.
Telephone	0539 21000
Contact	L.G. Walker, Principal Planner

310

Originator	DAIRY TRADE FEDERATION
Title	THE DAIRY INDUSTRY, annual
Coverage	Prices, consumption, market for milk and other dairy products.
Contents & Origin of Statistics	Tables per issue: 20pgs. Supporting text 80%
Currency	9-12 months
Response	1984
Availability	Members and selected requests
Cost	Free
Address	19 Cornwall Terrace, London, NW1 4QP
Telephone	01 486 7244; Telex: 262027

311

Originator	DE ZOETE AND BEVAN
Title	EQUITY AND FIXED INTEREST INVESTMENT FROM 1919, annual (with mid- year supplement). 1955-
Coverage	Indices on cost of living, De Zoete's equity, De Zoete's gilt, FT actuaries, all share, building society shares, treasury bills, and fund growth tables.
Contents & Origin of Statistics	Tables per issue: 8. Supporting text 30%
Comments	Other publications for clients and an international publication, 'International Equity Performance since 1919' which can be purchased generally. Not prepared to give figures over the 'phone due to staff and time limitations.

Currency	3-4 weeks
Response	1984
Availability	Primarily for clients but available generally if stocks available
Cost	£7.50
Address	25 Finsbury Circus, London FC2M 7EE
Telephone	01 588 4141; Telex: 888221/883179
Contact	Mrs N. Smith, Librarian

312

Originator	DEBENHAM, TEWSON AND CHINNOCKS
Title	DIGEST OF PROPERTY STATISTICS, annual
Coverage	Overview of the main variables affecting the property market. Divided into offices, shops, industrial property, agriculture and general.
Contents & Origin of Statistics	Tables per issue: 51. Own research + other non official source 60%, Government statistics 30%, Unstated 10%
Currency	Varies
Response	1984
Availability	General
Cost	Free to general public (may be charge made to companies, etc.)
Address	Bancroft House, Paternoster Square, London EC4P 4ET
Telephone	01 236 1520
Contact	Peter Evans, Geoffrey Prestridge, Information Services

313

Originator	DEBENHAM, TEWSON AND CHINNOCKS
Title	INDUSTRIAL RENTS AND RATES, annual
Coverage	Level of industrial rents and rates over a 10 year period in 16 industrial centres.
Contents & Origin of Statistics	Tables per issue: 6. Own research 100%
Response	1984
Availability	General
Cost	Free to general public (may be charge made to companies, etc.)
Address	Bancroft House, Paternoster Square, London EC4P 4ET
Telephone	01 236 1520
Contact	Peter Evans, Geoffrey Prestridge, Information Services

314

Originator	DEBENHAM, TEWSON AND CHINNOCKS
Title	MONEY INTO PROPERTY, annual
Coverage	Examines the amount of bank and institutional money being directed into the property sector.
Contents & Origin of Statistics	Tables per issue: 21. Own research + other non official source 25%, Unstated 75%
Comments	Although a large percentage of the individual tables are not acknowledged, a list of sources is given at the end of the publication.
Response	1984
Availability	General
Cost	Free to general public (may be charge made to companies, etc.)
Address	Bancroft House, Paternoster Square, London EC4P 4ET
Telephone	01 236 1520
Contact	Peter Evans, Geoffrey Prestridge, Information Services

315

Originator	DEBENHAM, TEWSON AND CHINNOCKS
Title	OFFICE FLOORSPACE SURVEY, quarterly
Coverage	Office floorspace available in main centres of Great Britain.
Contents & Origin of Statistics	Tables per issue: Own research 100%
Response	1984
Availability	General
Cost	Free, but charge may be imposed on certain requesters
Address	Bancroft House, Paternoster Square, London EC4P 4ET
Telephone	01 236 1520
Contact	Peter Evans, Geoffrey Prestridge, Information Services

316

Originator	DEBENHAM, TEWSON AND CHINNOCKS
Title	OFFICE RENTS AND RATES, annual
Coverage	Level of prime office rents and rates in main centres of Great Britain.
Contents & Origin of Statistics	Tables per issue: 13. Own research + other non official source 60%, Government statistics 15%, Unstated 25%
Response	1984
Availability	General
Cost	Free, but charge may be imposed on certain requesters

Address	Bancroft House, Paternoster Square, London EC4P 4ET
Telephone	01 236 1520
Contact	Peter Evans, Geoffrey Prestridge, Information Services

317

Originator	DECORATIVE LIGHTING ASSOCIATION LTD

Title	ANALYSIS OF TURNOVER, biennial
Coverage	Analysis of sales and imports

Contents & Origin of Statistics	Tables per issue: 10. Own research 100%. Supporting text 10%

Comments	1981 and 1982 results were insufficient to compile an analysis. Next summary due in 1986.
Currency	2 years
Response	1984
Availability	Members
Cost	Free
Address	Bryn House, Bryn, Bishops Castle, Shropshire SY9 5LE
Telephone	05884 658
Contact	J.W.L. Tengwall, Director

318

Originator	DEVON COUNTY COUNCIL

Title	DEVON IN FIGURES, annual
Coverage	Statistics for the county and for district councils. Includes data on population, housing, economy, transport, education, social services, crime, recreation, resources, water.

Contents & Origin of Statistics	Tables per issue: 85. Own research + other non official source 30%, Government statistics 70%

Response	1983
Availability	General
Address	Treasurer's Department, County Hall, Exeter EX2 4QJ
Telephone	0392 77977
Contact	T. Widdicombe

319

Originator	DIRECT RESPONSE

Title	MEDIA EXPENDITURE AND FULFILMENT ROAD TEST, annual in a monthly journal

Coverage	Media expenditure in mail order industry and data on how quickly goods are sent from advertisements.
Contents & Origin of Statistics	Tables per issue: Own research + other non official source 100%
Response	1984
Availability	A controlled subscription
Cost	£25
Address	Macro Publishing Ltd, 41B High St, Hoddesdon, Hertfordshire EN11 8TA
Telephone	0992 469556
Contact	Paul Rowney

320

Originator	DIRECTOR
Title	KEY BUSINESSS STATISTICS, monthly in a monthly journal
Coverage	General data on the economy including earnings, inflation, employment, interest rates, exchange rates and production.
Contents & Origin of Statistics	Tables per issue: 7. Government statistics 100%. Supporting text 10%
Currency	Varies
Response	1984
Availability	General
Cost	£18 or £1.50 for a single issue
ISSN	0012 3242
Address	Director Publications Ltd, Institute of Directors, 116 Pall Mall, London SW1Y 5ED
Telephone	01 839 1233
Contact	Carol Kennedy, Deputy Editor

321

Originator	DISTILLERS CO
Title	STATISTICAL TABLES, annual
Coverage	Covers Scotch whisky industry as a whole, giving production and stocks, home and export sales, shipments to major markets, exports and UK excise duty. Data for a 10 year period.
Contents & Origin of Statistics	Tables per issue: 5. Non official source 100%
Comments	Supplement to 'Distillers of Scotch'. Source of statistics given as Scotch Whisky Association.
Response	1984

Availability   At company's discretion
Cost   Free
Address   20 St James's Square, London SW1Y 4JF
Telephone   01 930 1040
Contact   Charles Piggott, Public Relations Department

322

Originator   DOOR AND SHUTTER MANUFACTURERS ASSOCIATION

Title   MEMBERS' SALES STATISTICS, quarterly
Coverage   Members' intake of orders for home and overseas markets.

Contents &   Tables per issue: Own research 100%
Origin of
Statistics

Response   1983
Availability   Members
Address   5 Greenfield Crescent, Edgbaston, Birmingham B15 3BE
Telephone   021 454 2177
Contact   Above address

323

Originator   DRAPERS CHAMBER OF TRADE

Title   MONTHLY SALES FIGURES, annual. 1981-
Coverage   As indicated in title.
Currency   3 months
Response   1984
Availability   Members
Cost   Free
Address   North Bar, Banbury, Oxfordshire
Telephone   0295 53601
Contact   R.W. Hylands, Secretary

324

Originator   DRAPERS CHAMBER OF TRADE

Title   OPERATING RESULTS, annual. 1981-
Coverage   Operating results of 5 groups of members according to turnover and
                   type of merchandise sold. For each gives sales index, gross margin
                   and expenses.

Contents &   Tables per issue: c.19. Own research 100%. Supporting text 15%
Origin of
Statistics

Currency   6 months

Response	1984
Availability	Members
Cost	Free
Address	North Bar, Banbury, Oxfordshire
Telephone	0295 53601
Contact	R.W. Hylands, Secretary

325

Originator	DRAWING OFFICE MATERIAL MANUFACTURERS AND DEALERS
Title	ANNUAL REPORT, annual
Coverage	Contains data on invoiced exports.
Contents & Origin of Statistics	Tables per issue: Own research 100%
Response	1983
Address	25-27 Oxford St, London W1R 1RJ
Contact	Above address

326

Originator	DRIVERS JONAS
Title	ABERDEEN COMMERCIAL AND INDUSTRIAL PROPERTY SURVEY, bi-annual. May 1975-
Coverage	Space available, space let or sold and index of rental levels.
Contents & Origin of Statistics	Tables per issue: 6. Own research 100%. Supporting text 50%
Comments	Includes list of office property available.
Currency	1 month
Response	1984
Availability	General
Cost	Free
Address	16 Suffolk St, London SW1Y 4HQ
Telephone	01 930 9731
Contact	D. Monti, Librarian

327

Originator	DRIVERS JONAS
Title	EAST ANGLIA INDUSTRIAL PROPERTY SURVEY, bi-annual. Autumn 1979-
Coverage	Space available and space let in the region.

Contents & **Origin of** **Statistics**	Tables per issue: 6. Own research 100%. Supporting text 50%
Response	1984
Availability	General
Cost	Free
Address	16, Suffolk St, London SW1Y 4HQ
Telephone	01 930 9731
Contact	D. Monti, Librarian

328

Originator	DUDLEY METROPOLITAN BOROUGH DISTRICT COUNCIL
Title	LAND RESOURCES REVIEW, annual
Coverage	Covers land demand and availability, ownership, distribution of uses among areas, uncommitted land. Also includes a series of maps of the area and its land use.
Contents & **Origin of** **Statistics**	Tables per issue: 9. Own research 100%
Response	1983
Address	The Council House, Dudley, West Midlands
Contact	Above address

329

Originator	DUDLEY METROPOLITAN BOROUGH DISTRICT COUNCIL
Title	PROFILE, annual
Coverage	Divided into sections on population, households, business and government.
Contents & **Origin of** **Statistics**	Tables per issue: 47. Own research + other non official source 50%, Government statistics 30%, Unstated 20%
Response	1983
Address	The Council House, Dudley, West Midlands
Contact	Above address

330

Originator	DUN & BRADSTREET LTD
Title	BUSINESS FAILURE STATISTICS, quarterly

Coverage	Company liquidations and bankruptcies analysed by trade and by region.
Contents & Origin of Statistics	Tables per issue: 3. Own research 100%. Supporting text 70%.
Comments	Issued as a press release.
Currency	1 week
Response	1984
Availability	General
Cost	Free
Address	26-32 Clifton St, London, EC2P 2LY
Telephone	01 377 4377; Telex: 886697
Contact	A. Priestley, Public Relations Officer

331

Originator	DUNDEE AND TAYSIDE CHAMBER OF COMMERCE AND INDUSTRY
Title	PAY SURVEY - CLERICAL AND SECRETARIAL, annual
Coverage	Survey of clerical and secretarial rates of pay. Data supplied by members.
Contents & Origin of Statistics	Tables per issue: Own research 100%
Response	1983
Availability	General
Cost	£20 to non-members
Address	Chamber of Commerce Buildings, Panmure St, Dundee DD1 1ED
Telephone	0382 22122
Contact	Above address

332

Originator	EAST SUSSEX COUNTY COUNCIL
Title	HOUSING LAND COMMITMENT, annual. 1974-
Coverage	Summary of outstanding planning permissions for housing development in each district in East Sussex together with details of large sites and land allocated for housing.
Contents & Origin of Statistics	Tables per issue: 16. Own research 100%. Supporting text 4%
Currency	5 months
Response	1984
Availability	General
Cost	£20

Address	Planning Department, Southover House, Southover Rd, Lewes, East Sussex, BN7 1YA
Telephone	07916 5400, ext 346
Contact	Peter Jackson, Senior Planner

333

Originator   EAST SUSSEX COUNTY COUNCIL

Title	INDUSTRIAL, OFFICE AND RETAIL LAND COMMIT-MENT, annual. 1975-
Coverage	Summary by ward and parish of the amount of land allocated or with planning permission for industrial, office or retail development. Includes maps of large sites allocated for industrial development.
Contents & Origin of Statistics	Tables per issue: 33. Own research 100%. Supporting text 7%
Currency	4 months
Response	1984
Availability	General
Cost	£15
Address	Planning Department, Southover House, Southover Rd, Lewes, East Sussex BN7 1YA
Telephone	07916 5400, Ext 346
Contact	Peter Jackson, Senior Planner

334

Originator   EAST SUSSEX COUNTY COUNCIL

Title	STATISTICS, annual
Coverage	Largely financial data but has sections on population, housing, services, tourism and leisure.
Contents & Origin of Statistics	Tables per issue: 13.
Currency	6 months
Response	1983
Availability	General
Address	P.O. Box 3, County Hall, St Anne's Crescent, Lewes, Sussex BN7 1SF
Telephone	07916 5400
Contact	J. Unsworth, County Treasurer

335

Originator   ECONOMIST INTELLIGENCE UNIT

Title   CAPITAL REPLACEMENT COSTS, quarterly. 1983-
Coverage   A continuous survey of over 160 items of capital equipment arranged
                    into 16 categories of machinery. Data presented in the form of an
                    index and is based on a survey of 50 manufacturers of equipment,
                    trade associations and other bodies.

Contents &   Tables per issue: Own research 100%
Origin of
Statistics

Comments   Also publishes 'one-off' reports and international publications.
Currency   2-3 months
Response   1984
Availability   General
Cost   £50 for standard index for each product category plus £30 for an
                    annual revision and £38 for a quarterly revision.
Address   Economist Publications Ltd, 40 Duke St, London W1M 5DG
Telephone   01 493 6711; Telex: 266353
Contact   Above address

336

Originator   ECONOMIST INTELLIGENCE UNIT

Title   MOTOR BUSINESS, quarterly
Coverage   Articles and features on the motor industry worldwide but includes
                    regular statistics on vehicle production and registrations in the UK
                    by type of vehicle and manufacturer plus a forecast for one year
                    ahead of car and commercial vehicle production. Comparative figures
                    for other major countries also given and vehicle prices also included.

Contents &   Tables per issue: 8. Own research + other non official source +
Origin of   government statistics 100%
Statistics

Comments   Also publish various 'one-off' reports and international publications.
Currency   1-2 months
Response   1984
Availability   General
Cost   £155 (£1.50 p+p)
ISSN   0027 1802
Address   Economist Publications Ltd, 40 Duke St, London W1M 5DG
Telephone   01 493 6711; Telex: 266353
Contact   Above address

337

Originator	ECONOMIST INTELLIGENCE UNIT
Title	RETAIL BUSINESS, monthly
Coverage	General trends in the retail trade plus regular monthly and six monthly sector and product reviews. Every quarter there is an economic review with special emphasis on trends and prospects for consumer spending and retail sales.
Contents & Origin of Statistics	Tables per issue: Varies
Comments	Also publish 'one-off' reports and international publications.
Currency	Varies
Response	1984
Availability	General
Cost	£155 (£4 p+p)
ISSN	0034 012
Address	Economist Publications Ltd, 40 Duke St, London W1M 5DG
Telephone	01 493 6711; Telex: 266353
Contact	Above address

338

Originator	ECONOMIST INTELLIGENCE UNIT
Title	UNITED KINGDOM QUARTERLY ECONOMIC REVIEW, quarterly
Coverage	General review of economic trends in the UK.
Contents & Origin of Statistics	Tables per issue: Varies. Government statistics 100%
Comments	Publish various other 'one-off' reports and international publications.
Currency	Varies
Response	1984
Availability	General
Cost	£45 (£1.50 p+p), includes annual supplement
Address	Economist Publications Ltd, 40 Duke St, London W1M 5DG
Telephone	01 493 6711; Telex: 266353
Contact	Above address

339

Originator	EDEN VALE
Title	REVIEW OF THE FRESH CHILLED DAIRY PRODUCTS MARKET, annual

Coverage	Sections on yoghurt, cream, cottage cheese, salad, desserts, etc. Covers sales in values and quantities. Gives projected data for following year and historical data for comparison.
Contents & Origin of Statistics	Tables per issue: 13. Own research 100%

Response	1983
Availability	General
Cost	Free
Address	Victoria Rd, South Ruislip, Middlesex HA4 0HF
Telephone	01 845 2345
Contact	Above address

340

Originator	EGGS AUTHORITY

Title	EGG STATISTICS, annual. 1978-
Coverage	Data on egg production, packing, household purchases, prices, imports/exports and chick placings. Some comparative figures for the EEC.
Contents & Origin of Statistics	Tables per issue: 40. Own research 70%, Other non official source 20%, Government statistics 10%.

Currency	2-3 months
Response	1984
Availability	General
Cost	Free
Address	Union House, Eridge Rd, Tunbridge Wells, Kent BR3 2QD
Telephone	0892 33987; Telex: 957346
Contact	Mrs K. Cole, Market Analyst

341

Originator	EGGS AUTHORITY

Title	MONTHLY DIGEST AND EGG FIGURES, monthly. Sept. 1981-
Coverage	Summary of UK market with data on household purchases, packing station supplies, prices, chick placings, and production costs. Includes a supplement titled 'Egg Figures'
Contents & Origin of Statistics	Tables per issue: 21. Own research 70%, Other non official source 20%, Government statistics 10%. Supporting text 35%

Currency	Varies
Response	1984
Availability	General
Cost	Free to egg producers, £25 to others

Address	Union House, Eridge Rd, Tunbridge Wells, Kent BR3 2QD
Telephone	0892 33987; Telex: 957346
Contact	Mrs K. Cole, Market Analyst

342

Originator	EGGS AUTHORITY

Title	WEEKLY REPORT, weekly. 1971-
Coverage	Producer and retail prices of eggs by region, and international comparisons, and packing station supplies.
Contents & Origin of Statistics	Tables per issue: 5-10. Own research 90%, Government statistics 10%. Supporting text 30%
Currency	1 week
Response	1984
Availability	Levy paying egg producers and packers
Cost	Unstated
Address	Union House, Eridge Rd, Tunbridge Wells, Kent BR3 2QD
Telephone	0892 33987; Telex: 957346
Contact	Mrs K. Cole, Market Analyst

343

Originator	ELECTRIC VEHICLE ASSOCIATION OF GREAT BRITAIN LTD

Title	ELECTRIC ROAD VEHICLE REGISTRATIONS, monthly
Coverage	Analysis of registrations of electric road vehicles.
Contents & Origin of Statistics	Tables per issue: Own research 100%
Response	1983
Availability	Members
Cost	Free
Address	Suite 713, Thames House North, Millbank, London SW1P 4QF
Telephone	01 630 5064
Contact	Above address

344

Originator	ELECTRICAL AND RADIO TRADING

Title	UNTITLED, quarterly in a weekly journal
Coverage	Statistics cover marketing and sales of domestic electrical appliances and home electronic equipment.

Contents & Origin of Statistics	Tables per issue: Non official source 50%. Government statistics 50%
Currency	Varies
Response	1984
Availability	Controlled Circulation
Cost	£20 or 4op for a single issue
Address	IPC Electrical-Electronic Press Ltd, Quadrant House, Sutton, Surrey, SM2 5AS
Telephone	01 661 35000
Contact	Alfred Sorkin, Editor

345

Originator	ELECTRICAL INSTALLATION EQUIPMENT MANUFAC-TURERS ASSOCIATION LTD
Title	ELECTRICAL INDUSTRIAL FUSES, HOME AND EXPORT SALES, quarterly
Coverage	Electrical fuses market.
Response	1984
Availability	Members
Cost	Free
Address	Leicester House, 8 Leicester St, London WC2H 7BN
Telephone	01 437 0678
Contact	K.H. Jackson, Director

346

Originator	ELECTRICAL INSTALLATION EQUIPMENT MANUFAC-TURERS ASSOCIATION LTD
Title	ELECTRICAL INSTALLATION EQUIPMENT GENERAL TRENDS SURVEY, quarterly
Coverage	General data on electrical equipment trends.
Response	1984
Availability	Members
Cost	Free
Address	Leicester House, 8 Leicester St, London WC2H 7BN
Telephone	01 437 0678
Contact	K.H. Jackson, Director

347

Originator	ELECTRICAL INSTALLATION EQUIPMENT MANUFAC-TURERS ASSOCIATION LTD
Title	ELECTRICAL WIRING ACCESSORIES, EXPORT SALES BY COUNTRY, quarterly

Coverage	Exports of wiring accessories.
Response	1984
Availability	Members
Cost	Free
Address	Leicester House, 8 Leicester St, London WC2H 7BN
Telephone	01 437 0678
Contact	K.H. Jackson, Director

348

Originator	ELECTRICAL INSTALLATION EQUIPMENT MANUFAC-TURERS ASSOCIATION LTD
Title	ELECTRICAL WIRING ACCESSORIES, HOME AND EXPORT SALES AND ORDERS, quarterly
Coverage	Wiring accessories market.
Response	1984
Availability	Members
Cost	Free
Address	Leicester House, 8 Leicester St, London WC2H 7BN
Telephone	Telephone:01 437 0678
Contact	K.H. Jackson, Director

349

Originator	ELECTRICAL INSTALLATION EQUIPMENT MANUFAC-TURERS ASSOCIATION LTD
Title	INDUSTRIAL PLUGS AND SOCKETS, HOME AND EXPORT SALES, quarterly
Coverage	Plugs and sockets market data.
Response	1984
Availability	Members
Cost	Free
Address	Leicester House, 8 Leicester St, London WC2H 7BN
Telephone	01 437 0678
Contact	K.H. Jackson, Director

350

Originator	ELECTRICAL INSTALLATION EQUIPMENT MANUFAC-TURERS ASSOCIATION LTD
Title	LOW VOLTAGE CIRCUIT-BREAKERS, HOME AND EXPORT ORDERS RECEIVED, VALUE AND UNITS, quarterly
Coverage	Circuit-breakers market data.
Response	1984
Availability	Members

Cost   Free
Address   Leicester House, 8 Leicester St, London WC2H 7BN
Telephone   01 437 0678
Contact   K.H. Jackson, Director

351

Originator   ELECTRICAL INSTALLATION EQUIPMENT MANUFAC-
                TURERS ASSOCIATION LTD

Title   LOW VOLTAGE DISTRIBUTION SWITCHBOARDS, HOME
                AND EXPORT SALES AND ORDERS, quarterly
Coverage   Distribution switchboards market data.
Response   1984
Availability   Members
Cost   Free
Address   Leicester House, 8 Leicester St, London WC2H 7BN
Telephone   01 437 0678
Contact   K.H. Jackson, Director

352

Originator   ELECTRICAL INSTALLATION EQUIPMENT MANUFAC-
                TURERS ASSOCIATION LTD

Title   LOW VOLTAGE SWITCH AND FUSEGEAR, HOME AND
                EXPORT SALES AND ORDERS, quarterly
Coverage   Switch and fusegear market data.
Response   1984
Availability   Members
Cost   Free
Address   Leicester House, 8 Leicester St, London WC2H 7BN
Telephone   01 437 0678
Contact   K.H. Jackson, Director

353

Originator   ELECTRICAL INSTALLATION EQUIPMENT MANUFAC-
                TURERS ASSOCIATION LTD

Title   SWITCH AND FUSEGEAR, EXPORT SALES BY COUNTRY,
                quarterly
Coverage   Switch and fusegear exports.
Response   1984
Availability   Members
Cost   Free
Address   Leicester House, 8 Leicester St, London WC2H 7BN

Telephone	01 437 0678
Contact	K.H. Jackson, Director

354

Originator	ELECTRICAL TIMES
Title	BEAMA INDEX, NEDO INDICES, PRICES OF CABLE-METALS AND MATERIALS, monthly in a monthly journal
Coverage	Labour and material price indices covering electrical equipment and specialised engineering installations plus prices of selected metals and materials.
Contents & Origin of Statistics	Tables per issue: 3. Non official source 30%, Government statistics 70%
Currency	2-4 months
Response	1985
Availability	General
Cost	£19.50 or 80p for a single issue
ISSN	0013 4414
Address	Business Press International Ltd, Quadrant House, The Quadrant, Sutton, Surrey SM2 5AS
Telephone	01 661 3115; Telex: 892084
Contact	Tim Turner, Deputy Editor

355

Originator	ELECTRICAL WHOLESALERS FEDERATION
Title	UNTITLED
Coverage	Data on sales of electrical goods.
Contents & Origin of Statistics	Tables per issue: Own research 100%
Response	1983
Availability	Members
Cost	Free
Address	Panton Hose, 25-27 Haymarket, London SW1Y 4EN
Telephone	01 930 2002
Contact	N. Ellis, Secretary

356

Originator	ELECTRICITY CONSUMERS' COUNCIL
Title	ELECTRICITY DISCONNECTIONS, quarterly. 1978-

Coverage	Disconnections of domestic customers by area board. Previous year's data for comparison. Given as % of total accounts and of domestic credit customers.
Contents & Origin of Statistics	Tables per issue: 2. Non official source 100%. Supporting text 25%
Comments	Issue tariff levels in different regions annually.
Currency	3 months
Response	1984
Availability	Selected distribution list
Cost	Free
Address	Brook House, 2-16 Torrington Place, London WC1E 7LL
Telephone	01 636 5703
Contact	Toby Harris, Deputy Secretary

357

Originator	ELECTRICITY COUNCIL
Title	ELECTRICITY SUPPLY INDUSTRY IN ENGLAND AND WALES - MEDIUM TERM DEVELOPMENT PLAN, annual
Coverage	Background information, objectives to 1990, medium term plans, resource requirements and sensitivity.
Contents & Origin of Statistics	Tables per issue: 20. Own research 100%. Supporting text 70%
Response	1984
Availability	General
Cost	Free
Address	30 Millbank, London SW1P 4RD
Telephone	01 834 2333
Contact	G.R. McCluskey, Intelligence Officer

358

Originator	ELECTRICITY COUNCIL
Title	HANDBOOK OF ELECTRICITY SUPPLY STATISTICS, annual
Coverage	Power stations, national grid system, distribution systems, transmission and distribution, generation finance, commercial data, tariff, appliances, employment. Some European and World data on electricity. Historical data.
Contents & Origin of Statistics	Tables per issue: 88. Own research 80%, Government statistics 20%.
Response	1984

Availability	General
Cost	Free
ISSN	0440 1905
Address	30 Millbank, London SW1P 4RD
Telephone	01 834 2333
Contact	G.R. McCluskey, Intelligence Officer

359

Originator	ELECTRICTY COUNCIL
Title	STATEMENT OF ACCOUNTS AND STATISTICS, annual
Coverage	Contains statistical appendices, covering supplies, sales, prices customers, generation, transmission, employees, accidents, salaries etc. Mainly consists of financial accounts of the Council.
Contents & Origin of Statistics	Tables per issue: 12. Own research 100%. Supporting text 5%
Response	1984
Availability	General
Cost	£2.25
ISSN	0307 1839
Address	30 Millbank, London SW1P 4RD
Telephone	01 834 2333
Contact	G.R. McCluskey, Intelligence Officer

360

Originator	ELECTRONIC COMPONENTS INDUSTRY FEDERATION
Title	UNTITLED
Coverage	Production data on electronic components. Data supplied by members.
Contents & Origin of Statistics	Tables per issue: Own research 100%
Response	1983
Availability	Members
Address	7-8 Savile Row, London W1X 1AF
Telephone	01 437 4127
Contact	Dudley Ollis, Technical Secretary

361

Originator	ELLIS, RICHARD
Title	CITY OF LONDON OFFICE ACCOMMODATION REVIEW, bi-annual
Coverage	In-depth analysis of office market which reviews recent patterns of supply and demand and examines medium-term trends.
Contents & Origin of Statistics	Tables per issue: 4. Own research 100%. Supporting text 80%.
Comments	Data in graph form. Other 'one-off' reports on other cities, e.g. Manchester, Glasgow, Reading and Bristol.
Currency	1-2 months
Response	1984
Availability	General
Cost	Unstated
Address	Berkeley Square House, London W1X 6AN
Telephone	01 629 6290; Telex: 262498
Contact	Beverley Nerden

362

Originator	ELLIS, RICHARD
Title	PROPERTY MARKET INDICATORS, annual
Coverage	Indices for regional capital growth rates, rentals in principal cities, estimated components of capital growth, changes in equated and prime yields and prime property yields. Based on a sample of approximately 1,000 properties.
Contents & Origin of Statistics	Tables per issue: 30-40. Own research 100%. Supporting text 10%.
Comments	'One off' reports on other cities, Manchester, Glasgow, Reading and Bristol.
Currency	2-3 months
Response	1984
Availability	General
Cost	Unstated
Address	Berkeley Square House, London W1X 6AN
Telephone	01 629 6290; Telex: 262498
Contact	Beverley Nerden

363

Originator	ELLIS, RICHARD
Title	U.K. PROPERTY, annual

Coverage	Reviews recent changes in property, construction, and professional practice. Covers the past year and outlook for the coming year for office, industrial and shop property.
Contents & Origin of Statistics	Tables per issue: 7. Own research 70%, Government statistics 30%. Supporting text 80%.
Comments	Data in graph form.'One-off' reports on property in particular cities, e.g. Manchester, Glasgow, Reading and Bristol.
Currency	Varies
Response	1984
Availability	General
Cost	Unstated
Address	Berkeley Square House, London W1X 6AN
Telephone	01 629 6290; Telex: 262498
Contact	Beverley Nerden

364

Originator	ENERGY PUBLICATIONS
Title	ENERGY FOR INDUSTRY AND COMMERCE QUARTERLY BULLETIN, quarterly
Coverage	Market trends and prospects for oil, gas, coal and electricity.
Contents & Origin of Statistics	Tables per issue: 6.
Currency	2 weeks
Response	1984
Availability	General
Cost	£47.50
ISBN	0 905332 07 5
Address	P.O. Box 147, Grosvenor House, High St, Newmarket CB8 9AL
Telephone	0638 663030
Contact	Mrs E. Sinclair, Sales

365

Originator	ENGINEERING COUNCIL
Title	SURVEY OF PROFESSIONAL ENGINEERS, biennial. c.1967-
Coverage	Employment, incomes, current occupation, field of work, qualifications, location, responsibility, trade unions, fringe benefits, overtime and further training for chartered engineers and technician engineers.
Contents & Origin of Statistics	Tables per issue: 50. Own research 100%. Supporting text 10%
Currency	4 months

Response	1984
Availability	General
Cost	£15
Address	6th Floor, Canberra House, 10-16 Maltravers St, London WC2R 3ER
Telephone	01 240 7891 ; Telex: 297177
Contact	Miss Laura Mason, Professional Institutions

366

Originator	ENGINEERING EMPLOYERS FEDERATION
Title	ENGINEERING SHORT TERM TRENDS, quarterly
Coverage	General trends in engineering production, sales and new orders with costs and prices and manpower figures. One issue per year contains a forecast.
Contents & Origin of Statistics	Tables per issue: 20-25. Own research 30%, Government statistics 70%. Supporting text 40%
Response	1984
Availability	General
Cost	£20 members, £50 non-members
Address	Broadway House, Tothill St, London SW1H 9NQ
Telephone	01 222 7777
Contact	Above address

367

Originator	ENGINEERING INDUSTRY TRAINING BOARD
Title	EITB ANNUAL REPORT AND ACCOUNTS, annual
Coverage	Includes a number of regular statistics on employment and training plus data on the levy, exemption and grant scheme and foundry statistics.
Contents & Origin of Statistics	Tables per issue: 50. Own research 90%. Supporting text 70%
Currency	1 year
Response	1984
Availability	General
Cost	£2.20
Address	54 Clarendon Rd, Watford, Herts WD1 1LB
Telephone	0923 38441
Contact	Tony Fidgett, Information Services

368

Originator	ENGINEERING INDUSTRY TRAINING BOARD
Title	EITB Sector Profiles, bi-annual. 1984-
Coverage	Employment data for various engineering sectors by occupation and region. Each profile covers a particular sector.
Contents & Origin of Statistics	Tables per issue: 10. Non official source 95%, Government statistics 5%. Supporting text 40%
Comments	EITB has a databank on employment in the engineering industry which is available to the public for analysis. Data from 1978 onwards.
Currency	1 year
Response	1984
Availability	General
Cost	£10 for each profile
Address	54 Clarendon Rd, Watford, Herts WD1 1LB
Telephone	0923 38441
Contact	Tony Fidgett, Information Services

369

Originator	ENGLISH TOURIST BOARD
Title	ENGLAND'S TOURISM, annual
Coverage	Fact sheets containing basic facts and figures about tourism in England.
Contents & Origin of Statistics	Tables per issue: 13. Own research 75%, Government statistics 25%
Currency	Varies
Response	1984
Availability	General
Cost	Free
Address	4 Grosvenor Gardens, London SW1W 0DU
Telephone	01 730 3400
Contact	I.M. Rickson, Planning Research Manager

370

Originator	ENGLISH TOURIST BOARD
Title	ENGLISH HOTEL OCCUPANCY SURVEY, monthly with an annual summary
Coverage	Includes data on average bed and room occupancy, duration of stay and proportion of arrivals from overseas. Results are given for different locations according to tariff levels and by the 12 ETB regions. Based on a sample of approximately 500 hotels.

Contents & Origin of Statistics	Tables per issue: Own research 100%

Response	1984
Availability	General
Cost	£15 plus £5 for the annual summary
Address	4 Grosvenor Gardens, London SW1W 0DU
Telephone	01 730 3400
Contact	I.M. Rickson, Planning Research Manager

371

Originator	ENGLISH TOURIST BOARD

Title	FORECASTS OF TOURISM BY BRITISH RESIDENTS, biennial
Coverage	Forecasts of tourist trips by British residents.

Contents & Origin of Statistics	Tables per issue: Own research 100%

Response	1984
Availability	General
Cost	£3.50
Address	4 Grosvenor Gardens, London SW1W 0DU
Telephone	01 730 3400
Contact	I.M. Rickson, Planning Research Manager

372

Originator	ENGLISH TOURIST BOARD

Title	HOLIDAY INTENTIONS SURVEY, annual
Coverage	Report of survey carried out before Easter to find out holiday intentions for forthcoming season.

Contents & Origin of Statistics	Tables per issue: Own research 100%

Response	1984
Availability	General
Cost	£3.50
Address	4 Grosvenor Gardens, London SW1W 0DU
Telephone	01 730 3400
Contact	I.M. Rickson, Planning Research Manager

373

Originator	ENGLISH TOURIST BOARD
Title	SIGHTSEEING IN 19.., annual
Coverage	Analysis of usage and capacity of England's attractions for visitors based on a survey of all main tourist sights.
Contents & Origin of Statistics	Tables per issue: Own research 100%
Response	1984
Availability	General
Cost	£2.50
Address	4 Grosvenor Gardens, London SW1W 0DU
Telephone	01 730 3400
Contact	I.M. Rickson, Planning Research Manager

374

Originator	ENGLISH TOURIST BOARD
Title	TOURISM REGIONAL FACTS, annual
Coverage	Statistical digests of all essential demand and basic supply information summarised separately for the 12 ETB regions. Volume for each region.
Contents & Origin of Statistics	Tables per issue: Own research 100%
Response	1984
Availability	General
Cost	Individual copies are free, £3.50 for set of 12
Address	4 Grosvenor Gardens, London SW1W 0DU
Telephone	01 730 3400
Contact	I.M. Rickson, Planning Research Manager

375

Originator	EQUIPMENT LEASING ASSOCIATION
Title	ANNUAL REPORT, annual
Coverage	Contains a statistical section covering assets of members, over a 10 year period. Also comparative European figures.
Contents & Origin of Statistics	Tables per issue: 10. Own research 100%. Supporting text 80%
Comments	Also publish a press release with statistics on new assets leased to industry.

Currency	6 months
Response	1984
Availability	General
Cost	Free
Address	18 Upper Grosvenor St, London W1X 97B
Telephone	01 491 2783
Contact	A.I. Warwood, Assistant Secretary

376

Originator	ESTATES GAZETTE
Title	FACTS AND FIGURES, monthly in a weekly journal. January 1977-
Coverage	General data relating to the property market including house prices farm prices, rent index, housing starts and completions, land prices, commercial property yields, Agricultural Mortgage Corporation, interest rates and compulsory acquisition rates of interest.
Contents & Origin of Statistics	Tables per issue: 14. Non official source 65%, Government statistics 35%
Currency	Varies
Response	1984
Availability	General
Cost	£49.50p or 60p for a single issue
ISSN	0014 1240
Address	The Estates Gazette Ltd, 151 Wardour St, London W1V 4BN
Telephone	01 437 0141; Telex: 892751
Contact	E.G. Speller, Editor

377

Originator	EURO MARKETORS PARTNERSHIP
Title	SURVEY OF EXPORT MANAGEMENT REMUNERATION AND BENEFITS, biennial. 1980-
Coverage	Levels of remuneration, benefits and responsibility areas of export executives in major food and drink companies in the UK.
Contents & Origin of Statistics	Tables per issue: 25. Own research 100%. Supporting text 10%
Currency	1 month
Response	1984
Availability	General
Cost	£25
Address	Aylescott House, Cookham Dean, Berkshire, SL6 9PU

Telephone	06284 2870 ; Telex: 8813246
Contact	Norman Boakes, Senior Partner

378

Originator	EUROMONITOR PUBLICATIONS LTD
Title	A-Z OF UK MARKETING DATA, biennial. 1982-
Coverage	Key marketing parameters, i.e. sales, market size, production etc, on 450 individual consumer markets, with some historical figures.
Contents & Origin of Statistics	Tables per issue: 400. Own research 30%, Other non official source 25%, Government statistics 45%.
Currency	Latest year available
Response	1984
Availability	General
Cost	£38
Address	87-88 Turnmill St, London EC1M 5QU
Telephone	01 251 8024 ; Telex: 21120
Contact	Nicola Webb, Marketing Executive

379

Originator	EUROMONITOR PUBLICATIONS LTD
Title	ADVANCED MEDICAL EQUIPMENT, biennial. 1984-
Coverage	Market overview and production and trade trends for medical imaging, lasers, renal dialysis, pacemakers, patient monitoring and other products.
Contents & Origin of Statistics	Tables per issue: 110. Own research 35%, Other non official source 45%, Government statistics 20%. Supporting text 40%
Currency	1 year
Response	1984
Availability	General
Cost	£160
ISBN	0 86338 049 2
Address	87-88 Turnmill St, London EC1M 5QU
Telephone	01 251 8024; Telex: 21120
Contact	Nicola Webb, Marketing Executive

380

Originator	EUROMONITOR PUBLICATIONS LTD
Title	ADVANCED OFFICE EQUIPMENT, biennial. 1982-

Coverage	Data on computers, electronic mail, reprographic equipment and micrographic equipment. Figures on sales, market shares, distribution.
Contents & Origin of Statistics	Tables per issue: 46. Own research 95%, Government statistics 5%. Supporting text Unknown
Currency	1 year
Response	1984
Availability	General
Cost	£185
ISBN	0 903706 70 9
Address	87-88 Turnmill St, London EC1M 5QU
Telephone	01 251 8024; Telex: 21120
Contact	Nicola Webb, Marketing Executive

381

Originator	EUROMONITOR PUBLICATIONS LTD
Title	BABY SURVEY, biennial. 1982-
Coverage	Market for all products for children under 2.
Contents & Origin of Statistics	Tables per issue: 155. Own research 75%, Other non official source 15%, Government statistics 10%. Supporting text 45%
Currency	1 year
Response	1984
Availability	General
Cost	£175
ISBN	0 903706 82 2
Address	87-88 Turnmill St, London EC1M 5QU
Telephone	01 251 8024; Telex: 21120
Contact	Nicola Webb, Marketing Executive

382

Originator	EUROMONITOR PUBLICATIONS LTD
Title	BEER REPORT, biennial. 1982-
Coverage	Five year trends and future prospects for beer consumption and consumer expenditure. Figures on individual market sectors, prices and margins, advertising and promotion, distribution and consumer profiles. Also details of companies.
Contents & Origin of Statistics	Tables per issue: 77. Own research 20%, Other non official source 60%, Government statistics 20%. Supporting text 35%
Currency	Latest year
Response	1984

Availability	General
Cost	£135
ISBN	0 980 37069 X
Address	87-88 Turnmill St, London EC1M 5QU
Telephone	01 251 8024 ; Telex: 21120
Contact	Nicola Webb, Marketing Executive

383

Originator	EUROMONITOR PUBLICATIONS LTD

Title	BOOK REPORT, annual. 1975-
Coverage	Survey of book trade and UK market for books with trend figures for the last 4 years. Includes publishers' sales, trade, home sales, retail market, book retailing, educational and library market and electronic publishing.
Contents & Origin of Statistics	Tables per issue: 63. Own research 65%, Other non official source 20%, Government statistics 15%. Supporting text 40%
Currency	6 months
Response	1984
Availability	General
Cost	£135
ISBN	0 86338 023 9
Address	87-88 Turnmill St, London EC1M 5QU
Telephone	01 251 8024 ; Telex: 21120
Contact	Nicola Webb, Marketing Executive

384

Originator	EUROMONITOR PUBLICATIONS LTD

Title	DIY REPORT, biennial. 1977-
Coverage	Data on purchasing patterns, market sizes, consumer expenditure and distribution of 60 DIY products. Also contains survey data from 2000 households.
Contents & Origin of Statistics	Tables per issue: 165. Own research 60%, Other non official source 30%, Government statistics 10%. Supporting text 40%
Currency	1 year
Response	1984
Availability	General
Cost	£95
ISBN	0 86338 039 S
Address	87-88 Turnmill St, London EC1M 5QU

Telephone	01 251 8024 ; Telex: 21120
Contact	Nicola Webb, Marketing Executive

385

Originator	EUROMONITOR PUBLICATIONS LTD

Title	HEALTH REPORT, biennial. 1981-
Coverage	Data on the health care market in the UK with special emphasis on the OTC market. Markets covered include home medicine, OTC products, family planning, spectacles, . Also includes the results of a sample survey of 1000 into OTC buying habits.

Contents & Origin of Statistics	Tables per issue: 168. Own research 50%, Other non official source 30%, Government statistics 20%. Supporting text 40%

Currency	1 year
Response	1984
Availability	General
Cost	£160
ISBN	0 86338 0212
Address	87-88 Turnmill St, London EC1M 5QU
Telephone	01 251 8024; Telex: 21120
Contact	Nicola Webb, Marketing Executive

386

Originator	EUROMONITOR PUBLICATIONS LTD

Title	HOTEL AND CATERING INDUSTRY, biennial. 1982-
Coverage	Trends and forecasts up to 1985 for restaurants, take-aways, motorway services, institutional catering, luncheon vouchers, pubs, clubs, wine bars, hotels and motels and holiday centres.

Contents & Origin of Statistics	Tables per issue: 86. Own research 45%, Other non official source 50%, Government statistics 5%. Supporting text 50%

Currency	1 year
Response	1984
Availability	General
Cost	£135
ISBN	0 903706 72 S
Address	87-88 Turnmill St, London EC1M 5QU
Telephone	01 251 8024 ; Telex: 21120
Contact	Nicola Webb, Marketing Executive

387

Originator	EUROMONITOR PUBLICATIONS LTD
Title	LEISURE FUTURE, biennial. 1984-
Coverage	Data on TV and video, audio, home computing, reading, dressmaking, musical instruments, toys and games, beer and wine making, hobbies, DIY, gardening, sport, photography, car maintenance, holidays, catering, gambling and alcoholic drinks. Projections for leisure spending 4 years ahead.
Contents & Origin of Statistics	Tables per issue: 132. Own research 55%, Other non official source 35%, Government statistics 10%
Currency	1 year
Response	1984
Availability	General
Cost	£96
ISBN	0 86338 052 2
Address	87-88 Turnmill St, London EC1M 5QU
Telephone	01 251 8024; Telex: 21120
Contact	Nicola Webb, Marketing Executive

388

Originator	EUROMONITOR PUBLICATIONS LTD
Title	SCOTLAND: A MARKET SURVEY, biennial. 1983-
Coverage	General market data on Scotland including consumer profiles of 120 product areas.
Contents & Origin of Statistics	Tables per issue: 149. Own research 50%, Other non official source 30%, Government statistics 20%. Supporting text 35%
Currency	1 year
Response	1984
Availability	General
Cost	£96
ISBN	0 86338 007 7
Address	87-88 Turnmill St, London EC1M 5QU
Telephone	01 251 8024; Telex: 21120
Contact	Nicola Webb, Marketing Executive

389

Originator	EUROMONITOR PUBLICATIONS LTD
Title	SECURITY REPORT, biennial. 1982-

Coverage   Market data on security services, intruder alarms, screens and grills, CCT, ID and access control, book detection, paging, fire security, X-ray and transaction phones.

Contents &   Tables per issue: 101. Own research 60%, Other non official source
Origin of   20%, Government statistics 20%. Supporting text 30%
Statistics

Currency   1 year
Response   1984
Availability General
Cost   £155
ISBN   0 903706 97 0
Address   87-88 Turnmill St, London EC1M 5QU
Telephone   01 251 8024 ; Telex: 21120
Contact   Nicola Webb, Marketing Executive

390

Originator   EUROMONITOR PUBLICATIONS LTD

Title   SLIMMING FOODS REPORT, biennial. 1983-
Coverage   A survey of the market for slimming foods including artificial sweeteners, soft drinks, vegetable juice, breakfast cereals etc. Also includes forecasts, distribution trends and details of major companies.

Contents &   Tables per issue: 68. Own research 65%, Other non official source
Origin of   20%, Government statistics 15%. Supporting text 40%
Statistics

Currency   1 year
Response   1984
Availability General
Cost   £160
ISBN   0 86338 021 2
Address   87-88 Turnmill St, London EC1M 5QU
Telephone   01 251 8024 ; Telex: 21120
Contact   Nicola Webb, Marketing Executive

391

Originator   EUROMONITOR PUBLICATIONS LTD

Title   SNACK FOODS REPORT, biennial. 1984-
Coverage   Retail sales, production, trade, distribution, market shares of crisps, savoury snacks, nuts, confectionery, ice cream and other snacks.

Contents &   Tables per issue: 124. Own research 25%, Other non official source
Origin of   35%, Government statistics 40%. Supporting text 40%
Statistics

Currency   1 year
Response   1984

Availability	General
Cost	£135
ISBN	08 6338 026 3
Address	87-88 Turnmill St, London EC1M 5QU
Telephone	01 251 8024; Telex: 21120
Contact	Nicola Webb, Marketing Executive

392

Originator	EUROMONITOR PUBLICATIONS LTD
Title	SPIRITS REPORT, biennial. 1983-
Coverage	Five year analysis and forecasts for consumption and expenditure on individual spirits. Also data on brands, prices, advertising, promotion and consumer profiles. Original research data on drinking patterns and brand awareness.
Contents & Origin of Statistics	Tables per issue: 124. Own research 18%, Other non official source 70%, Government statistics 12%. Supporting text 35%
Currency	1 year
Response	1984
Availability	General
Cost	£160
ISBN	0 86338 015 8
Address	87-88 Turnmil! St, London EC1M 5QU
Telephone	01 251 8024 ; Telex: 21120
Contact	Nicola Webb, Marketing Executive

393

Originator	EUROMONITOR PUBLICATIONS LTD
Title	TELECOMMUNICATIONS - UK PROSPECTS IN THE EIGHTIES, biennial. 1982-
Coverage	Survey of industry and markets covering telephones, telex, digital text transmission, facsimile, data networking and the major UK companies.
Contents & Origin of Statistics	Tables per issue: 15. Supporting text 90%
Response	1984
Availability	General
Cost	£180
ISBN	0 903706 84 9
Address	87-88 Turnmill St, London EC1M 5QU

Telephone   01 251 8024; Telex: 21120
Contact   Nicola Webb, Marketing Executive

394

Originator   EUROMONITOR PUBLICATIONS LTD

Title   TELEVISION: THE NEW ERA, biennial. 1981-
Coverage   Data on the TV market including viewing patterns, programmes,
             advertising, prices, imports, TV hire, distribution, colour and mono-
             chrome purchases, teletext, cable, viewdata and combination units.

Contents &   Tables per issue: 45. Own research 45%, Other non official source
Origin of   50%, Government statistics 5%. Supporting text 40%
Statistics

Currency   1 year
Response   1984
Availability General
Cost   £135
ISBN   0 86338 0174
Address   87-88 Turnmill St, London EC1M 5QU
Telephone   01 251 8024; Telex: 21120
Contact   Nicola Webb, Marketing Executive

395

Originator   EUROMONITOR PUBLICATIONS LTD

Title   TOYS AND GAMES REPORT, biennial. 1982-
Coverage   Production, trade, retail trends, and brand share figures for wheeled
             toys, dolls, soft toys, construction sets, die-cast models, electric trains,
             cars, sport and outdoor leisure equipment, indoor games, action dolls,
             electronic toys, books, and nursery toys. Also details of the major
             companies.

Contents &   Tables per issue: 90. Own research 25%, Other non official source
Origin of   25%, Government statistics 50%. Supporting text 50%
Statistics

Currency   1 year
Response   1984
Availability General
Cost   £160
ISBN   0 86338 087 0
Address   87-88 Turnmill St, London EC1M 5QU
Telephone   01 251 8024; Telex: 21120
Contact   Nicola Webb, Marketing Executive

396

Originator	EUROMONITOR PUBLICATIONS LTD
Title	UK AUTOMOTIVE INDUSTRY, biennial. 1984-
Coverage	Figures on the market for cars, cycles, mopeds and scooters, and auto parts. Also details of the petrol market and some international comparisons.
Contents & Origin of Statistics	Tables per issue: 75. Own research 30%, Other non official source 50%, Government statistics 20%. Supporting text 40%
Currency	1 year
Response	1984
Availability	General
Cost	£135
ISBN	0 86338 038 6
Address	87-88 Turnmill St, London EC1M 5QU
Telephone	01 251 8024; Telex: 21120
Contact	Nicola Webb, Marketing Executive

397

Originator	EUROMONITOR PUBLICATIONS LTD
Title	UK COSMETICS AND TOILETRIES CENSUS, biennial. 1983-
Coverage	Market overview and survey of fragrances, make up, skin care products, hair care, bathroom products, deodorants, oral hygiene, and mens' toiletries. Also includes details of the major companies and a sample survey of 2000 people.
Contents & Origin of Statistics	Tables per issue: 203. Own research 50%, Other non official source 40%, Government statistics 10%. Supporting text 40%
Currency	Current year
Response	1984
Availability	General
Cost	£160
ISBN	0 863801 82
Address	87-88 Turnmill St, London EC1M 5QU
Telephone	01 251 8024; Telex: 21120
Contact	Nicola Webb, Marketing Executive

398

Originator	EUROMONITOR PUBLICATIONS LTD
Title	VIDEO REPORT, biennial. 1982-
Coverage	Market profiles of VCRs, software, video discs and cameras.

Contents & Origin of Statistics	Tables per issue: 60. Own research 70%, Other non official source 20%, Government statistics 10%. Supporting text 40%
Currency	1 year
Response	1984
Availability	General
Cost	£135
ISBN	0 86338 0530
Address	87-88 Turnmill St, London EC1M 5QU
Telephone	01 251 8024; Telex: 21120
Contact	Nicola Webb, Marketing Executive

399

Originator	EUROMONITOR PUBLICATIONS LTD
Title	WHITE GOODS INDUSTRY, biennial. 1983-
Coverage	Survey of markets for 55 electrical products. Includes data on spending, prices, distribution, ownership, penetration and market structure.
Contents & Origin of Statistics	Tables per issue: 219. Own research 45%, Other non official source 35%, Government statistics 20%. Supporting text 40%
Currency	1 year
Response	1984
Availability	General
Cost	£160
ISBN	0 86338 019 0
Address	87-88 Turnmill St, London EC1M 5QU
Telephone	01 251 8024; Telex: 21120
Contact	Nicola Webb, Marketing Executive

400

Originator	EUROMONITOR PUBLICATIONS LTD
Title	WHOLESALE TRADE IN THE UK, biennial. 1983-
Coverage	Size, structure, profits and margins of the wholesale trade with data on major companies and suppliers and voluntary groups.
Contents & Origin of Statistics	Tables per issue: 62. Own research 40%, Other non official source 50%, Government statistics 10%. Supporting text 35%
Currency	Curency of data: 1 year
Response	1984
Availability	General
Cost	£96
ISBN	0 86338 011 S
Address	87-88 Turnmill St, London EC1M 5QU

Telephone	01 251 8024; Telex: 21120
Contact	Nicola Webb, Marketing Executive

401

Originator	EUROMONITOR PUBLICATIONS LTD
Title	WINE REPORT, biennial. 1984-
Coverage	Figures on the consumption, trade, market sectors, distribution, and consumers of various wines.
Contents & Origin of Statistics	Tables per issue: 75. Own research 20%, Other non official source 35%, Government statistics 45%. Supporting text 40%
Currency	1-2 years
Response	1984
Availability	General
Cost	£135
ISBN	0 86338 062 X
Address	87-88 Turnmill St, London EC1M 5QU
Telephone	01 251 8024 ; Telex: 21120
Contact	Nicola Webb, Marketing Executive

402

Originator	EUROPEAN PLASTICS NEWS
Title	ANNUAL SURVEY OF UK PLASTICS INDUSTRY, annual in a monthly journal
Coverage	Market performance of plastics raw materials in the UK with comments on exports, imports, prices and predictions for the coming year.
Contents & Origin of Statistics	Tables per issue: Own research 100%
Comments	Survey usually published in January issue.
Currency	2-3 weeks
Response	1985
Availability	General
Cost	£36 or £3 for a single issue
ISSN	0306 3534
Address	Business Press International, Quadrant House, The Quadrant, Sutton, Surrey M2 5AS
Telephone	01 661 3500; Telex: 892084
Contact	T. Tunbridge, Editor

403

Originator	EXETER AND DISTRICT CHAMBER OF COMMERCE AND TRADE
Title	BUSINESS OPINION SURVEY, annual
Coverage	Returns from members divided into the following categories - manufacturing, primary, retail, services, wholesale, commercial, and professional. Details of employment, changes in that area, changes in trading results and anticipated trading.
Contents & Origin of Statistics	Tables per issue: 13. Own research 100%. Supporting text 15%
Currency	6 weeks
Response	1984
Availability	Members and some others
Cost	Free
Address	31 Southernhay East, Exeter EX1 1NS
Telephone	0392 36641 ; Telex: 42603
Contact	Mrs Davina Everson, Assistant Director

404

Originator	EXHIBITION SURVEYS
Title	AUDIENCE PROFILE REPORTS, every 1-3 years (depending on exhibition)
Coverage	Produce reports for a large number of exhibitions, eg Interplas, International Business Show, IPEX, Hevac, Meatex, Boat Show, Commercial Motor Show, Which Computer, Royal Show, Smithfield Show. Detailed analysis of exhibition audiences, their product interest, purchasing role, status, behaviour, reactions and opinions, performance of named exhibition stands, most memorable exhibits, reasons for recall, and noting of new producers.
Contents & Origin of Statistics	Tables per issue: Own research 100%. Supporting text 20%
Response	1983
Availability	Exhibiting companies
Cost	£260 each
Address	P.O. Box 7, Melton Mowbray, Leicestershire LE13 0BR
Telephone	0664 67666
Contact	Harry McDermott

405

Originator	EXPORT TIMES
Title	ET INDEX, 6 times a year in a monthly journal. 1982-
Coverage	Competitiveness of UK exports calculated on the basis of prices and exchange rates for USA, Japan, West Germany, France and Italy.
Contents & Origin of Statistics	Tables per issue: 2. Government statistics 100%
Currency	6 months
Response	1984
Availability	General
Cost	£14.70
Address	Turret Wheatland, 886 High Rd, London N12 9SB
Telephone	01 446 2411; Telex: 268207
Contact	Ken Mactaggart

406

Originator	FARMLAND MARKET
Title	LAND VALUES, bi-annual in a bi-annual journal. 1973-
Coverage	Farmland auction prices analysed over the last 6 months. Also grass keep and other land values, borrowing charges, rents, and land loss in the tenanted sector.
Contents & Origin of Statistics	Tables per issue: 10. Own research 20%, Other non official source 50%, Government statistics 30%
Comments	Journal is published jointly by the Estates Gazette and Farmers Weekly
Currency	Varies
Response	1984
Availability	General
Cost	£24 or £12 for a single copy
Address	Estates Gazette, 151 Wardour St, London W1 and Farmers Weekly, 1 Throwley Way, Sutton, Surrey
Telephone	01 643 8040; Te;ex: 946564
Contact	Liz Rigbey, Joint Editor

407

Originator	FARMSTAT LTD
Title	FARMSTAT, quarterly
Coverage	Usage of different agricultural inputs on different crops. Covers particularly herbicides, fungicides, fertilizers, growth regulators, insecticides and seed dressings.

Contents & Origin of Statistics	Tables per issue: 15-40. Own research 99%, Government statistics 1%. Supporting text 60%
Comments	Also available on-line, and on floppy disc and magnetic tape. Also known as Produce Studies Ltd.
Currency	4-6 weeks
Response	1984
Availability	General
Cost	£800-£7,700, depending on the amount of data required
Address	Northcroft House, West St, Newbury, Berkshire
Telephone	Newbury 46112; Telex: 849228
Contact	Lesley Davies, Research Executive

408

Originator	FEDERATION OF BRITISH CREMATION AUTHORITIES
Title	ANNUAL REPORT, annual
Coverage	Cremation statistics for individual crematoria over a 5 year period. Data on disposition of ashes.
Contents & Origin of Statistics	Tables per issue: 4. Own research 100%. Supporting text 80%
Response	1984
Availability	General
Cost	Free
Address	Davis House, 69-77 High St, Croydon CR9 2RE
Telephone	01 681 2241
Contact	The Secretary

409

Originator	FEDERATION OF BRITISH ENGINEERS TOOL MANUFAC-TURERS
Title	UNTITLED, quarterly
Coverage	Summaries of production and trade over past 5-10 years.
Response	1983
Availability	Members
Cost	Free
Address	Light Trades House, Melbourne Avenue, Sheffield S10 2QJ
Telephone	0742 663084
Contact	Mrs T.P. Field, Statistics and Marketing Assistant

410

Originator	FEDERATION OF MASTER BUILDERS
Title	FMB STATE OF TRADE SURVEY, quarterly. November 1983-
Coverage	Results of survey of members concerning workload for the quarter and predictions for the coming quarter. Also methods of payment of wages by cash or cheque.
Contents & Origin of Statistics	Tables per issue: 8. Own research 100%. Supporting text 50%
Currency	1 month
Response	1984
Availability	General
Cost	On application
Address	33 John St, London, WC1N 2BB
Telephone	01 242 7583
Contact	Miss Susan Hunt, Research Executive

411

Originator	FEDERATION OF OPTICAL CORPORATE BODIES
Title	OPTICS AT A GLANCE, annual. 1982-
Coverage	Numbers of opticians, sight tests and average spectacle prices.
Contents & Origin of Statistics	Tables per issue: 3-4. Own research 65%, Government statistics 35%. Supporting text 50%
Comments	Content and date of publication may vary.
Currency	6 months
Response	1984
Availability	General
Cost	Free
Address	22 Nottingham Place, London W1M 4AT
Telephone	01 935 7411
Contact	A.P.D. Westhead, Secretary

412

Originator	FEDERATION OF PETROLEUM SUPPLIERS
Title	FPS INDEX, 2 issues per week. July 1980-
Coverage	Buying prices of various grades of petroleum product, as distinct from published wholesale general prices.
Contents & Origin of Statistics	Tables per issue: 3. Own research 100%. Supporting text 20%

Currency	1 day
Response	1984
Availability	Members
Address	Suite 24, 1st Floor, 500 Manchester Rd East, Worsley, Manchester M28 6NS
Telephone	061 799 5181
Contact	E. J. Rowson, Executive Secretary

413

Originator	FEDERATION OF SMALL MINES OF GREAT BRITAIN
Title	UNTITLED
Coverage	Mining.
Contents & Origin of Statistics	Tables per issue: Own research + government statistics 100%
Response	1983
Availability	District Associations
Cost	Free
Address	30 King St, Wigan, Lancashire WN1 1BS
Contact	J. Wainwright, Secretary

414

Originator	FEDERATION OF WHOLESALE DISTRIBUTORS
Title	TRADE STATISTICS YEARBOOK, annual
Coverage	General review of the wholesale trade including the cash and carry trade and delivered catering data.
Contents & Origin of Statistics	Tables per issue: 40. Own research 100%
Response	1984
Availability	General
Cost	Free to members, £195 to others
Address	18 Fleet St, London EC4Y 1AS
Telephone	01 353 8894
Contact	A.L. Paterson

415

Originator	FERRO ALLOYS AND METALS PRODUCERS ASSOCIATION
Title	UNTITLED
Coverage	Data on production and orders.

Response	1983
Availability	Members
Address	Peat, Marwick, Mitchell & Co, P.O. Box 121, Fountain Precinct, 1 Balm Green, Sheffield S1 3AF
Telephone	0742 751234
Contact	E. Green-Spikesley

416

Originator	FERTILISER MANUFACTURERS' ASSOCIATION
Title	FERTILISER REVIEW, annual
Coverage	Covers area of crops, consumption of inorganic fertilisers, straight fertilisers and compound fertilisers. Also concentration, application rates and usage of compound fertilisers.
Contents & Origin of Statistics	Tables per issue: 3. Own research 80%, Government statistics 20%. Supporting text 90%
Comments	Previously issued as 'Fertiliser Statistics'.
Currency	6 months
Response	1984
Availability	General
Cost	£3
Address	Greenhill House, 90-93 Cowcross St, London EC1M 6BH
Telephone	01 251 6001; Telex: 943763
Contact	M.F. Sandeman, Public Relations Officer

417

Originator	FIBRE BUILDING BOARD DEVELOPMENT ORGANISA-TION LTD
Title	HARDBOARD, MEDIUM BOARD AND INSULATING BOARD IMPORT STATISTICS, quarterly
Coverage	Imports of fibre building board, worked/unworked, into the UK by country of origin. Gives quantity and value. Cumulation at year end and comparison with previous year.
Contents & Origin of Statistics	Tables per issue: 3. Government statistics 100%
Response	1983
Availability	Members
Cost	Free
Address	1 Hanworth Rd, Feltham, Middlesex TW13 5AF
Telephone	01 751 6107
Contact	Mrs Y.M. Puzey

418

Originator	FIELDING, NEWSON-SMITH & CO
Title	COMPENDIUM OF UK BUILDING RELATED STATISTICS, 11 issues per year. September1981-
Coverage	Includes value of output, new orders, earnings, prices, building societies activities and materials deliveries, stocks and prices.
Contents & Origin of Statistics	Tables per issue: 80. Non official source 40%, Government statistics 60%.
Comments	Also publish international statistics on mining and oil.
Currency	Varies
Response	1984
Availability	Primarily clients but subscriptions available to certain organisations on request.
Cost	£60
Address	Garrard House, 31 Gresham St, London EC2V 7DX
Telephone	01 606 7711; Telex: 883395
Contact	Miss Marilyn Mincham, Statistician

419

Originator	FIELDING, NEWSON-SMITH & CO
Title	MONTHLY ECONOMIC INDICATORS, monthly
Coverage	Data on general economic trends, i.e. prices, unemployment, output, retail sales, earnings, PSBR, money supply etc.
Contents & Origin of Statistics	Tables per issue: 14. Government statistics 100%. Supporting text 20%
Comments	Also publish international statistics on mining and oil.
Currency	1 month
Response	1984
Availability	Primarily clients but subscriptions available to certain organisations on request
Cost	£75
Address	Garrard House, 31 Gresham St, London EC2V 7DX
Telephone	01 606 7711; Telex: 883395
Contact	Andrew Carpenter, Statistician

420

Originator	FIFE REGIONAL COUNCIL
Title	FIFE IN FIGURES, every 5 years. 1983-

Coverage	Population, births, employment, unemployment, dwellings, car ownership, rate charges, earnings, road lengths, water, education and social data.
Contents & Origin of Statistics	Tables per issue: 25. Own research 35%, Government statistics 65%. Supporting text 5%
Currency	Varies
Response	1984
Availability	General
Cost	Free
Address	Planning Dept, Rothesay House, Rothesay Place, Glenrothes, Fife
Telephone	0592 754411, ext 3321; Telex: 727461
Contact	Bruce McKay, Data Technician

421

Originator	FIFE REGIONAL COUNCIL
Title	POPULATION ESTIMATES, annual. 1983-
Coverage	Estimates of the population of every settlement in Fife having more than 100 residents. Also population of other areas eg Employment Office areas, structure plan sub-areas and local plan areas
Contents & Origin of Statistics	Tables per issue: 8. Own research 100%. Supporting text 20%
Currency	10 months
Response	1984
Availability	General
Cost	Free
Address	Planning Dept, Rothesay House, Rothesay Place, Glenrothes, Fife
Telephone	0592 754411, ext 3321; Telex: 727461
Contact	Bruce McKay, Data Technician

422

Originator	FIFE REGIONAL COUNCIL
Title	STRATEGIC PROJECTIONS, annual. 1983-
Coverage	Population projections, household projections, labour supply and demand.
Contents & Origin of Statistics	Tables per issue: 40. Own research 100%. Supporting text 30%
Currency	Varies
Response	1984
Availability	General
Cost	£2.50

Address	Planning Dept, Rothesay House, Rothesay Place, Glenrothes, Fife
Telephone	0592 754411, ext 3321; Telex: 727461
Contact	Bruce McKay, Data Technician

423

Originator	FINANCE DIRECTOR'S REVIEW
Title	ALL STOCKS INDEX AND MONEY MARKETS, fortnightly in a fortnightly journal
Coverage	Share prices by major sectors, interest rates and sterling values.
Contents & Origin of Statistics	Tables per issue: 3
Currency	1 week
Response	1984
Availability	General
Cost	£59
ISSN	0206 1176
Address	Tolley Publishing Co Ltd, 102-104 High St, Croydon, Surrey CRO 1ND
Telephone	01 686 9141
Contact	Alan Dobic, Editor

424

Originator	FINANCE HOUSES ASSOCATION
Title	CREDIT QUARTERLY REVIEW, quarterly
Coverage	Statistical section at the end covering outstanding credit to FHA members, new credit extended and finance house base rate. Remainder of the review comprises articles and book reviews.
Contents & Origin of Statistics	Tables per issue: 3. Own research 80%, Government statistics 20%. Supporting text 90%
Currency	Varies
Response	1984
Availability	General
Cost	Free
Address	18 Upper Grosvenor St, London W1X 9BB
Telephone	01 491 2783
Contact	A.I. Warwood, Assistant Secretary

425

Originator	FINANCE HOUSES ASSOCIATION
Title	ANNUAL REPORT, annual
Coverage	Small section of regular statistics on outstanding credit to FHA members and new credit extended for the last 5 year period.
Contents & Origin of Statistics	Tables per issue: 2. Own research 100%. Supporting text 95%
Currency	3 months
Response	1984
Availability	General
Cost	Free
Address	18 Upper Grosvenor St, London W1X 9BB
Telephone	01 491 2783
Contact	A.I. Warwood, Assistant Secretary

426

Originator	FINANCIAL TIMES
Title	VARIOUS STATISTICS, daily, weekly and regular in a daily newspaper
Coverage	A range of statistics including prices of securities, industrial share prices, actuaries indices, unit trust prices, insurance and property bonds, offshore and overseas funds, exchange rates and money rates, commodity prices and general economic data.
Contents & Origin of Statistics	Tables per issue: Varies
Comments	General information on the statistics available is contained in the 'Guide to Financial Times Statistics'. Weekly microfiche service from McCarthy Information Services brings together various FT statistics (see separate entry). FT also carry out a joint survey of property indicators with the Royal Institution of Chartered Surveyors (see separate entry).
Currency	Varies
Response	1984
Availability	General
Cost	35p for a single issue
Address	Financial Times Ltd, Bracken House, 10 Cannon St, London EC4P 4BY
Telephone	01 248 8000; Telex: 8811506
Contact	Above address

427

Originator	FINANCIAL TIMES BUSINESS INFORMATION LTD
Title	FT MONTHLY INDICES TABLES, monthly
Coverage	Gives daily information on the FT indices, main FT actuaries equity indices and the fixed interest index and gross redemption yield information. High, low and average figures for the month are highlighted for ease of reference.
Contents & Origin of Statistics	Tables per issue: 5. Own research 100%.
Comments	Also publish overseas currency and stock statistics.
Currency	1-2 weeks
Response	1984
Availability	General
Cost	£40
Address	Bracken House, 10 Cannon St, London EC4P 4BY
Telephone	01 248 8000; Telex: 8811506
Contact	Tony Northeast, Manager, Business Information Service

428

Originator	FINANCIAL TIMES BUSINESS INFORMATION LTD
Title	QUARTERLY FT ACTUARIES INDICES, quarterly. 1962-
Coverage	Mid and end of month figures for the index value, earnings yield and dividend yield for each of the FT sub-indices.
Contents & Origin of Statistics	Tables per issue: 1. Own research 100%.
Comments	The basis of the publication is a loose-leaf binder containing data from the start of the series in 1962. The binder is available for £75. Also publish overseas currency and stock statistics.
Currency	3 months
Response	1984
Availability	General
Cost	£25
Address	Bracken House, 10 Cannon St, London EC4P 4BY
Telephone	01 248 8000; Telex: 8811506
Contact	Tony Northeast, Manager, Business Information Service

429

Originator	FINANCIAL WEEKLY
Title	ISVA/FW HOUSING INDEX, quarterly in a weekly journal

Coverage   Nationwide analysis of house price movements in value terms and in index form. Based on a survey carried out by the Incorporated Society of Valuers and Auctioneers.

Contents &   Tables per issue: 2. Non official source 100%
Origin of
Statistics

Currency   2-3 weeks
Response   1984
Availability General
Cost   £39 or 75p for a single issue
Address   Waterlaw Publishers Ltd, Maxwell House, 74 Worship St, London EC2A 2EN
Telephone   01 377 4600; Telex: 888804
Contact   Above address

430

Originator   FINANCIAL WEEKLY

Title   STATISTICAL UPDATE, weekly in a weekly journal
Coverage   General economic statistics usually taken from official sources.

Contents &   Tables per issue: 2. Non official source 20%,Government statistics
Origin of   80%
Statistics

Currency   Varies
Response   1984
Availability General
Cost   £39 or 75p for a single issue
Address   Waterlaw Publishers Ltd, Maxwell House, 74 Worship St, London EC2A 2EN
Telephone   01 377 4600; Telex: 888804
Contact   Above address

431

Originator   FISH TRADER

Title   RETAIL FISH PRICES, PORT AND MARKET PRICES AND POTATO MARKET REPORT, weekly in a weekly journal
Coverage   Producers' and wholesale prices for potatoes,wholesale fish prices at Billingsgate, Aberdeen, Fraserburgh, Peterhead, Lowestoft, and Grimsby and retail fish prices nationally and by region. Prices are given for various species of fish.

Contents &   Tables per issue: 3. Non official source 100%
Origin of
Statistics

Currency   1 week

Response	1984
Availability	General
Cost	£17 or 34p for a single issue
ISSN	0143 7771
Address	Retail Journals Ltd, Queensway House, 2 Queensway, Redhill, Surrey RH1 1QS
Telephone	0737 68611, ext 287; Telex: 948669
Contact	James Pringle, Editor

432

Originator FLOWER TRADES JOURNAL

Title AIPH STATISTICS annual in a monthly journal. 1981-
Coverage Cultivation and production data on non-edible horticultural products.

Contents & Tables per issue: 1. Own research 100%
Origin of
Statistics

Currency	2 years
Response	1984
Availability	General
Cost	£18 or £1.20 for a single copy
Address	Lockwood Press Ltd, 430-438 Market Towers, New Covent Garden Market, London SW8 5NN
Telephone	01 622 6677; Telex: 915149
Contact	D. Hore-Mason, Managing Director

433

Originator FOOD AND DRINK INDUSTRIES COUNCIL

Title FDIC BULLETIN, 3 times per year
Coverage Articles on profitability of the food trade, with accompanying tables.

Contents & Tables per issue: 4. Non official source 100%
Origin of
Statistics

Response	1983
Availability	General
Cost	Free
Address	25 Victoria St, London SW1H 0EX
Telephone	01 222 1533
Contact	Above address

434

Originator	FOOD MANUFACTURERS' FEDERATION INC
Title	FMF ANNUAL STATISTICS, annual. 1971-
Coverage	Food exports by major country breakdown and by product category. Gives total EEC and world figure.
Contents & Origin of Statistics	Tables per issue: 14 pgs. Government statistics 100%.
Currency	4-5 months
Response	1984
Availability	General
Cost	£10 (free to members)
Address	6 Catherine St, London, WC2B 5JJ
Telephone	01 836 2460 ; Telex: 299388
Contact	Mrs. Anna Soh, Statistics Assistant

435

Originator	FOUNDRY TRADE JOURNAL
Title	UK METAL PRICES, twice monthly in a twice monthly journal
Coverage	Prices of various metals per 1,000 kg delivered in the UK.
Contents & Origin of Statistics	Tables per issue: 1. Non official source 100%
Currency	2-3 days
Response	1985
Availability	General
Cost	£54 or £3.75 for a single issue
Address	Fuel and Metallurgical Journals Ltd, Queensway House, 2 Queensway, Redhill, Surrey RH1 1QS
Telephone	0737 68611; Telex: 948669
Contact	Above address

436

Originator	FRASER OF ALLANDER INSTITUTE
Title	QUARTERLY ECONOMIC COMMENTARY, quarterly. 1975-
Coverage	Trends and outlook for the Scottish economy with individual reviews of industrial performance, service sector, labour market and the regions. Also includes feature articles and briefing papers.
Contents & Origin of Statistics	Tables per issue: 35-40. Own research 10%, Other non official source 10%, Government statistics 80%. Supporting text 50%

Currency	Varies
Response	1984
Availability	General
Cost	£20
ISSN	0306 7866
Address	University of Strathclyde, Curran Building, 100 Cathedral St, Glasgow G4 0LN
Telephone	041 552 4400, ext 3958
Contact	Frank Kirwan, Senior Research Fellow

437

Originator	FREIGHT INFORMATION SERVICES
Title	EXPORT/IMPORT TONNAGES, annual
Coverage	Guide to export and import tonnages to and from the UK and every country in the world. 41 product descriptions and summary tables covering 4 year period for major trading areas. Simplifies government data.
Contents & Origin of Statistics	Tables per issue: Government statistics 100%
Response	1983
Availability	General
Cost	£40
Address	Adelphi Chambers, Hoghton St, Southport, Merseyside PR9 0NZ
Telephone	0704 38515
Contact	M. Rounding

438

Originator	FREIGHT TRANSPORT ASSOCIATION
Title	COST AND RATES REPORTS, quarterly. 1972-
Coverage	Trends in vehicle operating costs and road haulage rates measured in actual values and indices.
Contents & Origin of Statistics	Tables per issue: 22. Own research 100%. Supporting text 15%
Currency	2 months
Response	1984
Availability	Members
Cost	£32
Address	Hermes House, St John's Rd, Tunbridge Wells, Kent TN4 9UZ
Telephone	0892 26171 ; Telex: 957158
Contact	M.S. Downer, Management Information Services

439

Originator	FREIGHT TRANSPORT ASSOCIATION
Title	DRIVERS WAGES REPORT, quarterly
Coverage	Rates of pay of drivers and fitters plus hours of work. Analysed by geographical area, operation, vehicle type and shift.
Contents & Origin of Statistics	Tables per issue: 5. Own research 100%.
Currency	2 months
Response	1984
Availability	Members
Cost	£29
Address	Hermes House, St John's Rd, Tunbridge Wells, Kent TN4 9UZ
Telephone	0892 26171 ; Telex: 957158
Contact	M.S. Downer, Management Information Services

440

Originator	FRESH FRUIT AND VEGETABLE INFORMATION BUREAU
Title	WEEKLY PRICE AND AVAILABILITY BULLETIN, weekly. September 1976-
Coverage	Latest retail prices for a wide range of fruit and vegetables. Categorised into best buys, good buys and produce 'just in'.
Contents & Origin of Statistics	Tables per issue: 4pgs. Own research 100%. Supporting text 25%
Response	1984
Availability	General
Cost	£76 (Free to Press)
Address	9 Walton St, London SW3 2JD
Telephone	01 589 6601
Contact	Nicolette Agnew, Executive

441

Originator	FRUIT IMPORTERS ASSOCIATION
Title	IMPORTED FRUIT AND VEGETABLES - LONDON MARKET PRICES, 3 per week (Mon, Wed, Fri)
Coverage	Prices of imported fruit and vegetables.
Contents & Origin of Statistics	Tables per issue: Own research 100%
Response	1983

Availability	General
Cost	£100
Address	114/115 Fruit and Vegetable Market, New Covent Garden, London SW8 5LP
Telephone	01 720 1387/8
Contact	Jonh Ellis, Secretary

442

Originator	FUEL OIL NEWS AND ROAD TANKER TRANSPORT
Title	PETROLEUM PRODUCT PRICE LISTINGS, monthly in a monthly journal. August 1978-
Coverage	Prices of wholesale and retail petroleum products by manufacturer.
Contents & Origin of Statistics	Tables per issue: 1. Unstated 100%
Response	1985
Availability	General
Cost	£24 or £2 for a single issue
Address	4 King St, Knutsford, Cheshire
Telephone	0565 53283
Contact	James Smith, Managing Editor

443

Originator	FURNITURE INDUSTRY RESEARCH ASSOCIATION
Title	QUARTERLY BULLETIN OF STATISTICS, quarterly
Coverage	General data on the industry. Updating the annual digest - see next entry.
Comments	Also publish 'Annual Statistical Digest'
Currency	2-3 months
Response	1984
Availability	General
Cost	£12 to FIRA members, £25 to non-members
Address	Maxwell Rd, Stevenage, Hertfordshire SG1 2EW
Telephone	0438 3423
Contact	Marketing Department

444

Originator	FURNITURE INDUSTRY RESEARCH ASSOCIATION
Title	STATISTICAL DIGEST FOR THE FURNITURE INDUSTRY, annual
Coverage	General data on the industry including turnover, sales, deliveries, consumption, trade, price and advertising expenditure.

Contents & Origin of Statistics	Tables per issue: 78. Own research 12.5%, Other non official source 12.5%, Government statistics 75%
Comments	Also publish 'Quarterly Bulletin'
Currency	Varies
Response	1984
Availability	General
Cost	£12 to FIRA members, £28 to non-members
ISSN	0142 9957
Address	Maxwell Rd, Stevenage, Hertfordshire SG1 2EW
Telephone	0438 3433
Contact	Marketing Department

445

Originator	GALLUP
Title	GALLUP POLITICAL INDEX, monthly. Jan 1960-
Coverage	Public opinion data on political, economic and social matters.
Contents & Origin of Statistics	Tables per issue: Varies. Own research 100%. Supporting text 5%
Comments	Data available on magnetic tape.
Currency	2-4 weeks
Response	1984
Availability	General
Cost	£50
Address	202 Finchley Rd, London NW3 6BL
Telephone	01 794 0461 ; Telex: 261712
Contact	R.J. Wybrow, Director

446

Originator	GARAGE AND TRANSPORT NEWS
Title	NEWSDESK - CAR SALES, monthly in a monthly journal
Coverage	Details of new car sales and the shares of the top five selling cars.
Contents & Origin of Statistics	Tables per issue: 0. Supporting text 100%
Comments	Figures obtained from SMMT. Also publish other regular statistics during the year but these largely refer to the individual car companies.
Currency	2 months
Response	1984
Availability	Controlled Circulation
Cost	£330 or £2.50 for a single issue
ISSN	0264 0163

Address	AGB HULTON Ltd, Warwick House, Azalfa Drive, Swanley, Kent BR8 8JF.
Telephone	0322 69411; Telex: 892629
Contact	Richard Gradeselli, Editor

447

Originator	GC & HTJ - THE HORTICULTURE AND AMENITY WEEKLY
Title	MARKET REPORTS, weekly in a weekly journal. 1968-
Coverage	Wholesale prices for horticultural products in leading wholesale markets.
Contents & Origin of Statistics	Tables per issue: 1. Government statistics 100%
Comments	Once a year the journal also contains the results of the MAFF annual census of horticultural holdings.
Currency	8 days
Response	1984
Availability	General
Cost	£28 or 45p for a single copy
Address	GC & HTJ Haymarket Publishing Ltd, 38-42 Hampton Rd, Teddington, Middlesex
Telephone	01 977 8787
Contact	Jim Deen, Editor

448

Originator	GENERAL AND MUNICIPAL WORKERS' UNION
Title	CHEMICALS AND ALLIED INDUSTRY WAGES AND CONDITIONS, annual
Coverage	Rates of pay, bonus, shiftwork, hours, overtime, leave and sick pay in the chemical industry.
Contents & Origin of Statistics	Tables per issue: Own research 100%
Response	1984
Availability	General
Cost	Free to officials, £30 to others
Address	Thorne House, Ruxley Ridge, Claygate, Esher, Surrey KT10 0TL
Telephone	0372 62081
Contact	S. Pryle

449

Originator	GENERAL AND MUNICIPAL WORKERS' UNION
Title	CONSTRUCTION INDUSTRY WAGES AND CONDITIONS SURVEY, bi-annual
Coverage	Rates of pay, bonus, shiftwork, hours, overtime, leave and sick pay in the building industry.
Contents & Origin of Statistics	Tables per issue: Own research 100%
Response	1984
Availability	General
Cost	Free to officials, £10 to others
Address	Thorne House, Ruxley Ridge, Claygate, Esher, Surrey KT10 0TL
Telephone	0372 62081
Contact	S. Pryle

450

Originator	GENERAL AND MUNICIPAL WORKERS' UNION
Title	ELECTRICAL, ELECTRONIC AND INSTRUMENT WAGES AND CONDITIONS SURVEY, bi-annual
Coverage	Rates of pay, bonus, shiftwork, overtime, leave and sick pay in the electrical and electronics sectors.
Contents & Origin of Statistics	Tables per issue: Own research 100%
Response	1984
Availability	General
Cost	Free to officials, £10 to others
Address	Thorne House, Ruxley Ridge, Claygate, Esher, Surrey KT10 0TL
Telephone	0372 62081
Contact	S. Pryle

451

Originator	GENERAL AND MUNICIPAL WORKERS' UNION
Title	FOOD AND DRINK INDUSTRY WAGES AND CONDITIONS SURVEY, annual
Coverage	Rates of pay, bonus, shiftwork, hours, overtime, leave and sick pay in the food and drink industry.
Contents & Origin of Statistics	Tables per issue: Own research 100%

Response	1984
Availability	General
Cost	Free to officials, £30 to others
Address	Thorne House, Ruxley Ridge, Claygate, Esher, Surrey KT10 0TL
Telephone	0372 62081
Contact	S. Pryle

452

Originator	GENERAL AND MUNICIPAL WORKERS' UNION
Title	MECHANICAL ENGINEERING WAGES AND CONDITIONS SURVEY, bi-annual
Coverage	Rates of pay, bonus, shiftwork, hours, overtime, leave and sick pay in the mechanical engineering sector.
Contents & Origin of Statistics	Tables per issue: Own research 100%
Response	1984
Availability	General
Cost	Free to officials, £10 to others
Address	Thorne House, Ruxley Ridge, Claygate, Esher, Surrey KT10 0TL
Telephone	0372 62081
Contact	S. Pryle

453

Originator	GENERAL AND MUNICIPAL WORKERS' UNION
Title	METAL GOODS WAGES AND CONDITIONS SURVEY, bi-annual
Coverage	Rates of pay, bonus, shiftwork, hours, overtime, leave and sick pay in the metal goods industry.
Contents & Origin of Statistics	Tables per issue: Own research 100%
Response	1984
Availability	General
Cost	Free to officials, £10 to others
Address	Thorne House, Ruxley Ridge, Claygate, Esher, Surrey KT10 0TL
Telephone	0372 62081
Contact	S. Pryle

454

Originator	GENERAL AND MUNICIPAL WORKERS' UNION
Title	METALS WAGES AND CONDITIONS SURVEY, bi-annual
Coverage	Rates of pay, bonus, shiftwork, hours, overtime, leave and sick pay in the metals sector.
Contents & Origin of Statistics	Tables per issue: Own research 100%
Response	1984
Availability	General
Cost	Free to officials, £10 to others
Address	Thorne House, Ruxley Ridge, Claygate, Esher, Surrey KT10 0TL
Telephone	0372 62081
Contact	S. Pryle

455

Originator	GENERAL AND MUNICIPAL WORKERS' UNION
Title	PLASTIC LUBRICATION AND OTHER WAGES AND CONDITIONS SURVEY, bi-annual
Coverage	Rates of pay, bonus, shiftwork, hours, overtime, leave and sick pay in plastic lubrication.
Contents & Origin of Statistics	Tables per issue: Own research 100%
Response	1984
Availability	General
Cost	Free to officials, £10 to others
Address	Thorne House, Ruxley Ridge, Claygate, Esher, Surrey KT10 0TL
Telephone	0372 62081
Contact	S. Pryle

456

Originator	GENERAL AND MUNICIPAL WORKERS' UNION
Title	RUBBER INDUSTRY WAGES AND CONDITIONS SURVEY, annual
Coverage	Rates of pay, bonus, shiftwork, overtime, leave and sick pay in the rubber industry.
Contents & Origin of Statistics	Tables per issue: Own research 100%
Response	1984

Availability	General
Cost	Free to officials, £25 to others
Address	Thorne House, Ruxley Ridge, Claygate, Esher, Surrey KT10 0TL
Telephone	0372 62081
Contact	S. Pryle

457

Originator	GENERAL AND MUNICIPAL WORKERS' UNION
Title	SHIFTWORK, annual
Coverage	Rates paid in continuous and non-continuous shifts.
Contents & Origin of Statistics	Tables per issue: Own research 100%
Response	1984
Availability	General
Cost	Free to officials, £5 to others
Address	Thorne House, Ruxley Ridge, Claygate, Esher, Surrey KT10 0TL
Telephone	0372 62081
Contact	S. Pryle

458

Originator	GENERAL AND MUNICIPAL WORKERS' UNION
Title	VEHICLE AND AUTOMOTIVE COMPONENTS WAGES AND CONDITIONS SURVEY, bi-annual
Coverage	Rates of pay, bonus, shiftwork, hours, overtime, leave and sick pay in the vehicle and automotive components industry.
Contents & Origin of Statistics	Tables per issue: Own research 100%
Response	1984
Availability	General
Cost	Free to officials, £10 to others
Address	Thorne House, Ruxley Ridge, Claygate, Esher, Surrey KT10 0TL
Telephone	0372 62081
Contact	S. Pryle

459

Originator	GENERAL COUNCIL OF BRITISH SHIPPING
Title	BRITISH SHIPPING STATISTICS, annual
Coverage	Covers UK fleet, shipbuilding, laid-up shipping, earnings, finance trade and number of seafarers. Also gives international data.

Contents &	Tables per issue: 48. Own research + other non official source 100%
Origin of	
Statistics	

Response	1983
Availability	General
Cost	£8
Address	30-32 St Mary Axe, London EC3A 8ET
Telephone	01 283 2922/01 626 8131; Telex: 884008
Contact	Susana Turner

460

Originator	GENERAL COUNCIL OF BRITISH SHIPPING

Title	TRAMP TIME CHARTER INDEX, quarterly
Coverage	Index of chartered tramp time.

Contents &	Tables per issue: 2. Non official source 100%
Origin of	
Statistics	

Response	1983
Availability	General
Cost	£20 or £5 for a single issue
Address	30-32 St Mary Axe, London EC3A 8ET
Telephone	01 283 2922/01 626 8131; Telex: 884008
Contact	Susana Turner

461

Originator	GENERAL COUNCIL OF BRITISH SHIPPING

Title	TRAMP TRIP CHARTER INDEX, monthly
Coverage	Index of chartered tramp trips.

Contents &	Tables per issue: 3. Non official source 100%
Origin of	
Statistics	

Response	1983
Availability	General
Cost	£20 or £5 for a single issue
Address	30-32 St Mary Axe, London EC3A 8ET
Telephone	01 283 2922/01 626 8131; Telex: 884008
Contact	Susana Turner

462

Originator	GLASGOW CHAMBER OF COMMERCE

Title	ECONOMIC SURVEY, quarterly

Coverage	Survey of business activities in the West of Scotland. Issued as press release.
Contents & Origin of Statistics	Tables per issue: c14. Own research 100%. Supporting text 50%
Comments	Survey also included in the Chamber's Journal.
Currency	1 month
Response	1984
Availability	General
Cost	Free
Address	30 George St, Glasgow G2 1EQ
Telephone	041 204 2121; Telex: 777967
Contact	Mr Marwick, Secretary

463

Originator	GLASS MANUFACTURERS ASSOCIATION
Title	BOTTLE BANK PROGRESS REPORT, quarterly. 1979-
Coverage	Data on every bottle bank scheme in the UK plus a list of the best sites.
Contents & Origin of Statistics	Tables per issue: 16 pgs. Own research 100%. Supporting text 5%
Currency	3 months
Response	1984
Availability	General
Cost	Under review
Address	19 Portland Place, London W1N 4BH
Telephone	01 580 6952; Telex: 27470
Contact	P.G. Mansfield

464

Originator	GLAZED AND FLOOR TILE HOME TRADE ASOCIATION
Title	UK IMPORTS OF CERAMIC TILES, monthly
Coverage	Imports of ceramic tiles.
Contents & Origin of Statistics	Tables per issue: Government statistics 100%
Response	1983
Availability	Members
Cost	Free
Address	Federation House, Stoke-on-Trent ST4 2RU

Telephone	0782 45147
Contact	Contact:G.H.J. Goodwin, Secretary

465

Originator	GLAZED AND FLOOR TILE HOME TRADE ASSOCIATION
Title	MEMBERS' SALES OF CERAMIC TILES, monthly
Coverage	Sales of ceramic tiles.
Contents & Origin of Statistics	Tables per issue: Own research 100%
Response	1983
Availability	Members
Cost	Cost (pa):Free
Address	Federation House, Stoke-on-Trent ST4 2RU
Telephone	0782 45147
Contact	G.H.J. Goodwin, Secretary

466

Originator	GLENROTHES DEVELOPMENT CORPORATION
Title	GLENROTHES EMPLOYMENT, annual
Coverage	Gives total employment figures by sex plus employment figures by SIC group. Also details of working days lost. Based on a survey of all firms and establishments in Glenrothes.
Contents & Origin of Statistics	Tables per issue: 3. Own research 30%, Government statistics 70%. Supporting text 40%
Currency	2 months
Response	1984
Availability	General
Cost	Free
Address	Balbirnie House, Glenrothes, Fife
Telephone	0592 754343
Contact	Nancy Finnie, Planning Department

467

Originator	GORDON SIMMONS RESEARCH LTD
Title	CONFECTIONERY PROFILES, annual

Coverage	Annual reports on the confectionery market covering total market, chocolate and sugar confectionery, brands. Gives consumer expenditure, expenditure profiles, source of purchase, day of week, time of day, amount spent per item, pack type, gift market, consumer profiles, childrens' market. Around 40,000 items checked at 1,000 outlets.
Contents & Origin of Statistics	Tables per issue: Own research 100%
Response	1984
Availability	General
Cost	(pa): On request
Address	80 St Martin's Lane, London WC2N 2AA
Telephone	01 240 0256
Contact	Above address

468

Originator	GOWER PUBLISHING CO
Title	BRITISH SOCIAL ATTITUDES, annual. 1984-
Coverage	National survey of contemporary British attitudes towards the whole spectrum of British life, including views on the constitution, coalition government, protest action, industrial relations, social policy, public expenditure, educational issues and priorities, social and moral values, including views on prejudice and discrimination.
Contents & Origin of Statistics	Tables per issue: Own research 100%
Comments	Report of a survey deposited in the data archive at Essex University, available to all bona fide academics for a nominal fee. Survey conducted by Professor Roger Jowell and Mr. Colin Airey for the Social and Community Planning Research
Currency	Current year
Response	1984
Availability	General
Cost	£9.99 paper, £18.50 hardback with microfiche tables
Address	Gower House, Croft Rd, Aldershot, Hampshire GU11 3HR
Telephone	0252 331551
Contact	Above address

469

Originator	GOWLING MARKETING SERVICES
Title	UK HOME COMPUTER AND SOFTWARE MARKET, annual 1983-

Coverage	Based on a national survey of 1500 households it provides data on ownership, market size, market shares, manufacturers, sales forecasts, ownership of peripheral equipment and outlets purchased from.
Contents & Origin of Statistics	Tables per issue: 13. Own research 100%. Supporting text 60%
Currency	3 weeks
Response	1984
Availability	General
Cost	£75
Address	Britannia Buildings, Fenwick St, Liverpool L2 7NA
Telephone	051 236 6036
Contact	Paul Stoddart, Marketing Executive

470

Originator	GOWLING MARKETING SERVICES
Title	UK SMALL BUSINESS MICROCOMPUTER MARKET, annual. 1983-
Coverage	Ownership and applications of micros in small businesses with less than 50 employees. Ownership profiles, market shares, manufacturers, sales forecasts, outlets purchased from, buying decisions, user problems and readership of newspapers. The report is based on a quarterly survey of 2000 small businesses.
Contents & Origin of Statistics	Tables per issue: 19. Own research 100%. Supporting text 50%
Currency	3 weeks
Response	1984
Availability	General
Cost	£75
Address	Britannia Buildings, Fenwick St, Liverpool L2 7NA
Telephone	051 236 6036
Contact	Paul Stoddart, Marketing Executive

471

Originator	GOWLING MARKETING SERVICES LTD
Title	ATTITUDES OF PARENTS AND CHILDREN TO HOME COMPUTERS AND SOFTWARE, annual. July 1984-
Coverage	Attitudes and behaviour patterns with information on motives for purchase, usage patterns, evaluation of different types of software, impact on family routines, buying frequency, influence of opinion leaders and key markets and segmentation variables.

Contents & Origin of Statistics	Tables per issue: 10. Own research 100%. Supporting text 80%

Currency	1-3 weeks
Response	1984
Availability	General
Cost	£90
Address	Britannia Buildings, Fenwick St, Liverpool L2 7NA
Telephone	051 236 6036
Contact	Paul Stoddart, Marketing Executive

472

Originator	GOWLING MARKETING SERVICES LTD
Title	MICROCOMPUTERS IN FINANCIAL SERVICE ORGANIS-ATIONS, annual. July 1984-
Coverage	Ownership and applications of micros amongst accountants, banks, building societies, insurance brokers etc. Data on market size, ownership profiles, manufacturers, market shares, sales forecast, applications, buying decisions and user problems. Based on a survey of 2000 organisations.
Contents & Origin of Statistics	Tables per issue: 19. Own research 95%, Government statistics 5%. Supporting text 50%
Currency	1-3 weeks
Response	1984
Availability	General
Cost	£75
Address	Britannia Buildings, Fenwick St, Liverpool L2 7NA
Telephone	051 236 6036
Contact	Paul Stoddart, Marketing Executive

473

Originator	GOWLING MARKETING SERVICES LTD
Title	UK HOME COMPUTER SOFTWARE INDUSTRY, annual. April 1984-
Coverage	Data on definition and structure of the industry, product range and new product development, distribution, discount structure and promotional strategies.
Contents & Origin of Statistics	Tables per issue: 13. Own research 100%. Supporting text 60%
Currency	1-3 weeks
Response	1984
Availability	General

Cost	£90
Address	Britannia Buildings, Fenwick St, Liverpool L2 7NA
Telephone	051 236 6036
Contact	Paul Stoddart, Marketing Executive

474

Originator   GOWLING MARKETING SERVICES LTD

Title   UK MARKET FOR PHOTOCOPIERS, annual. March 1984-

Coverage   Ownership of photocopiers amongst small businesses based on a survey of 4000 businesses. Data on market size, ownership profiles, manufacturers, market shares, sales estimates, product specifications and customer service requirements.

Contents & Origin of Statistics   Tables per issue: 16. Own research 100%. Supporting text 50%

Currency	1-3 weeks
Response	1984
Availability	General
Cost	£90
Address	Britannia Buildings, Fenwick St, Liverpool L2 7NA
Telephone	051 236 6036
Contact	Paul Stoddart, Marketing Executive

475

Originator   GOWLING MARKETING SERVICES LTD

Title   UK SMALL HOTEL MICROCOMPUTER MARKET, annual. Oct 1983 -

Coverage   Ownership and applications in UK small hotels defined as hotels with 4-50 bedrooms. Based on a survey of 621 hotels it provides data on market size, ownership profiles, manufacturers, market shares, sales forecasts, hotel needs, sources of purchase and readership of trade journals.

Contents & Origin of Statistics   Tables per issue: 39. Own research 99%, Government statistics 1%. Supporting text 50%

Currency	1-3 weeks
Response	1984
Availability	General
Cost	£75
Address	Britannia Buildings, Fenwick St, Liverpool L2 7NA
Telephone	051 236 6036
Contact	Paul Stoddart, Marketing Executive

476

Originator	GRAMPIAN REGIONAL COUNCIL
Title	FORECASTS OF POPULATION, EMPLOYMENT AND HOUSING, annual
Coverage	Forecasts for districts and structure plan areas based upon the latest projections of demographic rates together with an assessment of current market trends, local authority policies and their likely future variations.
Contents & Origin of Statistics	Tables per issue: 30 pgs.
Response	1984
Availability	General
Cost	£2.50
Address	Woodhill House, Ashgrove Rd West, Aberdeen AB9 2LU
Telephone	0224 682222; Telex: 739277
Contact	Planning Department

477

Originator	GRAMPIAN REGIONAL COUNCIL
Title	QUARTERLY ECONOMIC SURVEY, quarterly
Coverage	Analysis of trends in the local economy, the labour market and land development over the preceding quarter and reports on developments which are likely to affect future prospects.
Contents & Origin of Statistics	Tables per issue: 30 pgs.
Currency	3 months
Response	1984
Availability	General
Cost	£12
Address	Woodhill House, Ashgrove Rd West, Aberdeen AB9 2LU
Telephone	0224 682222; Telex: 739277
Contact	Planning Department

478

Originator	GRAMPIAN REGIONAL COUNCIL
Title	SCHOOL ROLL FORECASTS, annual
Coverage	Information on roll, type, capacity and catchment area for each school and roll forecasts for the period to 1991. Also description of forecasting method.

Contents & **Origin of** **Statistics**	Tables per issue: 35 pgs.
Response	1984
Availability	General
Cost	£3
Address	Woodhill House, Ashgrove Rd West, Aberdeen AB9 2LU
Telephone	0224 682222; Telex: 739277
Contact	Planning Department or Education Department

479

Originator	GRAMPIAN REGIONAL COUNCIL
Title	SMALL AREA POPULATIONS, annual
Coverage	Details of current electorate, housing stock and population totals by parish and settlement.
Contents & **Origin of** **Statistics**	Tables per issue: 17 pgs.
Response	1984
Availability	General
Cost	£2
Address	Woodhill House, Ashgrove Rd West, Aberdeen AB9 2LU
Telephone	0224 682222; Telex: 739277
Contact	Planning Department

480

Originator	GRAMPIAN TELEVISION PLC
Title	MARKETING FACTS BOOK, annual
Coverage	Data on population, employment, oil, agriculture, finance, lifestyle, motoring, leisure, and retailing for the Grampian area
Contents & **Origin of** **Statistics**	Tables per issue: 53. Non official source 85%, Government statistics 15%. Supporting text 10%
Currency	1-2 years
Response	1984
Availability	Advertising agencies
Cost	Free
Address	29 Glasshouse St, London W1
Telephone	01 439 3141; Telex: 267912
Contact	Ms. A. Millwood, Research Manager

481

Originator	GRANADA TELEVISION LTD
Title	GRANADA RETAIL AND SERVICES DIRECTORY, annual. 1980-
Coverage	Number of outlets by type of business in the area and for GB as a whole. Detailed breakdown of major multiple groups both nationally and in Granada based on intensive trade enquiries.
Contents & Origin of Statistics	Tables per issue: 60. Own research 90%, Other non official source 10%.
Comments	This directory is one of three. The others are 'The area, communications, employment and industry' and 'The Granada Market', but these are not issued regularly.
Currency	3 months
Response	1984
Availability	General
Cost	Free
Address	36 Golden Square, London W1
Telephone	01 734 8080
Contact	Helen Elliot, Librarian

482

Originator	GREATER LONDON COUNCIL
Title	ANNUAL ABSTRACT OF GREATER LONDON STATISTICS, annual. 1966-
Coverage	Demographic, economic and central and local government statistics for Greater London.
Contents & Origin of Statistics	Tables per issue: 160. Non official source 50%, Government statistics 50%.
Currency	1 year
Response	1984
Availability	General
Cost	£13
ISSN	716 1288 6
Address	The County Hall, London SE1 7PB
Telephone	01 633 7139; Telex: 919443
Contact	Michael Minors, DG/I/P

483

Originator	GREATER MANCHESTER PASSENGER TRANSPORT EXECUTIVE
Title	ANNUAL REPORT AND ACCOUNTS, annual
Coverage	Contains a section of statistical information covering operations, staff, assets, direct bus operating activities and selected key indicators for last 6 years. Includes passenger journeys, vehicle miles and fares.
Contents & Origin of Statistics	Tables per issue: 21. Own research 100%
Response	1983
Address	P.O. Box 429, County Hall, Piccadilly Gardens, Manchester M60 1HX
Telephone	061 273 3322
Contact	Barbara Cheetham

484

Originator	GREENE, BELFIELD-SMITH AND CO
Title	GREAT BRITAIN PROPERTY TIMESHARING SURVEY, annual
Coverage	Trends in the timesharing industry. Covers facilities and year on year changes.
Contents & Origin of Statistics	Tables per issue: Own research 100%
Response	1984
Availability	General
Cost	£10
Address	20 Kingsway, London WC2B 6LH
Telephone	01 405 3861
Contact	Above address

485

Originator	GREENE, BELFIELD-SMITH AND CO
Title	HOTEL TARIFF STUDY OF GREAT BRITAIN, annual
Coverage	Survey of two star to five star hotels, by grade and geographical area. Sample of 272 hotels.
Contents & Origin of Statistics	Tables per issue: 24. Own research 100%
Response	1983

Availability	General
Cost	£17.50
Address	20 Kingsway, London WC2B 6LH
Telephone	01 405 3861
Contact	Above address

486

Originator	GREENE, BELFIELD-SMITH AND CO
Title	TRENDS IN HOTEL SALES AND PROFITS, annual
Coverage	Covers a sample of 74 hotels. Comparisons with tariff survey, retail price index and Hillier Parker rent index.
Contents & Origin of Statistics	Tables per issue: 9. Own research 100%
Response	1983
Availability	General
Cost	£10
Address	20 Kingsway, London WC2B 6LH
Telephone	01 405 3861
Contact	Above address

487

Originator	GREENWELL, W. AND CO
Title	MONETARY BULLETIN, monthly
Coverage	Gives different measures of money supply.
Contents & Origin of Statistics	Tables per issue: Government statistics 100%
Response	1983
Availability	Clients
Address	Bow Bells House, Bread St, London EC4M 9EL
Telephone	01 236 2040; Telex: 883006
Contact	Above address

488

Originator	GRIEVESON, GRANT AND CO
Title	QUARTERLY PSBR FORECASTS, quarterly
Coverage	Covers control of public expenditure, PSBR, Central Government reviews and spending, local authorities' borrowing requirement and public corporations' borrowing requirement.

Contents & Origin of Statistics	Tables per issue: 12. Government statistics 10%, Unstated 90%

Response	1983
Availability	Clients
Address	P.O. Box 191, 59 Gresham St, London EC2P 2DS
Telephone	01 606 4433; Telex: 887336
Contact	Above address

489

Originator	GROCER

Title	WHOLESALE AND RETAIL PRICES, weekly in a weekly journal
Coverage	Prices of various foods including vegetables, meat, salad, cheese, eggs, butter, sugar and lard.

Contents & Origin of Statistics	Tables per issue: 7. Own research + other non official source 100%. Supporting text 15%

Currency	1 week
Response	1985
Availability	General
Cost	£15 or 30p for a single issue
Address	William Reed Ltd, 5-7 Southwark St, London SE1 1RQ
Telephone	01 407 6981; Telex: 8812648
Contact	Above address

490

Originator	GWENT COUNTY COUNCIL

Title	ECONOMIC PROGRESS REPORT, quarterly. 1977-
Coverage	Largely concerned with the employment situation in the county covering unemployment, vacancies and redundancies. Also a section on industrial development covering industrial and commercial news and planning permissions.

Contents & Origin of Statistics	Tables per issue: 6. Own research 20%, Government statistics 80%. Supporting text 40%

Comments	Replaced publication titled 'Employment and Industrial Trends' which appeared from 1961 to 1976.
Currency	2-3 weeks
Response	1984
Availability	General
Cost	£3.50
Address	County Planning Department, County Hall, Cwmbran, Gwent NP44 2XF

Telephone   06333 67111, ext 480
Contact   Mr P.R. Eaton, Principal Planning Officer

491

Originator   H.P. INFORMATION

Title   INDIVIDUAL MARKET SHARE ANALYSIS - PRIVATE
             CARS, bi-annual
Coverage   HP agreements on private motor cars.

Contents &   Tables per issue: Own research 100%
  Origin of
  Statistics

Response   1984
Availability Restricted
Cost   On application
Address   P.O. Box 44, 9 Grosvenor Gardens, London SW1W 0BH
Telephone   01 828 0851
Contact   Elizabeth Gibbings, Market Development Manager

492

Originator   H.P. INFORMATION

Title   PRIVATE CARS - HP REGISTRATIONS BY DATE AND
             LENGTH OF AGREEMENT, monthly
Coverage   HP data on retail sales of motor cars.

Contents &   Tables per issue: Own research 100%
  Origin of
  Statistics

Response   1984
Availability Restricted
Cost   £15 plus VAT
Address   P.O. Box 44, 9 Grosvenor Gardens, London SW1W 0BH
Telephone   01 828 0851
Contact   Elizabeth Gibbings, Market Development Manager

493

Originator   H.P. INFORMATION

Title   STATISTICAL RETURN OF REGISTRATIONS RECEIVED,
             monthly
Coverage   Monthly hire purchase registrations for consumer goods.

Contents & **Origin of** **Statistics**	Tables per issue: Own research 100%

Response	1984
Availability	On application
Cost	£120 plus VAT
Address	P.O. Box 44, 9 Grosvenor Gardens, London SW1W 0BH
Telephone	01 828 0851
Contact	Elizabeth Gibbings, Market Development Manager

494

Originator	HALIFAX BUILDING SOCIETY

Title	THE NEW HALIFAX HOUSE PRICE INDEX NATIONAL BULLETIN, monthly. March 1984-
Coverage	Indices of house prices and average prices for all buyers, first-time buyers, and former owner-occupiers. Also general comment on mortgage demand.

Contents & **Origin of** **Statistics**	Tables per issue: 4. Own research 95%, Government statistics 5%. Supporting text 30%

Comments	A separate booklet 'The Halifax House Price Index - Technical Details' is available free.
Currency	1-2 weeks
Response	1984
Availability	General
Cost	Free
Address	PO Box 60, Trinity Rd, Halifax, West Yorkshire, HX1 2RG
Telephone	0422 65777 ; Telex: 517441
Contact	Miss M. Nash, Librarian, Research Department

495

Originator	HALIFAX BUILDING SOCIETY

Title	THE NEW HALIFAX HOUSE PRICE INDEX REGIONAL BULLETIN, quarterly. March 1984-
Coverage	Indices and average prices of different types of houses by economic planning regions. Average prices also by age of property.

Contents & **Origin of** **Statistics**	Tables per issue: 5. Own research 100%. Supporting text 20%

Currency	1-2 weeks
Response	1984
Availability	General
Cost	Free
Address	PO Box 60, Trinity Rd, Halifax, West Yorkshire, HX1 2RG

Telephone	0422 65777 ; Telex: 517441
Contact	Miss M. Nash, Librarian, Research Department

496

Originator	HAMBLIN, MARTIN RESEARCH
Title	RETAIL PHARMACISTS' RECOMMENDATIONS OF OVER-THE-COUNTER AND CONSUMER MEDICINES, approx. every 2 years. 1976-
Coverage	Investigates the pharmacists' influence on the customer with regard to OTC medicines and sources of influence on the pharmacist. It covers approximately 20 therapeutic areas and approximately 200 pharmacists.
Contents & Origin of Statistics	Tables per issue: 590. Own research 100%. Supporting text 10%
Comments	Much of the data obtained is illustrated by computer graphics. Facility to add individual questions to survey.
Currency	2 months
Response	1984
Availability	General
Cost	Depends on amount of data purchased and individual requirements
Address	14-20 Headfort Place, London, SW1X 7HN
Telephone	01 235 544
Contact	Katy Goulden, Research Executive

497

Originator	HAMPSHIRE COUNTY COUNCIL
Title	EMPLOYMENT NEWSLETTER, quarterly. September 1981-
Coverage	General labour market news plus data on national unemployment trends, Hampshire unemployment and youth unemployment.
Contents & Origin of Statistics	Tables per issue: 6. Own research 40%, Government statistics 60%. Supporting text 60%
Currency	1 month
Response	1984
Availability	General
Cost	Free
Address	County Planning Department, The Castle, Winchester Hampshire, SO23 8UJ.
Telephone	0962 54411
Contact	Maureen Booth, Research Assistant

498

Originator	HAMPSHIRE COUNTY COUNCIL
Title	HAMPSHIRE EDUCATION STATISTICS, annual
Coverage	Pupil numbers, teaching staff, further education student numbers, student awards, special education numbers, external examination statistics and career details for young people.
Contents & Origin of Statistics	Tables per issue: 76. Own research 50%, Government statistics 10%, Unstated 40%. Supporting text 5%
Currency	2 months
Response	1984
Availability	General
Address	The Castle, Winchester SO23 8UJ
Telephone	0962 54411
Contact	Verna Clark, Planning Dept

499

Originator	HAMPSHIRE COUNTY COUNCIL
Title	HAMPSHIRE FACTS AND FIGURES, annual. 1977-
Coverage	Summary of trends in the county including sections on population, employment, housing, transportation, social services, education, other services and finance. Each issue also has a 'special topic' section - 1983 issue topic covers 'The Coast'.
Contents & Origin of Statistics	Tables per issue: 80. Own research 75%, Government statistics 25%. Supporting text 60%
Comments	Most data given in the form of graphs.
Currency	Varies
Response	1984
Availability	General
Cost	£33 (plus 50p, p+p)
Address	County Planning Department, The Castle, Winchester, Hampshire, SO23 8UJ
Telephone	0962 54411
Contact	Karen Harding, Administrative Officer

500

Originator	HAMPSHIRE COUNTY COUNCIL
Title	HOUSING NEWSLETTER, bi-annual. 1982-
Coverage	Housing trends in the county.

Contents & Origin of Statistics	Tables per issue: 5. Own research 40%, Government statistics 60%. Supporting text 70%
Response	1984
Availability	General
Cost	Free
Address	County Planning Department, The Castle, Winchester, Hampshire SO23 8UJ.
Telephone	0962 54411
Contact	Kate Barnard, Research Officer

501

Originator	HARDWARE TODAY
Title	TODAY'S TRADING TRENDS, quarterly in a monthly journal
Coverage	Performance trends, i.e. profits, sales, wages, stocks etc, in 3 hardware sectors - homecentres, merchants and retailers.
Contents & Origin of Statistics	Tables per issue: 5. Own research 100%. Supporting text 30%
Currency	2-3 months
Response	1984
Availability	General
Cost	£10
Address	British Hardware Federation, 20 Holborn Rd, Edgbaston, Bir- mingham B15 3AB
Telephone	021 454 4385; Telex: 338024
Contact	R. Petitjean, Managing Director

502

Originator	HARDWARE TRADE JOURNAL
Title	BUSINESS NEWS, monthly in a weekly journal. 1983-
Coverage	Average price movements in hardware, paint, paper, glass, pottery, DIY and garden products.
Contents & Origin of Statistics	Tables per issue: Own research 20%, Government statistics 80%
Currency	1 month
Response	1984
Availability	General
Cost	£33 or 55p for a single issue
ISSN	0017 7741
Address	Benn Publications Ltd, Sovereign Way, Tonbridge, Kent TN9 1RW

Telephone	0732 364422; Telex: 95132
Contact	B.D. Farthing, Editor

503

Originator	HARDWARE TRADE JOURNAL
Title	PRICEWATCH, monthly in a weekly journal. 1983-
Coverage	Retail prices in the major DIY multiples.
Contents & Origin of Statistics	Tables per issue: Own research 100%
Currency	1 week
Response	1984
Availability	General
Cost	£33 or 55p for a single issue
ISSN	0017 7741
Address	Benn Publications Ltd, Sovereign Way, Tonbridge, Kent TN9 1RW
Telephone	0732 364422; Telex: 95132
Contact	B.D. Farthing, Editor

504

Originator	HAY/MSL MANAGEMENT CONSULTANTS
Title	HAY BOARDROOM PAY GUIDE, annual
Coverage	Pay levels and employee benefits for directors usually paid about £20,000 upwards. Analysis of pay practice is both by company and function and by sector. There are also sections on incentives and other benefits.
Contents & Origin of Statistics	Tables per issue: Own research 100%
Response	1984
Availability	Participants
Cost	On application
Address	52 Grosvenor Gardens, London SW1W 0AJ
Telephone	01 730 8371
Contact	Mrs. K. Hilton-Johnson

505

Originator	HAY/MSL MANAGEMENT CONSULTANTS
Title	HAY REGIONAL SURVEYS, bi-annual
Coverage	Regional survey of pay levels and employee benefits in 7 regions.

Contents & **Origin of** **Statistics**	Tables per issue: Own research 100%

Response	1984
Availability	Participants
Cost	On application
Address	52 Grosvenor Gardens, London SW1W 0AJ
Telephone	01 730 8371
Contact	Mrs. K. Hilton-Johnson

506

Originator	HAY/MSL MANAGEMENT CONSULTANTS

Title	HAY REMUNERATION COMPARISON, quarterly
Coverage	Pay levels and employee benefits within the UK by industry sector, job function, location and level. The survey is arranged in two parts - industrial and service organisations and financial organisations.

Contents & **Origin of** **Statistics**	Tables per issue: Own research 100%

Response	1984
Availability	Participants
Cost	On application
Address	52 Grosvenor Gardens, London SW1W 0AJ
Telephone	01 730 8371
Contact	Mrs. K. Hilton-Johnson

507

Originator	HAY/MSL MANAGEMENT CONSULTANTS

Title	HAY SURVEY OF DATA PROCESSING STAFF, bi-annual
Coverage	Survey of pay levels and employment benefits in data processing. The survey covers a wide range of job titles, analysed by industrial sector and region.

Contents & **Origin of** **Statistics**	Tables per issue: Own research 100%

Response	1984
Availability	Participants
Cost	On application
Address	52 Grosvenor Gardens, London SW1W 0AJ
Telephone	01 730 8371
Contact	Mrs. K. Hilton-Johnson

508

Originator	HAY/MSL MANAGEMENT CONSULTANTS
Title	HAY/MSL SURVEY OF EMPLOYEE BENEFITS, annual
Coverage	General survey of employee benefits.
Contents &	Tables per issue: Own research 100%
Origin of	
Statistics	
Response	1984
Availability	Participants
Cost	On application
Address	52 Grosvenor Gardens, London SW1W 0AJ
Telephone	01 730 8371
Contact	Mrs. K. Hilton-Johnson

509

Originator	HAY/MSL MANAGEMENT CONSULTANTS
Title	INVESTMENT FUND MANAGERS, annual
Coverage	Survey of pay and benefits of investment fund managers.
Contents &	Tables per issue: Own research 100%
Origin of	
Statistics	
Response	1984
Availability	Participants
Cost	On application
Address	52 Grosvenor Gardens, London SW1W 0AJ
Telephone	01 730 8371
Contact	Mrs. K. Hilton-Johnson

510

Originator	HAY/MSL MANAGEMENT CONSULTANTS
Title	LIFE ASSURANCE SALES SURVEY, annual
Coverage	Salaries and benefits of life assurance sales staff.
Contents &	Tables per issue: Own research 100%
Origin of	
Statistics	
Response	1984
Availability	Participants
Cost	On application
Address	52 Grosvenor Gardens, London SW1W OAJ

Telephone	01 730 8371
Contact	Mrs. K. Hilton-Johnson

511

Originator	HAY/MSL MANAGEMENT CONSULTANTS
Title	RETAIL SURVEY, annual
Coverage	Salaries and benefits in the retail sector.
Contents & **Origin of** **Statistics**	Tables per issue: Own research 100%
Response	1984
Availability	Participants
Cost	On application
Address	52 Grosvenor Gardens, London SW1W 0AJ
Telephone	01 730 8371
Contact	Mrs. K. Hilton-Johnson

512

Originator	HEATING AND VENTILATING CONTRACTORS' ASSOCI-ATION
Title	COSTING SURVEY, annual
Coverage	Profitability/accounting ratios.
Contents & **Origin of** **Statistics**	Tables per issue: Own research 100%
Response	1983
Availability	Members
Cost	Free
Address	ESCA House, 34 Palace Court, Bayswater, London W2 4JG
Telephone	01 229 2488
Contact	R.J. Higgs, Deputy Director

513

Originator	HEATING AND VENTILATING CONTRACTORS' ASSOCI-ATION
Title	STATE OF TRADE ENQUIRY, bi-annual
Coverage	Current and anticipated volume of work.
Contents & **Origin of** **Statistics**	Tables per issue: Own research 100%

Response	1983
Availability	Members
Cost	Free
Address	ESCA House, 34 Palace Court, Bayswater, London W2 4JG
Telephone	01 229 2488
Contact	R.J. Higgs, Deputy Director

514

Originator	HEATING, VENTILATING AND AIR CONDITIONING MANUFACTURERS ASSOCIATION
Title	UNTITLED
Coverage	Members' returns.
Contents & Origin of Statistics	Tables per issue: Own research 100%
Response	1983
Availability	Members
Cost	Free
Address	Unit 3, Phoenix House, Phoenix Way, Heston, Middlesex TW5 9ND
Telephone	01 897 2848/9
Contact	Miss C.J. Ayers, Administrative Secretary

515

Originator	HENLEY CENTRE FOR FORECASTING
Title	COSTS AND PRICES, quarterly
Coverage	General overview followed by data on a wide range of key industrial prices such as energy, metal, property etc. Final section presents cost/price forecasts for 26 major industrial sectors.
Contents & Origin of Statistics	Tables per issue: 60pgs
Comments	Also produce international publications and CENTREX, a computer database accessible by telephone.
Response	1984
Availability	General
Cost	£350 or £105 for a single issue
Address	2 Tudor St, Blackfriars, London EC4Y 0AA
Telephone	01 353 9961; Telex: 298817
Contact	Above address

516

Originator	HENLEY CENTRE FOR FORECASTING
Title	DIRECTOR'S GUIDE, monthly
Coverage	Summary document containing statistics, commentary and forecasts up to 5 years ahead.
Contents & Origin of Statistics	Tables per issue: 16pgs.
Comments	Also produce international publications and CENTREX, a computer database accessible by telephone.
Currency	Varies
Response	1984
Availability	General
Cost	£125 or £20 for a single issue
Address	2 Tudor St, Blackfriars, London EC4Y 0AA
Telephone	01 353 9961; Telex: 298817
Contact	Above address

517

Originator	HENLEY CENTRE FOR FORECASTING
Title	FRAMEWORK FORECASTS FOR THE UK ECONOMY, monthly
Coverage	Data on the UK economy with 5 years actual and 5 years forecasts with a detailed commentary.
Contents & Origin of Statistics	Tables per issue: 60pgs.
Comments	Also produce international publications and CENTREX, a computer database accessible by telephone.
Currency	Varies
Response	1984
Availability	General
Cost	£675 or £182 for a single copy
Address	2 Tudor St, Blackfriars, London EC4Y 0AA
Telephone	01 353 9961; Telex: 298817
Contact	Above address

518

Originator	HENLEY CENTRE FOR FORECASTING
Title	INVESTMENT MARKETS, quarterly
Coverage	Statistics, commentary and forecasts for investment funds in the UK.

Contents & Origin of Statistics	Tables per issue: 40pgs
Comments	Also produce international publications and CENTREX, a computer database accessible by telephone.
Response	1984
Availability	General
Cost	£375 or £115 for a single issue
Address	2 Tudor St, Blackfriars, London EC4Y 0AA
Telephone	01 353 9961; Telex: 298817
Contact	Above address

519

Originator	HENLEY CENTRE FOR FORECASTING
Title	LEISURE FUTURES, quarterly
Coverage	Forecasts and data on the UK leisure business.
Comments	Also produce international publications and CENTREX, a computer database accessible by telephone.
Response	1984
Availability	General
Cost	£575 or £155 for a single issue
Address	2 Tudor St, Blackfriars, London EC4Y 0AA
Telephone	01 353 9961; Telex: 298817
Contact	Above address

520

Originator	HENLEY CENTRE FOR FORECASTING
Title	PLANNING CONSUMER MARKETS, quarterly
Coverage	Forecasts, commentary and statistical data on the UK consumer economy.
Contents & Origin of Statistics	Tables per issue: 100pgs
Comments	Also produce international publications and CENTREX, a computer database accessible by telephone.
Response	1984
Availability	General
Cost	£500 or £150 for a single issue
Address	2 Tudor St, Blackfriars, London EC4Y 0AA
Telephone	01 353 9961; Telex: 298817
Contact	Above address

521

Originator	HENLEY CENTRE FOR FORECASTING
Title	PLANNING FOR SOCIAL CHANGE, annual
Coverage	Statistics, forecast and analysis of changes in social attitudes and their economic significance in the UK.
Comments	Also publish international publications and CENTREX, a computer database accessible by telephone.
Currency	Varies
Response	1984
Availability	General
Cost	£2000
Address	2 Tudor St, Blackfriars, London EC4Y 0AA
Telephone	01 353 9961; Telex: 298817
Contact	Above address

522

Originator	HEREWARD RADIO PLC
Title	SURVEY OF THE RADIO AUDIENCE, annual
Coverage	Results of a survey of radio listening. Data gathered by diary technique. Data on cumulative weekly audience (reach) and average half-hour audience. Covers ILR, Radio Luxembourg and BBC. Also data on rate card segment audiences and results of special reach and frequency package analyses. Data by sex, age and social class.
Contents & Origin of Statistics	Tables per issue: 8. Own research 100%
Response	1983
Availability	General
Cost	Free
Address	P.O. Box 225, Bridge St, Peterborough
Telephone	0733 46225
Contact	Above address

523

Originator	HIGHLANDS AND ISLANDS DEVELOPMENT BOARD
Title	HIDB ANNUAL REPORT, annual. 1967-
Coverage	Review of HIDB activities and the Highland economy with statistical appendices on population, unemployment, HIDB aid etc.
Contents & Origin of Statistics	Tables per issue: 20. Own research 50%, Other non official source 20%, Government statistics 30%. Supporting text 80%
Currency	6 months

Response	1984
Availability	General
Cost	Free
ISSN	0265 6698
Address	Bridge House, 27 Bank St, Inverness IV1 1QR
Telephone	0463 234171; Telex: 75267
Contact	Press and Public Relations Branch

524

Originator	HILLIER PARKER MAY AND ROWDEN
Title	CENTRAL LONDON SHOPS SURVEY, every 3 or 4 years
Coverage	Number of shops by types, general trading trends and number of shops in 4 main areas - Oxford St, Regent St, Bond St and Brompton Rd.
Contents & Origin of Statistics	Tables per issue: 20. Own research 100%
Comments	Other 'one-off' surveys published.
Response	1984
Availability	General
Cost	Free
Address	77 Grosvenor St, London W1A 2BT
Telephone	01 629 7666
Contact	Research Department

525

Originator	HILLIER PARKER MAY AND ROWDEN
Title	A FORECAST OF INDUSTRIAL RENTS, annual
Coverage	General forecasts of industrial rents, up to 18 months ahead.
Contents & Origin of Statistics	Tables per issue: 11. Own research 90%, Government statistics 10%
Comments	Other 'one-off' surveys published, plus a regular 'Industrial Contour Map' showing rents and yields.
Response	1984
Availability	General
Cost	Free
Address	77 Grosvenor St, London W1A 2BT
Telephone	01 629 7666
Contact	Research Department

526

Originator	HILLIER PARKER MAY AND ROWDEN
Title	A FORECAST OF SHOP RENTS, annual
Coverage	General forecasts of shop rents, up to 18 months ahead.
Contents & Origin of Statistics	Tables per issue: 12. Own research + other non official source 80%, Government statistics 20%
Comments	Other 'one-off' surveys published.
Response	1984
Availability	General
Cost	Free
Address	77 Grosvenor St, London W1A 2BT
Telephone	01 629 7666
Contact	Research Department

527

Originator	HILLIER PARKER MAY AND ROWDEN
Title	INVESTORS CHRONICLE HILLIER PARKER RENT INDEX, bi-annual
Coverage	Data on rents for the shop, office and industrial sector over a 5 year period with a regional breakdown. Gives current and constant prices.
Contents & Origin of Statistics	Tables per issue: 25. Own research + other non official source 100%
Comments	Other 'one-off' surveys published.
Response	1984
Availability	General
Cost	£3.50
Address	77 Grosvenor St, London W1A 2BT
Telephone	01 629 7666
Contact	Research Department

528

Originator	HILLIER PARKER MAY AND ROWDEN
Title	SURVEY OF BUILDING SOCIETY BRANCHES, annual
Coverage	Building society branch numbers and expansion trends.
Contents & Origin of Statistics	Tables per issue: 8. Own research + other non official source 60% Unstated 40%
Comments	Other 'one-off' surveys published.
Response	1984

Availability	General
Cost	Free
Address	77 Grosvenor St, London W1A 2BT
Telephone	01 629 7666
Contact	Research Department

529

Originator HILLIER PARKER MAY AND ROWDEN

Title SURVEY OF OFFICE MARKET ACTIVITY, bi-annual
Coverage Data on national office space availability.

Contents & Origin of Statistics Tables per issue: 7. Own research 100%

Comments Other 'one-off' surveys published, plus a regular 'Office Contour Map' showing rents and yields.
Response 1984
Availability General
Cost Free
Address 77 Grosvenor St, London W1A 2BT
Telephone 01 629 7666
Contact Research Department

530

Originator HIRE NEWS

Title HIRE RATES NATIONAL ANNUAL REVIEW, annual in a journal published ten times a year
Coverage Average national hire rates, weekly and daily, for various tools and machinery. Information is based on a survey of approximately 55 companies.

Contents & Origin of Statistics Tables per issue: 1. Own research 100%. Supporting text 30%

Response 1984
Availability Controlled circulation to hire industry but general subscription available
Cost Free to hire industry, £12 to others
Address Togher Promotions, 100 Cecil St, Watford, Hertfordshire WD2 5AP
Telephone 0923 27211
Contact The Editor

531

Originator	HOARE GOVETT LTD
Title	CORPORATE SECTOR QUARTERLY TRENDS, quarterly
Coverage	Retrospective analysis of previous year and forecasts for coming year. Regular features include profits, dividends, working capital, capital spending and gearing. Also sector earnings indices, yield analysis and PER analysis. Indices are derived from the Hoare Govett Aggregate Model, 150 UK companies, 65% of London Market Capitalisation. Uses the FTA industrial group and FTA 500 index as divisions.
Contents & Origin of Statistics	Tables per issue: 24. Own research 50%, Government statistics 17%, Unstated 33%
Response	1983
Availability	General
Cost	£100 or £25 for a single issue
Address	Heron House, 319-325 High Holborn, London WC1V 7PB
Telephone	01 404 0344
Contact	Andrew K. Lansdown

532

Originator	HOARE GOVETT LTD
Title	ECONOMIC OUTLOOK, monthly
Coverage	Analysis of the UK economy. Includes overview, article, recurring features (political framework and international economy) and detailed forecasts of GDP, consumer expenditure, investment, employment and productivity, inflation, external position, financial framework and company profits. Forecasts 18-24 months ahead.
Contents & Origin of Statistics	Tables per issue: 23. Own research + other non official source 5%, Government statistics 30%, Unstated 65%
Response	1983
Availability	General
Cost	£250
Address	Heron House, 319-325 High Holborn, London WC1V 7PB
Telephone	01 404 0344
Contact	Andrew K. Lansdown

533

Originator	HOARE GOVETT LTD
Title	STORES QUARTERLY, quarterly

Coverage	Largely consists of company information, including forecasts. Also covers sector as a whole, with outlook for coming year and monthly data on past year forr non-food retail sales.
Contents & Origin of Statistics	Tables per issue: 31. Non official source 80%, Government statistics 10%, Unstated 10%
Response	1983
Availability	General
Cost	£100
Address	Heron House, 319-325 High Holborn, London WC1V 7PB
Telephone	01 404 0344
Contact	Andrew K. Lansdown

534

Originator	HOGSTON, JOHN ASSOCIATES LTD
Title	SILVER BOOK - A REVIEW OF THE COSMETICS AND TOILETRIES INDUSTRIES, quarterly
Coverage	Divided into sections on make-up, skin care, men's products, hair preparations and dental preparations. Gives data on consumer expenditure and retail sales. Twice a year provides 5 year trends.
Contents & Origin of Statistics	Tables per issue: 84. Own research + other non official source 10%, Government statistics 90%
Response	1983
Availability	General
Cost	£35 plus postage
Address	23 Golden Square, London W1
Telephone	01 439 8639
Contact	Above address

535

Originator	HOME GROWN CEREALS AUTHORITY
Title	ANNUAL REPORT, annual
Coverage	General review of cereals with some statistics.
Contents & Origin of Statistics	Tables per issue: Own research + government statistics 100%
Response	1984
Availability	General
Cost	£1
Address	Hamlyn House, Highgate Hill, London N19 5PR

Telephone   01 263 3391
Contact   J. Ellis

536

Originator   HOME GROWN CEREALS AUTHORITY

Title   CEREAL QUALITY SURVEY, annual
Coverage   National survey of the quality of wheat and barley crops.

Contents &   Tables per issue: Own research 100%
  Origin of
  Statistics

Comments   A joint survey with a number of agricultural organisations.
Response   1984
Availability General
Cost   £1.50
Address   Hamlyn House, Highgate Hill, London N19 5PR
Telephone   01 263 3391
Contact   J. Ellis

537

Originator   HOME GROWN CEREALS AUTHORITY

Title   CEREAL STATISTICS, annual
Coverage   Sections covering UK prices, production, supplies, and trade. EEC
             and world figures are also given.

Contents &   Tables per issue: 43. Own research + other non official source 35%,
  Origin of Government statistics 65%
  Statistics

Currency   Varies
Response   1984
Availability General
Cost   £5
Address   Hamlyn House, Highgate Hill, London N19 5PR
Telephone   01 263 3391
Contact   J. Ellis

538

Originator   HOME GROWN CEREALS AUTHORITY

Title   CEREALS MARKET INFORMATION, monthly
Coverage   Grain usage by human and industrial processors plus imports and
             exports. There are 2 statistical appendices giving estimates of annual
             supplies and consumption and cumulative monthly statistics covering
             usage of cereals by processors, etc.

Contents &	Tables per issue: 4. Own research + other non official source 50%,
Origin of	Government statistics 50%
Statistics	

Comments	Issued in the form of a press release.
Response	1984
Availability	General
Cost	Free
Address	Hamlyn House, Highgate Hill, London N19 5PR
Telephone	01 263 3391
Contact	J. Ellis

539

Originator	HOME GROWN CEREALS AUTHORITY

Title	WEEKLY BULLETIN, weekly
Coverage	Data on prices, trade and futures market, with some EEC and world figures.

Contents &	Tables per issue: 10. Government statistics 20%, Unstated 80%
Origin of	
Statistics	

Currency	Varies
Response	1984
Availability	General
Cost	£20 (including 'Weekly Digest')
Address	Hamlyn House, Highgate Hill, London N19 5PR
Telephone	01 263 3391
Contact	J. Ellis

540

Originator	HOME GROWN CEREALS AUTHORITY

Title	WEEKLY DIGEST, weekly
Coverage	Data on cereal output, prices, grain fed to livestock, and compound feed production.

Contents &	Tables per issue: 6. Own research + other non official source 50%,
Origin of	Government statistics 50%
Statistics	

Response	1984
Availability	General
Cost	£20 (including 'Weekly Bulletin')
Address	Hamlyn House, Highgate Hill, London N19 5PR
Telephone	01 263 3391
Contact	J. Ellis

541

Originator	HOPS MARKETING BOARD LTD
Title	PROVISIONAL ESTIMATE OF TOTAL PRODUCTION OF ENGLISH HOPS, annual
Coverage	Production of hops.
Contents & Origin of Statistics	Tables per issue: 1. Own research 100%
Response	1983
Availability	General
Cost	Free
Address	Hop Pocket Lane, Paddock Wood, Tonbridge, Kent TN12 6BY
Telephone	089 283 3415
Contact	Mr K. Waller, Secretary

542

Originator	HOPS MARKETING BOARD LTD
Title	STATEMENT OF TOTAL AREA UNDER HOPS, annual
Coverage	Total area under hops.
Contents & Origin of Statistics	Tables per issue: 1. Own research 100%
Response	1983
Availability	General
Cost	Free
Address	Hop Pocket Lane, Paddock Wood, Tonbridge, Kent TN12 6BY
Telephone	089 283 3415
Contact	Mr K. Waller, Secretary

543

Originator	HOPS MARKETING BOARD LTD
Title	STATEMENT OF TOTAL PRODUCTION OF ENGLISH HOPS, annual
Coverage	Production of hops.
Contents & Origin of Statistics	Tables per issue: 1. Own research 100%
Response	1983
Availability	General
Cost	Free
Address	Hop Pocket Lane, Paddock Wood, Tonbridge, Kent TN12 6BY

Telephone   089 283 3415
Contact   Mr K. Waller, Secretary

544

Originator   HORWATH AND HORWATH (UK) LTD

Title   UK LODGING INDUSTRY, annual ·
Coverage   Part of worldwide survey of first class hotels. Comparison between London, provincial UK and Scotland. 140 hotels responded, representing 31,200 rooms. Previous year's data for comparison. Covers room occupancy and rates, analysis of guests, methods of payment, distribution of revenue and expenses, operational data, food and drink, departmental revenues and expenses.

Contents &   Tables per issue: 52. Own research 100%
Origin of
Statistics

Response   1983
Availability General
Cost   £10
Address   84 Baker St, London W1M 1DL
Telephone   01 486 5191
Contact   H.R. Fraser

545

Originator   HOSIERY AND ALLIED TRADES RESEARCH ASSOCI-ATION (HATRA)

Title   KNITSTATS, bi-annual. 1976-
Coverage   UK production, imports, exports, sales, yarn consumption, capacity wages, hours of working of the U.K. knitting industry.

Contents &   Tables per issue: 36pgs. Own research 10%, Other non official source
Origin of   20%, Government statistics 70%. Supporting text 25%
Statistics

Comments   Data stored in computer form from 1985
Currency   9-12 months
Response   1984
Availability General
Cost   £20
ISSN   0260 8855
Address   7 Gregory Boulevard, Nottingham NG7 6LD
Telephone   0602 623311; Telex: 378230
Contact   J.A. Smirfitt, Information Officer

546

Originator	HOUSING CORPORATION
Title	HC NEWS SUPPLEMENT FACT SHEET, annual. 1982-
Coverage	Figures relating to housing associations in England and Wales, and based on returns from these associations (80% return in 1983). Covers stock, new building, development pipeline, vacant units, and staffing.
Contents & Origin of Statistics	Tables per issue: 4-8. Own research 100%. Supporting text 20%
Currency	1 year
Response	1984
Availability	Housing Associations and general
Cost	Free
Address	149 Tottenham Court Rd, London W1P OBN
Telephone	01 387 9466
Contact	Ian Brown, Press and Publicity Officer

547

Originator	HUMBERSIDE COUNTY COUNCIL
Title	HUMERSIDE FACTS AND FIGURES, annual. 1973-
Coverage	Background information, services and communications, economic development, financial assistance, labour, population and housing, administrative background.
Contents & Origin of Statistics	Tables per issue: 41. Own research 40%, Other non official source 10%, Government statistics 50%. Supporting text 30%
Comments	Published in March each year.
Currency	Varies
Response	1984
Availability	General
Cost	£2.75
ISSN	0262 5555
Address	Manor Rd, Beverley, North Humberside, HU17 7BX
Telephone	0482 867131
Contact	Colin Day, Senior Planning Officer

548

Originator	HUMBERSIDE COUNTY COUNCIL
Title	JOINT DEVELOPMENT ANALYSIS SYSTEM PROGRES. REPORT, annual. December 1974-

Coverage	All forms of development, including residential, industrial and commercial.
Contents & Origin of Statistics	Tables per issue: 16. Own research 100%. Supporting text 25%
Comments	More data available.
Currency	1 year
Response	1984
Availability	General
Cost	Free
Address	Manor Rd, Beverley, North Humberside, HU17 7BX
Telephone	0482 867131
Contact	I. Biddick, Senior Planning Officer

549

Originator	IMAC RESEARCH
Title	UK MARKET SIZE, annual. 1976-
Coverage	Output for some 4000 separate products, covering all manufacturing industry. 3 years figures by value and volume where available.
Contents & Origin of Statistics	Tables per issue: 200pgs. Non official source 10%, Government statistics 90%.
Currency	Less than 1 year
Response	1984
Availability	General
Cost	£85
Address	Lancaster House, More Lane, Esher, Surrey KT10 8AP
Telephone	0372 63121
Contact	Ian MacLean

550

Originator	INCOME DATA SERVICES LTD
Title	INCOMES DATA REPORT, bi-monthly. 1966-
Coverage	Changes to rates of pay and other terms of employment in the private and public sectors of industry plus sections on economic forecasts and official statistics on earnings etc.
Contents & Origin of Statistics	Tables per issue: 32pgs. Supporting text 50%
Comments	Publish other non-statistical reports.
Currency	2 weeks
Response	1984
Availability	Subscribers to IDS

Cost	On application
Address	140 Great Portland St, London W1N 5TA
Telephone	01 580 0521/9
Contact	Mrs Greta Iredale, Subscription Secretary

551

Originator	INCOMES DATA SERVICES LTD
Title	IDS PAY DIRECTORY, 3 issues per year. 1982-
Coverage	Rates of pay by job title of manual and white collar workers in companies and industries.
Contents & Origin of Statistics	Tables per issue: 176pgs. Own research 100%.
Comments	Publish other non-statistical reports
Currency	Varies
Response	1984
Availability	Subscribers to IDS
Cost	On application
Address	140 Great Portland St, London W1N 5TA
Telephone	01 580 0521/9
Contact	Mrs Greta Iredale, Subscription Secretary

552

Originator	INCORPORATED BREWERS' GUILD
Title	SALARY SURVEY, biennial. 1978-
Coverage	Survey of members' salaries, by age, educational qualifications, size of plant, status, location.
Contents & Origin of Statistics	Tables per issue: 11. Own research 100%. Supporting text 5%
Response	1984
Availability	Members
Cost	Free
Address	8 Ely Place, London EC1N 6SD
Telephone	01 405 4565
Contact	J.H. Griffiths, Secretary

553

Originator	INCORPORATED ENGINEER
Title	SURVEY OF MEMBERS, every 2 years in a monthly journal
Coverage	Data on employment by sector and earnings trends.

Contents & Origin of Statistics	Tables per issue: Own research 100%
Comments	The survey is normally conducted in January every 2 years.
Currency	3-4 months
Response	1984
Availability	General
Cost	£2.20
ISSN	0306 8552
Address	Institution of Electrical and Electronics Incorporated Engineers, 2 Savoy Hill, London WC2R 0BS
Telephone	01 836 3357
Contact	Secretary

554

Originator	INCORPORATED NATIONAL ASSOCIATION OF BRITISH AND IRISH MILLERS LTD
Title	FACTS ABOUT THE UK FLOUR MILLING INDUSTRY, annual
Coverage	Structure of the industry, wheat usage by millers, total production, flour production by type, sales revenue, costs, exports, consumption of flour.
Contents & Origin of Statistics	Tables per issue: 6. Non official source 10%, Government statistics 90%. Supporting text 40%
Response	1984
Availability	Members and researchers
Cost	Free
Address	21 Arlington St, London SW1A 1RN
Telephone	01 493 2621-5; Telex: 28878
Contact	Mr. P.G. Davies, Director-General

555

Originator	INCORPORATED SOCIETY OF BRITISH ADVERTISERS LTD
Title	EXHIBITION EXPENDITURE SURVEY, annual
Coverage	Expenditure by UK exhibitors on trade and consumer exhibitions, expenditure by venue, advertising expenditure by media, agricultural shows, private exhibitions, members' participation by venue in private events, overseas exhibition expenditure by UK companies, index of media rate increases.
Contents & Origin of Statistics	Tables per issue: 8. Own research 50%, Other non official source 50%. Supporting text 10%

Response	1984
Availability	General
Cost	£5
Address	44 Hertford St, London W1Y 8AE
Telephone	01 499 7502; Telex: 22525
Contact	Ann Harris, External Affairs Manager

556

Originator	INCORPORATED SOCIETY OF VALUERS AND AUC-TIONEERS
Title	ISVA HOUSING INDEX, quarterly
Coverage	Analysis and comment on the movement of house prices by region and nationally.
Contents & Origin of Statistics	Tables per issue: 2. Own research 100%. Supporting text 50%
Currency	2 weeks
Response	1984
Availability	Members and general
Cost	£10 (Free to members and the press)
Address	3 Cadogan Gate, London SW1
Telephone	01 235 2282
Contact	Mrs N. Eadon, Public Relations Officer

557

Originator	INDEPENDENT GROCER
Title	PRICES, fortnightly in a fortnightly journal
Coverage	Prices of basic foodstuffs and other household goods in main super-market chains.
Contents & Origin of Statistics	Tables per issue: 1. Own research 100%
Currency	2 weeks
Response	1984
Availability	Controlled circulation but general subscription available
Cost	Free to controlled circulation list, £35 to others
Address	Industrial Media Ltd, Blair House, 184-186 High St, Tonbridge, Kent TN9 1BE
Telephone	0732 359990; Telex: 957329
Contact	The Editor

558

Originator	INDEPENDENT TELEVISION COMPANIES ASSOCIATION
Title	ITV FACTS AND FIGURES, annual. 1979-
Coverage	ITV coverage for regions, profiles of ITV population viewing levels, distribution of commercials by length, index of media rates, advertising expenditure by media, distribution of expenditure, consumer income and expenditure.
Contents & Origin of Statistics	Tables per issue: 16. Non official source 90%, Government statistics 10%. Supporting text 50%
Currency	Varies
Response	1984
Availability	General
Cost	Free
Address	Knighton House, 56 Mortimer St, London W1N 8AN
Telephone	01 636 6866; Telex: 262988
Contact	Maggie Shrubshall, Librarian

559

Originator	INDUSTRIAL LIFE OFFICES ASSOCIATION
Title	PRESS RELEASES, bi-annual
Coverage	New life business release in February and progress statement on the home service life assurance business in June.
Contents & Origin of Statistics	Tables per issue: 1. Own research 100%. Supporting text 50%
Currency	2-3 months
Response	1984
Availability	General
Cost	Free
Address	Aldermary House, Queen St, London EC4N 1TL
Telephone	01 248 4477
Contact	B.J. Sharp, Secretary

560

Originator	INDUSTRIAL SOCIETY
Title	CATERING PRICES, COSTS AND SUBSIDIES AND OTHER INFORMATION, biennial
Coverage	Analysis by location of companies, number of meal sales, day/shift working.

Contents & Origin of Statistics	Tables per issue: 70. Own research 100%
Comments	Details of statistical techniques used. Also issue a survey supplement at £3 to update data.
Currency	1 year
Response	1984
Availability	General
Cost	£12
Address	Peter Runge House, 3 Carlton House Terrace, London SW1Y 5DG
Telephone	01 839 4300
Contact	Sandra Turner

561

Originator	INSTITUTE OF ADMINISTRATIVE MANAGEMENT
Title	OFFICE SALARIES ANALYSIS, annual
Coverage	Salary data for office staff in all industries, analysed by area, industry and size of establishment.
Contents & Origin of Statistics	Tables per issue: 120. Own research 99%, Government statistics 1%. Supporting text 30%
Comments	Information on office hours, working conditions and holidays often included.
Currency	3 months
Response	1984
Availability	General
Cost	£70 (discount for particpants)
ISSN	0307 0727
Address	40 Chatsworth Parade, Petts Wood, Orpington, Kent BR5 1RW
Telephone	0689 75555
Contact	Graham Noakes, Information Department

562

Originator	INSTITUTE OF DIRECTORS
Title	BUSINESS OPINION SURVEY, bi-monthly. October 1983-
Coverage	Results of an opinion survey of 200 business leaders asking for comments on UK economic trends, company performance, the state of confidence in British boardrooms and future government action wanted.
Contents & Origin of Statistics	Tables per issue: 13-15. Own research 100%. Supporting text 30%
Comments	Press release giving summary results also prepared.
Currency	Few weeks

Response	1984
Availability	General
Cost	£30
Address	116 Pall Mall, London SW1Y 5ED
Telephone	01 839 1233; Telex: 21614
Contact	Wendy Hutton, Press Officer

563

Originator	INSTITUTE OF GROCERY DISTRIBUTION
Title	ECONOMIC BULLETIN, monthly
Coverage	Commentary on recent economic developments and a review and interpretation of economic forecasts. Plus a summary of relevant economic statistics.
Contents & Origin of Statistics	Tables per issue: 23. Own research + other non official source 10%, Government statistics 90%
Currency	Varies
Response	1984
Availability	General
Cost	£20 to members, £40 to others
Address	Letchmore Heath, Watford WD2 8DQ
Telephone	09276 7141
Contact	Mrs M. Bradshaw

564

Originator	INSTITUTE OF GROCERY DISTRIBUTION
Title	FOOD INDUSTRY STATISTICS DIGEST, monthly
Coverage	Regular indicators for the national economy plus consumption and expenditure patterns. Retailing trends by sector, company and region and the number and size of shops. Costs, profits, employment, stocks and capital are also included.
Contents & Origin of Statistics	Tables per issue: 101. Own research + other non official source 42%, Government statistics 58%
Comments	Loose-leaf format with binder.
Currency	Varies
Response	1984
Availability	General
Cost	£30
Address	Letchmore Heath, Watford WD2 8DQ
Telephone	09276 7141
Contact	Mrs M. Bradshaw

565

Originator	INSTITUTE OF GROCERY DISTRIBUTION
Title	GROCERY DISTRIBUTION, annual
Coverage	Outlines current trading conditions and strategies in 3 sections: market forces at work; statistical summary of food chain; review of economy and forecasts for the food industry.
Contents & Origin of Statistics	Tables per issue: 77. Own research + other non official source 30%, Government statistics 70%
Currency	Varies
Response	1984
Availability	General
Cost	£15
Address	Letchmore Heath, Watford WD2 8DQ
Telephone	09276 7141
Contact	Mrs M. Bradshaw

566

Originator	INSTITUTE OF GROCERY DISTRIBUTION
Title	RETAIL GROCERY TRADE REVIEW, annual
Coverage	Analysis of structural changes in the trade. Data on number and size of grocery outlets, average sizes, total sales area, and area devoted to food, characteristics of new stores, product range, etc.
Contents & Origin of Statistics	Tables per issue: 107. Own research + other non official source 80%, Government statistics 20%
Currency	Varies
Response	1984
Availability	General
Cost	£20 to members, £40 to others
Address	Letchmore Heath, Watford WD2 8DQ
Telephone	09276 7141
Contact	Mrs M. Bradshaw

567

Originator	INSTITUTE OF GROCERY DISTRIBUTION
Title	UK ECONOMY: A REVIEW OF PERFORMANCE AND FORECASTS, annual
Coverage	General economic data plus a comparison of 24 forecasts over the next 2 years.

Contents & Origin of Statistics	Tables per issue: 20. Own research + other non official source 20%, Government statistics 80%

Currency	Varies
Response	1984
Availability	General
Cost	£30
Address	Letchmore Heath, Watford WD2 8DQ
Telephone	09276 7141
Contact	Mrs M. Bradshaw

568

Originator	INSTITUTE OF INFORMATION SCIENTISTS
Title	IIS REMUNERATION SURVEY, annual
Coverage	Pay statistics for Institute members in full time employment in the UK. Analysis by grade of membership, age,and industries/ sectors of employment.
Contents & Origin of Statistics	Tables per issue: 4-5. Own research 100%. Supporting text 50%.

Currency	9 months
Response	1984
Availability	Members and purchasers of Institute journal 'INFORM'
Cost	£10
Address	44 Museum St, London WC1A 1LY
Telephone	01 831 8003
Contact	Mrs J.E. Rowley, Survey Compiler

569

Originator	INSTITUTE OF MATHEMATICS AND ITS APPLICATIONS
Title	REMUNERATION SURVEY, every 2/3 years
Coverage	Survey of members, includes analysis of occupations by grade and age, employment by age and sector of women members, remuneration by age and grade for all occupations in selected employment groups, remuneraton by age up to 29 years.
Contents & Origin of Statistics	Tables per issue: 6. Own research 100%

Response	1983
Availability	General
Cost	Free
Address	Maitland House, Warrior Square, Southend-on-Sea, Essex SS1 2JY

Telephone	0702 612177
Contact	Above address

570

Originator	INSTITUTE OF PETROLEUM
Title	PRESS RELEASE, quarterly
Coverage	Deliveries into inland consumption of petroleum products and motor spirit deliveries to retail and commercial consumers. Gives change over previous year.
Contents & Origin of Statistics	Tables per issue: 2-3. Own research 100%. Supporting text 10%
Comments	Produce about 25 'Oil data sheets' covering various aspects of the oil industry, plus 'Know more about oil: world statistics' and an information card 'Petroleum Statistics'.
Currency	3 months
Response	1984
Availability	Press, companies etc
Cost	Free
Address	61 New Cavendish St, London W1M 8AR
Telephone	01 636 1004/9359
Contact	Jean Etherton, Information Department

571

Originator	INSTITUTE OF PETROLEUM
Title	UK PETROLEUM INDUSTRY STATISTICS: CONSUMPTION AND REFINERY PRODUCTION, annual
Coverage	Deliveries, end use and production of petroleum and petroleum products. 2 years data given.
Contents & Origin of Statistics	Tables per issue: 9. Own research 100%. Supporting text 10%
Comments	Also produce 'Know more about oil: world statistics' and an information card 'Petroleum Statistics'. both are free. Also 25 data sheets on the industry.
Currency	5 months
Response	1984
Availability	General
Cost	Free
ISSN	0141 4305
Address	61 New Cavendish St, London W1M 8AR

Telephone	01 636 1004/9359
Contact	Jean E Etherton, Information Department

572

Originator	INSTITUTE OF PHYSICS
Title	REMUNERATION SURVEY, annual. 1948-
Coverage	Analysis of salaries of members by age, sex, class of membership, type of work etc.
Contents & Origin of Statistics	Tables per issue: 15. Own research 100%. Supporting text 10%
Comments	Available in house journal 'Physics Bulletin' or as an offprint. Full survey only every 3 years, annually a sample is taken (10%).
Currency	3 months
Response	1984
Availability	General
Cost	Free
Address	47 Belgrave Square, London SW1X 8QX
Telephone	01 235 6111; Telex: 918453
Contact	Maurice Ebison, Education Officer

573

Originator	INSTITUTE OF PHYSICS
Title	STATISTICS RELATING TO PHYSICS AND EDUCATION, every 5-6 years. 1979-
Coverage	Data on physics education at all levels from CSE to Postgraduate. Covers entrants, passes and employment.
Contents & Origin of Statistics	Tables per issue: 50. Own research 10%, Other non official source 10%, Government statistics 80%. Supporting text 20%
Comments	Supplement was produced in 1982.
Currency	1-2 years
Response	1984
Availability	General
Cost	£4
Address	47 Belgrave Square, London SW1X 8QX
Telephone	01 235 6111; Telex: 918453
Contact	Maurice Ebison, Education Officer

574

Originator	INSTITUTE OF PRACTITIONERS IN ADVERTISING
Title	IPA SALARIES ANALYSIS, annual
Coverage	Numbers of staff at various salary levels by position and by size and location of agencies.
Contents & Origin of Statistics	Tables per issue: 48. Own research 100%.
Currency	3 months
Response	1984
Availability	Members (participating members only)
Cost	Free
Address	44 Belgrave Square, London SW1X 8QS
Telephone	01 235 7020; Telex: 918352
Contact	E.H. Goater, Treasurer

575

Originator	INSTITUTE OF PRACTITIONERS IN ADVERTISING
Title	IPA AGENCY CENSUS, annual. pre-1960-
Coverage	Estimated number of people employed in IPA member advertising agencies by location, size of agency and staff category.
Contents & Origin of Statistics	Tables per issue: 3. Own research 100%. Supporting text 10%
Currency	4-5 months
Response	1984
Availability	Members
Cost	Free to participants and £3 to non-participating members
Address	44 Belgrave Square, London SW1X 8QS
Telephone	01 235 7020; Telex: 918352
Contact	E.H. Goater, Treasurer

576

Originator	INSTITUTE OF PRACTITIONERS IN ADVERTISING
Title	IPA ANNUAL ANALYSIS OF AGENCY COSTS, annual. 1960-
Coverage	Analysis of agency turnovers, costs, profits, payroll and capital, in percentage terms and by size of agency.
Contents & Origin of Statistics	Tables per issue: 25. Own research 100%.
Currency	3 months

Response	1984
Availability	Members
Cost	Free to participants and £100 to non-participating members
Address	44 Belgrave Square, London SW1X 8QS
Telephone	01 235 7020; Telex: 918352
Contact	E.H. Goater, Treasurer

577

Originator	INSTITUTION OF CHEMICAL ENGINEERS
Title	REMUNERATION SURVEY, bi-annual
Coverage	Remuneration and employment statistics for members in the UK.
Contents & Origin of Statistics	Tables per issue: 33. Own research 100%
Response	1983
Availability	General
Cost	£25, free to members
Address	George E Davis Building, 165-171 Railway Terrace, Rugby CV21 3HQ
Telephone	0788 78214
Contact	Chris Pacey-Day, Assistant Secretary

578

Originator	INSTITUTION OF CIVIL ENGINEERS
Title	ICE SALARY SURVEY, every 2/3 years
Coverage	Published in weekly New Civil Engineer. Analysis of salaries of civil engineers by employer, age, type of work, overtime payment, location, size of firm, qualifications, company cars and pensions.
Contents & Origin of Statistics	Tables per issue: 23. Own research 100%
Response	1983
Availability	General
Address	Great George St, Westminster, London SW1P 3AA
Telephone	01 222 7722
Contact	Library

579

Originator	INSTITUTION OF ELECTRICAL ENGINEERS
Title	SALARY SURVEY, annual. 1976-

Coverage	Survey of salaries of a random sample of 40% of members. Analysis by age, position, class and field of employment, type of work, levels of responsibility, size of work, qualification, location of employment, fringe benefits.
Contents & Origin of Statistics	Tables per issue: 29. Own research 100%. Supporting text 15%
Comments	Appears as a supplement to journal 'IEE News'.
Currency	2 months
Response	1984
Availability	General
Cost	£35 (Free to members)
Address	Station House, Nightingale Rd, Hitchin, Herts SG5 IRJ
Telephone	0462 53331; Telex: 825962
Contact	Alison Schroeder, Professional Services

580

Originator	INSTITUTION OF ENVIRONMENTAL HEALTH OFFICERS
Title	ENVIRONMENTAL HEALTH REPORT, annual
Coverage	Annual report containing 8 statistical appendices on food, working environment, pollution control, noise control, housing, caravanning and camping, ports, and Northern Ireland.
Contents & Origin of Statistics	Tables per issue: 47. Own research: 100%
Response	1983
Availability	General
Cost	£4
Address	Chadwick House, Rushworth St, London SE1 0RB
Telephone	01 928 6006/7/8
Contact	K.J. Tyler, Secretary

581

Originator	INSURANCE PERSONNEL SELECTION LTD
Title	LONDON INSURANCE MARKET SALARIES REPORT, annual
Coverage	A guide to salaries paid by employers to insurance staff employed in London, based on approximately 1000 staff placed in work by the publishing body. Age breakdown given.
Contents & Origin of Statistics	Tables per issue: 1. Own research 100%. Supporting text 50%
Currency	Same year

Response	1984
Availability	Restricted to London broking houses, Lloyds and London insurance companies
Cost	£25
Address	Lloyds Avenue House, 6 Lloyde Ave, London EC3N 3ES
Telephone	01 481 8111
Contact	Mr Hugh Allen, Principal Consultant

582

Originator	INTER COMPANY COMPARISONS LTD (ICC)
Title	INDUSTRIAL PERFORMANCE ANALYSIS, annual. 1975-
Coverage	Financial situation of 109 industrial and commercial sectors with details of industry balance sheets, sales and profits.
Contents & Origin of Statistics	Tables per issue: 270. Own research 100%. Supporting text 5%
Comments	More detailed reports on specific sectors also published.
Currency	12-18 months
Response	1984
Availability	General
Cost	£32
Address	28-42 Banner St, London EC1Y 8QE
Telephone	01 253 3906; Telex: 23678
Contact	Liam Hogan, Business Ratio Manager

583

Originator	INTERNATIONAL TEA COMMITTEE
Title	MONTHLY STATISTICAL SUMMARY, monthly
Coverage	Tea production, exports, stocks, imports and auction prices but many tables just cover the UK.
Contents & Origin of Statistics	Tables per issue: 10pgs. Own research 10%, Government statistics 90%.
Comments	Another publication ' Annual Bulletin of Statistics and Supplement' gives international figures with some UK tables.
Currency	Varies
Response	1984
Availability	General
Cost	£35
ISSN	0309 0477
Address	Sir John Lyon House, 5 High Timber St, London EC4V 3NH

| Telephone | 01 248 4672; Telex: 887911 |
| Contact | Mrs Carnegie-Brown, Executive Secretary |

584

Originator	INVESTORS CHRONICLE
Title	MARKET INDICATORS/ECONOMIC INDICATORS/ SECTOR PERFORMANCE, weekly in a weekly journal
Coverage	'Market Indicators' covers UK and international stockmarkets, interest rates, exchange rates and commodity prices. 'Economic Indicators' covers output, demand, prices and trade plus a summary of the main economic forecasts. 'Sector peformance' covers a different sector each week.
Contents & Origin of Statistics	Tables per issue: 20. Non official source 50%, Government statistics 50%
Comments	Various other statistics on individual companies and international stockmarkets are also published.
Currency	Varies
Response	1984
Availability	General
Cost	£49 or 95p for a single issue
ISSN	0261 3115
Address	Financial Times Business Publishing Ltd, Greystoke Place, off Fetter Lane, London EC4A 1ND
Telephone	01 405 6969; Telex: 883694
Contact	Robert C. Ansted, Head of Statistics

585

Originator	INVESTORS IN INDUSTRY PLC
Title	SMALL FIRM SURVEY, every 4-5 years
Coverage	Survey on the financial development, growth and profitability of a sample of companies backed by Investors in Industry. The latest issue covers 687 companies over a 9 year period.
Contents & Origin of Statistics	Tables per issue: 13. Own research 100%
Response	1984
Availability	General
Cost	Unstated
Address	91 Waterloo Rd, London SE1
Telephone	01 928 7822
Contact	Above address

586

Originator	IPC MAGAZINES LTD
Title	ALCOHOLIC DRINKS FOR THE HOME WHO BUYS WHAT, annual
Coverage	Buying drinks for home consumption or to give as a present, participation by members of the household in purchase and consumption, tables for individual drinks and places where men and women buy drinks - levels of personal buying by men and women.
Contents & Origin of Statistics	Tables per issue: 99. Own research 100%. Supporting text 5%
Comments	Includes notes on statistical techniques employed.
Response	1984
Availability	General
Cost	£240
Address	King's Reach Tower, Stamford St, London SE1 9LS
Telephone	01 261 5000
Contact	Mary O'Sullivan, Marketing Library

587

Originator	ITEM CLUB
Title	ITEM CLUB REPORT, quarterly. 1978-
Coverage	Economic forecast using H.M. Treasury Model. Consists of report and computer print-out of data. Forecast for 2-3 years ahead by quarter.
Contents & Origin of Statistics	Tables per issue: 170. Supporting text 5%
Comments	Report consists of 8 tables, 22 charts plus text (50pgs) referring to print-out. Forecasts appear regularly in the 'Guardian'.
Currency	1 month
Response	1984
Availability	Members
Cost	£350
Address	c/o Scicon Ltd, 49 Berners St, London W1P 4AG
Telephone	01 580 5599 ; Telex: 24293
Contact	Rob Marshall, Senior Consultant

588

Originator	JOHNSEN JORGENSEN & WETTRE LTD
Title	A DIGEST OF UNITED KINGDOM WOODPULP IMPORTS AND PRICE REVIEW, annual. March 1964-

Coverage	Woodpulp imports and prices on a running ten year basis. Also comment on the UK market situation and the consumption and production of paper and board.
Contents & Origin of Statistics	Tables per issue: 21. Unstated 100%. Supporting text 15%
Currency	1 year
Response	1984
Availability	Limited distribution at their discretion
Cost	Free
Address	Johnsen House, Wellington Rd, Wokingham, Berks RG11 2LB
Telephone	0734 793033 ; Telex: 848308
Contact	E. Baynes, Pulp sales

589

Originator	JOINT INDUSTRY COMMITTEE FOR NATIONAL READERSHIP SURVEYS (JICNARS)
Title	NATIONAL READERSHIP SURVEY, bi-annual. 1968-
Coverage	Readership of national newspapers and a number of consumer magazines.
Contents & Origin of Statistics	Tables per issue: 329. Own research 100%. Supporting text 20%
Comments	Available online and batch via computer bureaux.
Currency	2 months
Response	1984
Availability	General
Cost	£550
Address	44 Belgrave Square, London SW1X 8QS
Telephone	01 235 7020; Telex: 918352
Contact	Janet Mayhew, Secretary

590

Originator	JONES LANG WOOTTON
Title	JLW CENTRAL LONDON OFFICES RESEARCH, quarterly
Coverage	Trends in availability, take-up and development activity. In addition detailed information on construction and planning permissions.
Contents & Origin of Statistics	Tables per issue: 14. Own research 95%, Other non official source 5%. Supporting text 20%
Response	1984
Availability	General
Cost	Free

Address	103 Mount St, London W1Y 6AS
Telephone	01 493 6040
Contact	Gillian Fleming, Librarian

591

Originator	JONES LANG WOOTTON
Title	JLW PROPERTY INDEX, quarterly
Coverage	Growth of capital and rental values in property sectors by sector. Portfolio statistics by region.
Contents & Origin of Statistics	Tables per issue: 10. Own research 60%, Other non official source 30%, Government statistics 10%. Supporting text 10%
Comments	Issue 'International property review' annually.
Response	1984
Availability	General
Cost	Free
Address	103 Mount St, London W1Y 6AS
Telephone	01 493 6040
Contact	Gillian Fleming, Librarian

592

Originator	JONES LANG WOOTTON
Title	50 CENTRES : A GUIDE TO OFFICE AND INDUSTRIAL RENTAL TRENDS IN ENGLAND AND WALES
Coverage	Rental trends in 50 selected office and industrial centres.
Contents & Origin of Statistics	Tables per issue: 51. Own research 50%, Other non official source 50%. Supporting text 20%
Response	1984
Availability	General
Cost	Free
Address	103 Mount St, London W1Y 6AS
Telephone	01 493 6040
Contact	Gillian Fleming, Librarian

593

Originator	JOURNAL OF ADVERTISING
Title	ADVERTISING EXPENDITURE IN THE UK, annual in a quarterly journal
Coverage	Data on advertising expenditure from the Advertising Association's annual survey. Expenditure by type, media, sector, product etc.

Contents &	Tables per issue: 19. Own research + other non official source 90%,
Origin of	Government statistics 10%. Supporting text 20%
Statistics	
Comments	Published by Holt, Rinehart and Winston for the Advertising Association.
Currency	8 months
Response	1984
Availability	General
Cost	£15 or £6 for a single issue
ISSN	0261 9903
Address	Holt, Rinehart and Winston Ltd, 1 St. Anne's Rd, Eastbourne East Sussex BN21 3UN
Telephone	0323 638211
Contact	The Editor

594

Originator	KING AND CO
Title	INDUSTRIAL FLOORSPACE SURVEY, 3 times a year. 1975-
Coverage	Details of the availability of industrial property (warehouses and factories) for England and Wales with regional breakdown and historical comparisons
Contents &	Tables per issue: 2. Own research 100%. Supporting text 25%
Origin of	
Statistics	
Currency	1 month
Response	1984
Availability	General
Cost	Free
Address	1 Snow Hill, London EC1A 2DL
Telephone	01 236 3000; Telex: 885485
Contact	Nicholas Griffiths, Research Surveyor

595

Originator	KIRKLEES AND WAKEFIELD CHAMBER OF COMMERCE AND INDUSTRY
Title	STATE OF TRADE SURVEY, quarterly
Coverage	Data on performance of member firms.
Contents &	Tables per issue: 12. Own research 100%.
Origin of	
Statistics	
Currency	1-2 weeks
Response	1984
Availability	Members
Cost	Free

Address	New North Rd, Huddersfield, West Yorkshire HD1 5PJ
Telephone	0484 26591; Telex: 51458
Contact	Mr. K.P. Welton, Director/Secretary

596

Originator	KIRKLEES AND WAKEFIELD CHAMBER OF COMMERCE AND INDUSTRY
Title	WAGES SURVEY, bi-annual
Coverage	Wage rates, hours of work and overtime rates in various industries.
Contents & Origin of Statistics	Tables per issue: 53. Own research 100%.
Currency	1 month
Response	1984
Availability	General
Cost	£30 (Participants), £100 (Others)
Address	New North Rd, Huddersfield, West Yorkshire HD1 5PJ
Telephone	0484 26591; Telex: 51458
Contact	A.L. Moxham, Administrative Assistant

597

Originator	KORN/FERRY INTERNATIONAL
Title	BOARDS OF DIRECTORS STUDY, annual
Coverage	Compiled from questionnaires sent to the Times 1000 companies. It covers composition of boards, special committees, salaries of executives, fringe benefits, days served, period of services, issues and government policies important to them, pay rises etc. Broken down by company type, business, market and number of employees.
Contents & Origin of Statistics	Tables per issue: Own research 100%
Comments	Available from Institute of Chartered Secretaries and Administrators, 16 Park Crescent, London W1N 4AH
Response	1984
Availability	General
Cost	£25
Address	2-4 King St, St James's, London SW1Y 6QL
Telephone	01 930 4334
Contact	Graham Lindsay

598

Originator	KP FOODS LTD
Title	SNACK FOOD REVIEW, annual
Coverage	Summary of the snack food market with market share figures and analysis of specific markets for crisps, nuts and savoury snacks. Also sales by outlet, products and packaging and growth prospects.
Contents & Origin of Statistics	Tables per issue: 6. Own research 100%. Supporting text 60%
Currency	3 months
Response	1984
Availability	General
Cost	Free
Address	Heathgate House, 57 Colne Rd, Twickenham, Middlesex TW2 6QA
Telephone	01 894 5600; Telex: 936246

599

Originator	LABOUR RESEARCH
Title	STATISTICS AND ECONOMIC NOTES, monthly in a monthly journal
Coverage	General economic statistics.
Contents & Origin of Statistics	Tables per issue: 1
Currency	Varies
Response	1984
Availability	General
Cost	£13
ISSN	0023 7000
Address	Labour Research Department, 78 Blackfriars Rd, London SE1 8H
Telephone	01 928 3649
Contact	Above address

600

Originator	LABOUR RESEARCH
Title	SURVEY OF TOP DIRECTORS PAY, annual in a monthly journal
Coverage	Monitors 50 company directors and gives percentage increase and average pay per employee as comparison and salary as multiple of this.
Response	1984
Availability	General
Cost	£13

ISSN	0023 7000
Address	Labour Research Department, 78 Blackfriars Rd, London SE1 8HF
Telephone	01 928 3649
Contact	Above address

601

Originator	LAING & CRUIKSHANK
Title	BUILDING MATERIALS AND CONSTRUCTION QUARTERLY REVIEW, quarterly. 1980-
Coverage	Summary of construction output plus an industry outlook. Also includes relative price performance, stock market assessment, profits, overseas markets and share price graphs and statistics.
Contents & Origin of Statistics	Tables per issue: 40-50.
Comments	Other reports produced on various industrial sectors
Response	1984
Availability	Clients
Cost	Free
Address	Piercy House, 7 Copthall Avenue, London EC2R 7BE
Telephone	01 588 2800; Telex: 888397/8
Contact	F. Wellings, Construction Analyst

602

Originator	LAING & CRUIKSHANK
Title	ECONOMIC AND MONETARY REVIEW, monthly. May 1977-
Coverage	Includes summary UK economic forecast for up to 21 years ahead and detailed forecasts for various economic variables by quarter up to 2 years ahead. Plus sections on the international framework the equity market and gilt-edged market.
Contents & Origin of Statistics	Tables per issue: 30-40. Own research 50%, Government statistics 50%. Supporting text 45%
Currency	2 months
Response	1984
Availability	General
Cost	£250 (Free to Clients)
Address	Piercy House, 7 Copthall Avenue, London EC2R 7BE
Telephone	01 588 2800; Telex: 888397/8
Contact	M. Roberts, Senior Economist

603

Originator	LAING & CRUIKSHANK
Title	FORECASTS OF ECONOMIC INDICATORS, monthly. May 1977-
Coverage	Summary forecasts for hire purchase, producer prices, output, retail sales, earnings, PSBR and overseas trade.
Contents & Origin of Statistics	Tables per issue: 2. Own research 50%, Government statistics 50%.
Comments	Statistics produced on a sheet of A4 paper.
Currency	2 weeks
Response	1984
Availability	General
Cost	Free
Address	Piercy House, 7 Copthall Avenue, London EC2R 7BE
Telephone	01 588 2800; Telex: 888397/8
Contact	M. Roberts, Senior Economist

604

Originator	LEASING DIGEST
Title	UK INTEREST AND LEASING RATES, monthly in a monthly journal
Coverage	Interest rates and leasing rates in London with minimum and average leasing rate figures
Contents & Origin of Statistics	Tables per issue: 3
Comments	Also publish an annual review of the world leasing business and figures on vehicle second hand values and IBM computer second hand values.
Currency	2 weeks
Response	1984
Availability	General
Cost	£45
ISSN	0309 5258
Address	Hawkins Publishers Ltd, Laxfield House, 2 Church St, Coggeshall Essex CO6 1TV
Telephone	0376 62262
Contact	The Editor

605

Originator	LEATHER
Title	MARKET REPORT, monthly in a monthly journal
Coverage	Data on slaughterings and hide prices.
Contents & Origin of Statistics	Tables per issue: 1.
Comments	Also contains international price of hides etc
Currency	2-3 weeks
Response	1984
Availability	General
Cost	£35 or £2.80 for a single copy
Address	Benn Publications Ltd, Benn House, Sovereign Way, Tonbridge, Kent TN9 1UX
Telephone	0732 364422; Telex: 95132
Contact	I.R. Howie, Editor

606

Originator	LEATHER PRODUCERS' ASSOCIATION
Title	UNTITLED, bi-annual
Coverage	Data collected from members on number of employees, hours and earnings.
Contents & Origin of Statistics	Tables per issue: Own research 100%
Response	1983
Availability	Members
Address	Leather Trade House, 9 St. Thomas St, London SE1 9SA
Telephone	01 407 1522/4
Contact	J.A. Cox, Secretary

607

Originator	LEEDS CHAMBER OF COMMERCE
Title	LOCAL ECONOMIC SURVEY, quarterly
Coverage	Survey of local member companies.
Contents & Origin of Statistics	Tables per issue: Own research 100%. Supporting text 40%
Comments	Issued in the form of a press release.
Response	1984
Availability	Members

Cost	£6.50
Address	Commerce House, St Albans Place, Wade Lane, Leeds 2
Telephone	0532 430491; Telex: 55293
Contact	Ron Taylor or Mary Walker

608

Originator	LEEDS PERMANENT BUILDING SOCIETY
Title	HOUSING FINANCE, quarterly. March 1980-
Coverage	Average house prices by type of property and region.
Contents & Origin of Statistics	Tables per issue: 2. Own research 100%. Supporting text 50%
Currency	1 month
Response	1984
Availability	General
Cost	Free
Address	72 The Headrow, Leeds LS1 1NS
Telephone	0532 438181
Contact	Mr P.J. Green, Economist

609

Originator	LEICESTERSHIRE COUNTY COUNCIL
Title	FACTS, FIGURES AND LEICESTERSHIRE, quarterly
Coverage	A number of different bulletins issued on such topics as unemployment, population, production.
Contents & Origin of Statistics	Tables per issue: Varies
Response	1984
Availability	General
Cost	Free
Address	County Hall, Glenfield, Leicester LE3 8RJ
Telephone	0533 871313; Telex: 341478
Contact	Graham Winter, Senior Planning Officer.

610

Originator	LEISURE CONSULTANTS
Title	LEISURE FORECASTS, annual (half-yearly update). Septembe 1983-

Coverage	All leisure markets covered, eg media leisure, hobbies and pastimes, entertainment and sport, catering and holidays. These appear in 5 separate reports with a general overview. Forecasts for 5 years ahead for consumer spending and prices and key market indicators.
Contents & Origin of Statistics	Tables per issue: 28 (per sector report). Own research 80%, Other non official source 10%, Government statistics 10%. Supporting text 50%
Currency	1-2 months
Response	1984
Availability	General
Cost	Cost (pa):£200 (1 sector). Reduced rates available for academic institutions
Address	Lint Growis, Foxearth, Sudbury, Suffolk
Telephone	0787 75777
Contact	Bill Martin/Sandra Mason, Principals

611

Originator	LIBRARY ASSOCIATION RECORD
Title	AVERAGE BOOK PRICES, 3 times a year in a monthly journal
Coverage	Average book prices by type and subject of book based on all works listed in the British National Bibliography.
Contents & Origin of Statistics	Tables per issue: 2. Non official source 100%
Comments	Also publish periodical prices data - see other entry
Currency	2 months
Response	1984
Availability	General
Cost	Free to Library Association members, £39.50p to others
ISSN	0024 2195
Address	The Library Association, 7 Ridgmount St, London WC1E 7AE
Telephone	01 636 7543; Telex: 21897
Contact	The Editor

612

Originator	LIBRARY ASSOCIATION RECORD
Title	PERIODICAL PRICES, annual in a monthly journal
Coverage	Average prices of periodicals analysed by subject and country of origin and based on a survey by Blackwell's Periodical Division.
Contents & Origin of Statistics	Tables per issue: 3. Non official source 100%

Comments	Survey usually appears in May issue. Also publish book price data - see previous entry
Response	1984
Availability	General
Cost	Free to Library Association members, £39.50 to others
ISSN	0024 2195
Address	The Library Association, 7 Ridgmount St, London WC1E 7AE
Telephone	01 636 7543; Telex: 21897
Contact	The Editor

613

Originator	LIFE OFFICES ASSOCIATION
Title	LIFE INSURANCE IN THE UNITED KINGDOM, annual
Coverage	Summary of the life insurance business plus details of new individual business, individual business in force, pension and life insurance schemes, permanent health insurances, income and expenditure and life insurance funds.
Contents & Origin of Statistics	Tables per issue: 25. Own research 100%. Supporting text 25%
Comments	Published jointly with the Associated Scottish Life Offices and the Industrial Life Offices Association. List of contributors to the survey is given.
Currency	8 months
Response	1984
Availability	General
Cost	Free
ISSN	0265 7341
Address	Aldermary House, Queen St, London EC4N 1TP
Telephone	01 236 1101; Telex: 885004
Contact	G.G. Luffrum, Assistant Secretary

614

Originator	LIFE OFFICES ASSOCIATION
Title	QUARTERLY NEW INDIVIDUAL BUSINESS FIGURES quarterly. 1978-
Coverage	New business for ordinary individual life assurances.
Contents & Origin of Statistics	Tables per issue: 2. Own research 100%. Supporting text 30%
Comments	Issued in the form of a press release and published jointly with th Associated Scottish Life Offices and the Industrial Life Office Association
Currency	5 weeks

Response	1984
Availability	General
Cost	Free
Address	Aldermary House, Queen St, London EC4N 1TP
Telephone	01 236 1101; Telex: 885004
Contact	G.G. Luffrum, Assistant Secretary

615

Originator	LIGHT METAL FOUNDERS' ASSOCIATION
Title	MONTHLY TONNAGE DESPATCH STATISTICS, monthly. 1977-
Coverage	Aggregate monthly despatches by members, shown by process type (eg sand casting, gravity diecasting, low pressure and high pressure diecasting) with a quarterly analysis of trends.
Contents & Origin of Statistics	Tables per issue: 1. Own research 100%. Supporting text 10%
Currency	2 months
Response	1984
Availability	Members
Cost	Free
Address	136 Hagley Rd, Edgbaston, Birmingham B16 9PN
Telephone	021 454 4141 ; Telex: 336993
Contact	Dr R.F. Smart, Research Manager

616

Originator	LIVERPOOL COTTON ASSOCIATION LTD.
Title	WEEKLY RAW COTTON REPORT, weekly
Coverage	Liverpool market for cotton, UK cotton supply and consumption, world futures markets, conference freight rates to Liverpool, world raw cotton markets.
Contents & Origin of Statistics	Tables per issue: 12. Unstated: 100%.
Currency	Varies
Response	1984
Availability	General
Cost	£16.50 (£11 to members)
Address	620 Cotton Exchange Building, Edmund St, Liverpool L3 9LH
Telephone	051 236 6041; Telex: 627849
Contact	Mr H.L. Billington, Arbitration Manager

617

Originator	LIVESTOCK AUCTIONEERS' MARKET COMMITTEE FOR ENGLAND AND WALES
Title	THROUGHPUT AND TURNOVER LIVESTOCK AUCTION MARKETS, annual. 1975-
Coverage	Sales of cattle, sheep, pigs and calves for store and for slaughter. 5 years of data given.
Contents & Origin of Statistics	Tables per issue: 3. Own research 100%. Supporting text 100%
Response	1984
Availability	Members and some others
Cost	Free
Address	Norden House, Basing View, Basingstoke, Hants, RG21 2HN
Telephone	04862 64934
Contact	A.W. Carter, Secretary

618

Originator	LIVINGSTON DEVELOPMENT CORPORATION
Title	FACTS AND FIGURES, annual
Coverage	Population, housing, employment, industrial premises, shops, offices, education and leisure.
Contents & Origin of Statistics	Tables per issue: 12. Unstated 100%.
Response	1984
Availability	General
Cost	Free
Address	Livingston, West Lothian, Scotland
Telephone	0506 414177; Telex: 727178

619

Originator	LIVINGSTON DEVELOPMENT CORPORATION
Title	QUARTERLY STATISTICAL ABSTRACT, quarterly
Coverage	Population, housing, industrial premises, shops, offices and employment.
Contents & Origin of Statistics	Tables per issue: 6. Unstated 100%
Response	1984
Availability	General

Cost	Free
Address	Livingston, West Lothian, Scotland
Telephone	0506 414177; Telex: 727178

620

Originator	LLOYD INCOMES RESEARCH
Title	MERCHANT AND INTERNATIONAL BANKING SURVEY, annual
Coverage	A comparison of pay and employment conditions in London-based merchant and international banks. Analysis by type, size and location of companies.
Contents & Origin of Statistics	Tables per issue: 72. Own research 100%. Supporting text 10%
Comments	Gives details of techniques used in compilation.
Response	1984
Address	11 John Princes St, London W1M 9HB
Telephone	01 409 2141; Telex: 269550

621

Originator	LLOYD INCOMES RESEARCH
Title	REWARDS OF MANAGEMENT, annual. 1975-
Coverage	Survey of UK management pay and employment conditions in industry and commerce. Analysis by type, size and location of companies and the extent of supplementary income and company cars is detailed against the various salary levels for each job.
Contents & Origin of Statistics	Tables per issue: 80. Own research 100%. Supporting text 10%
Comments	Gives details of techniques used in compilation.
Response	1984
Address	11 John Princes St, London W1M 9HB
Telephone	01 409 2141; Telex: 269550

622

Originator	LLOYDS BANK LTD.
Title	BRITISH ECONOMY IN FIGURES, annual
Coverage	National income, production, balance of payments, adult earnings, public expenditure and purchasing power of the £.

Contents &	Tables per issue: 12.
Origin of	
Statistics	
Comments	Similarly they produce 'Scottish economy in figures' and the 'Welsh economy in figures'.
Currency	3 months
Response	1984
Availability	General
Cost	Free
Address	Group Economics Dept, 71 Lombard St, London EC3P 3BS
Telephone	01 626 1500; Telex: 2219
Contact	Mr Whitley, Group Economics

623

Originator	LLOYDS BANK LTD.
Title	ECONOMIC PROFILE OF BRITAIN, annual
Coverage	As indicated by title.
Contents &	Tables per issue: 21. Own research 10%, Other non official source
Origin of	20%, Government statistics 70%. Supporting text 65%
Statistics	
Currency	3 months
Response	1984
Availability	General
Cost	Free
Address	Group Economics Dept, 71 Lombard St, London EC3P 3BS
Telephone	01 626 1500; Telex: 2219
Contact	Mr Whitley, Group Economics

624

Originator	LONDON BANKS' PERSONNEL MANAGEMENT GROUP
Title	CLERICAL AND SUPERVISORY SALARY SURVEY, annual
Coverage	Data on 126 non-managerial positions in the following functions: banking, accounts, secretarial, administration, communications, data processing and catering.
Contents &	Tables per issue: Own research 100%
Origin of	
Statistics	
Response	1983
Availability	Participants in survey
Cost	£55
Address	129 Windmill Street, Gravesend,Kent DA12 1BL

Telephone　0474 358383
Contact　J. Clark on 01 621 1111

625

Originator　LONDON BANKS' PERSONNEL MANAGEMENT GROUP

Title　MANAGEMENT SALARIES AND BENEFITS SURVEY, annual

Coverage　Data on 26 management positions including foreign exchange and money management, lending, corporate finance, investment, accounts, operation and administration.

Contents & Origin of Statistics　Tables per issue: Own research 100%

Response　1984
Availability　Participants in survey
Cost　£55
Address　129 Windmill Street, Gravesend, Kent DA12 1BL
Telephone　0474 358383
Contact　J. Clark on 01 621 1111

626

Originator　LONDON BUSINESS SCHOOL

Title　ECONOMIC OUTLOOK, monthly
Coverage　3 major forecasts and 9 intermediate forecasts releases per annum. Forecast summary followed by forecast in detail and topical articles. Forecasts up to 3 years ahead.

Contents & Origin of Statistics　Tables per issue: 50-70. Supporting text 50%

Comments　Published by Gower Publishing, Gower House, Croft Rd, Aldershot GU11 3HR. LBS also publish, through Gower, an international publication 'Exchange rate outlook'.

Currency　1 month
Response　1984
Availability　General
Cost　£95
Address　Sussex Place, Regent's Park, London NW1 4SA
Telephone　01 262 5050; Telex: 27461
Contact　Bill Robinson

627

Originator	LONDON BUSINESS SCHOOL
Title	FINANCIAL OUTLOOK, quarterly
Coverage	Four-year forecasts of financial flows in the UK economy and for 9 sectors within it. A breakdown of assets held by each sector is also given.
Contents & Origin of Statistics	Tables per issue: 50-60. Supporting text 40%
Comments	Published by Gower Publishing, Gower House, Croft Rd, Aldershot GU11 3HR. LBS also publish, through Gower, an international publication 'Exchange Rate Outlook'.
Currency	2-3 months
Response	1984
Availability	General
Cost	£370
Address	Sussex Place, Regent's Park, London NW1 4SA
Telephone	01 262 5050; Telex: 27461
Contact	Giles Keating

628

Originator	LONDON CHAMBER OF COMMERCE AND INDUSTRY
Title	LCCI ECONOMIC REPORT AND SURVEY, quarterly
Coverage	General economic review of London and the South-East
Contents & Origin of Statistics	Tables per issue: 30. Own research 90%. Supporting text 50%
Currency	1 month
Response	1984
Availability	General
Cost	£17.50, free to participants
Address	69 Cannon St London EC4N 5AB
Telephone	01 248 4444
Contact	Richard Walsh, Research Officer

629

Originator	LONDON COMMODITY EXCHANGE NEWSLETTER
Title	TURNOVER STATISTICS, quarterly in a quarterly journal. 1888-
Coverage	CCE Turnover statistics, high and low trades, annual turnover in lots, non-transferable options and the total number of lots registered from 1969-1983.

Contents & Origin of Statistics	Tables per issue: 6. Non official source 100%

Comments	Figures for tables supplied by the ICCH Ltd
Currency	2 weeks
Response	1984
Availability	General
Cost	Free
Address	London Commodity Exchange Company Ltd, Ceral House, 58 Mark Lane, London EC3R 7NE
Telephone	01 481 2080; Telex: 884370
Contact	Joanne Healy, Public Relations Assistant

630

Originator	LONDON CORN CIRCULAR

Title	MARKET PRICES, weekly in a weekly journal. 1843-
Coverage	Prices of cereals and other crops. Some forecasts of future prices.
Contents & Origin of Statistics	Tables per issue: Varies

Currency	Varies
Response	1984
Availability	General
Cost	£35
Address	Dittonfern Ltd, 54 Wentworth Crescent, Ash Vale, nr Aldershot, Hampshire GU12 5LF
Telephone	0252 29082
Contact	D.S. Alexander, Editor

631

Originator	LONDON TOURIST BOARD

Title	LONDON'S TOURIST STATISTICS, annual
Coverage	Facts about London, volume and value of tourism, purpose of visit and accommodation used, hotel occupancy, known stock of tourist accommmodation, day trips to London and visitors to selected attractions.
Contents & Origin of Statistics	Tables per issue: 25. Own research 55%, Other non official source 5%, Government statistics 40%. Supporting text 5%

Currency	8 months
Response	1984
Availability	General
Cost	£3
Address	26 Grosvenor Gardens, London SW1W 0DU

Telephone	01 730 3450; Telex: 919041
Contact	R.A. Chenery, Manager of Resource Development

632

Originator	LONDON TRANSPORT EXECUTIVE
Title	ANNUAL REPORT AND ACCOUNTS, annual. 1983-
Coverage	Basically annual report but includes much data in the text, for example passenger miles, waiting times, cost, commuting, traffic operations, number of buses, summary of underground statistics.
Contents & Origin of Statistics	Tables per issue: 10. Own research 100%. Supporting text 50%
Comments	Issue a summary 'Report Extra' which is free
Response	1984
Availability	General
Cost	£1
ISSN	0308 1615
Address	55 Broadway, London SW1H 0BD
Telephone	01 222 5600; Telex: 893633
Contact	A.G. Shaw, Assistant Secretary

633

Originator	LONDON WEEKEND TELEVISION
Title	MARKETING MANUAL, annual. 1980-
Coverage	Population; TV equipment, durables and vehicles; incomes, savings and expenditure; education and employment; leisure; retailing; population distribution; standard of living for the television area.
Contents & Origin of Statistics	Tables per issue: 23. Non official source 75%, Government statistics 25%. Supporting text 5%
Comments	Produce monthly 'Marketing Review' which occasionally features results of statistical surveys.
Response	1984
Availability	Controlled circulation at their discretion
Cost	Free
Address	South Bank Television Centre, Kent House, Upper Ground, London SE1 9LT
Telephone	01 261 3137/2; Telex: 918123
Contact	R.D. Byatt, Research Department

634

Originator	LYONS MAID LTD

Title	BRITAIN'S ICE CREAM BUSINESS, annual. 1980-
Coverage	3 sectors:- confectionery lines eg cones, wafers, lollies; grocery products eg packs; in-hand and bulk products. Examines market for each.

Contents & Origin of Statistics	Tables per issue: 25. Own research 20%, Other non official source 60%, Government statistics 20%. Supporting text 50%

Comments	Produced by Chambers Cox and Company
Response	1984
Availability	General
Cost	£20
Address	Glacier House, Brook Green, London W6 7BT
Telephone	01 603 2040; Telex: 22420
Contact	D.Brown, Public Relations Manager

635

Originator	MACHINE TOOL TRADES ASSOCIATION

Title	BASIC FACTS, annual. 1977-
Coverage	Summary information on the machine tool industry.

Contents & Origin of Statistics	Tables per issue: 4. Non official source 20%, Government statistics 80%. Supporting text 20%

Comments	Produced in pocket book format.
Currency	6 months
Response	1984
Availability	General
Cost	Free
Address	62 Bayswater Rd, London W2 3PH
Telephone	01 402 6671; Telex: 27829
Contact	G.J. Shortell, Marketing Department

636

Originator	MACHINE TOOL TRADES ASSOCIATION

Title	MACHINE TOOL STATISTICS, annual. 1980-
Coverage	Machine tool production, orders, imports, exports, population, prices and employment.

Contents & Origin of Statistics	Tables per issue: 20. Non official source 20%, Government statistics 80%. Supporting text 10%

Currency	6 months
Response	1984
Availability	General
Cost	£15
Address	62 Bayswater Rd, London W2 3PH
Telephone	01 402 6671; Telex: 27829
Contact	G.J. Shortell, Marketing Department

637

Originator	MAIL ORDER TRADERS ASSOCIATION
Title	TURNOVER FIGURES, annual
Coverage	Mail order sales and the share of total retail and of non-food retail. Also general economic data. Some estimates for the coming year.
Contents & Origin of Statistics	Tables per issue: 3. Unstated 100%.
Comments	In the form of an information sheet.
Response	1984
Availability	General
Cost	Free
Address	25 Castle St, Liverpool L2 4TD
Telephone	051 236 7581; Telex 628169
Contact	K.M. Tamlin, Secretary

638

Originator	MAN-MADE FIBRES INDUSTRY TRAINING ADVISORY BOARD
Title	REPORT AND ACCOUNTS, annual. 1982-
Coverage	Production data for the industry, numbers employed in occupational groups, new entrants to the workforce, apprentice data, and finance.
Contents & Origin of Statistics	Tables per issue: 6. Own research 100%. Supporting text 60%
Currency	4-5 months
Response	1984
Availability	General
Cost	Free
Address	Langwood House, 63-81 High St, Rickmansworth, Herts WD3 1EQ
Telephone	0923 778371
Contact	Mr. D.W. Ashby, General Manager

639

Originator	MANAGEMENT PERSONNEL
Title	SALARY SURVEY, annual. 1972-
Coverage	Survey of 50 companies in the South Eastern home counties. Salaries and fringe benefits for a wide range of management and administrative positions. Size of sample and age group given.
Contents & Origin of Statistics	Tables per issue: 15. Own research 100%. Supporting text 60%
Comments	Good notes on sampling.
Currency	8-12 weeks
Response	1984
Availability	General
Cost	£35
Address	York House, Chertsey St, Guildford, Surrey GU1 4ET
Telephone	0483 64857
Contact	L.F. Lock, Director

640

Originator	MANCHESTER POLYTECHNIC
Title	HOLLINGS APPAREL INDUSTRY REVIEW, 3 times a year
Coverage	Includes data on production, expenditure, prices, sales, employment unemployment, international trade, turnover, wages, stoppages, capital and finance and regional data for the clothing industry.
Contents & Origin of Statistics	Tables per issue: 61. Government statistics 100%
Response	1983
Availability	General
Cost	£15
Address	Hollings Faculty, Department of Clothing Design and Technology, Old Hall Lane, Manchester M14 6HR
Telephone	061 224 7341
Contact	Richard Jones, Editor

641

Originator	MANPOWER LTD
Title	SURVEY OF EMPLOYMENT PROSPECTS, quarterly.
Coverage	Forecasts of employment by industry and region based on the stated intentions of approximately 1288 British organisations. Also covers special topics occasionally.

Contents & Origin of Statistics	Tables per issue: 4. Own research 100%. Supporting text 50%

Currency	2-3 months
Response	1984
Availability	General
Cost	Free
ISSN	0260 8146
Address	Manpower House, 270-272 High St, Slough SL1 1LJ
Telephone	0753 73111; Telex: 848704
Contact	Mr A.A. Hoskins, Marketing Manager

642

Originator	MANUFACTURING CHEMIST
Title	AEROSOL REVIEW, annual and as a separate item from the journal
Coverage	Listing of all aerosols filled in the United Kingdom and imported. Also lists all types of aerosols filled by company, brand name, type of aerosol etc.
Contents & Origin of Statistics	Tables per issue: 2. Non official source 100%
Response	1984
Availability	General
Cost	£16
ISSN	0568 062X
Address	Morgan-Grampian (Process Press) Ltd, 30 Calderwood St, London SE18 69H
Telephone	01 855 7777; Telex: 896238
Contact	Neil Esberg, Editor

643

Originator	MARKET AND OPINION RESEARCH INTERNATIONAL (MORI)
Title	BRITISH PUBLIC OPINION, ten issues per year
Coverage	A digest of MORI polls published plus a summary of polls published by other polling companies.
Contents & Origin of Statistics	Tables per issue: 20-25. Own research 100%. Supporting text 60%.
Currency	1 month
Response	1984
Availability	General
Cost	£50

ISSN	0265 6175
Address	32 Old Queen St, London SW1H 9HP
Telephone	01 222 0232 ; Telex: 295230
Contact	Theresa Moss, Research Executive

644

Originator	MARKET ASSESSMENT INFORMATION SERVICES
Title	GROCERY AND CHEMIST MARKET ASSESSMENT, quarterly
Coverage	100 food and toiletries market survey reports produced annually.
Contents & Origin of Statistics	Tables per issue: Own research + other non official source + government statistics 100%
Comments	Part of BLA Management Services Group
Response	1983
Availability	General
Cost	£460
Address	2 Duncan Terrace, London N1 8BZ
Telephone	01 278 9517/8
Contact	Ian Bramble

645

Originator	MARKET ASSESSMENT INFORMATION SERVICES
Title	NON FOOD MARKET ASSESSMENT, quarterly
Coverage	96 non food market survey reports produced annually. Each issue contains 24 surveys.
Contents & Origin of Statistics	Tables per issue: Own research + government statistics 100%
Comments	Part of BLA Management Services Group
Response	1983
Availability	General
Cost	£500
Address	2 Duncan Terrace, London N1 8BZ
Telephone	01 278 9517/8
Contact	Ian Bramble

646

Originator	MARKET LOCATION LTD
Title	STATISTICAL ANALYSES OF BRITISH INDUSTRY, irregular

Coverage	Includes maps showing distribution of industry and 3 industrial profiles for each of 73 separate geographic areas. Industry in each area analysed by activity and size of unit (numbers of employees) and indexed to show any divergence from national average. Indexed tables for 10 economic regions show how these diverge from national average.
Contents & Origin of Statistics	Tables per issue: 225. Own research 100%
Response	1983
Availability	General
Cost	£70
Address	17 Waterloo Place, Warwick St, Leamington Spa, Warwicks CV32 5LA
Telephone	0926 34235
Contact	Mr. Kendall

647

Originator	MARKET STUDIES INTERNATIONAL
Title	UK TRADE DEVELOPMENTS SURVEYS, annual
Coverage	Individual reports on air pumps, compressors and hydraulic equipment; industrial fasteners; springs and wire; ferrous and non-ferrous valves. Production, imports and exports.
Response	1983
Availability	General
Cost	£68 each
Address	Inter Company Comparisons Ltd, 28-42 Banner St, London EC1Y 8QE
Telephone	01 250 3922
Contact	V.G. Cumming, Director

648

Originator	MARKETING
Title	MEDIAFACT, weekly in a weekly journal
Coverage	General data on the media industry, e.g. radio listening, readership of national newspapers, advertising trends etc.
Contents & Origin of Statistics	Tables per issue: 2-3. Non official source 100%
Currency	Varies
Response	1984
Availability	General
Cost	£40
Address	Haymarket Magazines Ltd, 22 Lancaster Gate, London W2 3LY

Telephone	01 402 4200
Contact	Ann MacDonald, Libraries

649

Originator	MARKETING IMPROVEMENTS
Title	SURVEY OF INCENTIVES, biennial
Coverage	Covers incentives in use, reasons for use, and results for salesmen.
Contents & Origin of Statistics	Tables per issue: Own research 100%. Supporting text 50%
Response	1983
Availability	General
Cost	Free
Address	Ulster House, 17 Ulster Terrace, Outer Circle, Regents Park, London NW1P 4PJ
Contact	Robin J. Birn

650

Originator	MARKETING WEEK
Title	DATABANK, weekly in a weekly journal
Coverage	General economic trends, consumer expenditure, top advertising spenders, advertising revenue etc.
Contents & Origin of Statistics	Tables per issue: 9. Non official source 80%, Government statistics 20%
Currency	Varies
Response	1984
Availability	General
Cost	Free controlled circulation but available to others at £40
Address	Marketing Week Communications Ltd, 60 Kingly St, London W1R 5LH
Telephone	01 439 4222; Telex: 261352
Contact	Martin Shelley, Information Services

651

Originator	MARKETPOWER LTD
Title	CATERING INDUSTRY POPULATION PROFILE, monthly

Coverage	Data covering 5 sections of the industry: market structure divided into 17 main sectors and a further 70 sub-sectors; regional information giving the distribution of 56 sub-sectors across 14 regions by outlet type; food purchases by market sector; group purchasing by catering groups and independent outlets; distribution trends in the regions. The data is based on approximately 350 interviews per month.
Contents & Origin of Statistics	Tables per issue: 46pgs. Own research 100%
Comments	Also offer a general information service known as the 'Catering Industry Database'.
Currency	1 month
Response	1984
Availability	General
Cost	£400
Address	Capital House, Market Place, London W3 6AL
Telephone	01 993 5998-9/5191
Contact	Peter Backman or Simon Southern

652

Originator	MARKS, ALFRED BUREAU LTD
Title	SURVEY OF FRINGE BENEFITS FOR OFFICE STAFF, annual. 1975-
Coverage	Monitors changes in legislation and company practice concerning non-wage benefits to office staff. Covers pensions, life and medical insurance, holidays, meal facilities and bonus incentive schemes.
Contents & Origin of Statistics	Tables per issue: 46. Own research 100%
Response	1983
Availability	General
Cost	£48, £24 to participating companies
Address	ADIA House, 84-86 Regent St, London W1R 5PA
Telephone	01 437 7855; Telex: 298240
Contact	Beverley Howard, Statistical Services Division

653

Originator	MARKS, ALFRED BUREAU LTD
Title	SURVEY OF SECRETARIAL AND CLERICAL SALARIES, quarterly. 1967-

Coverage   Salary figures for 8 categories of staff and 6 age groups covering Central London, suburban London and various centres in the UK. Also gives movements in turnover and demand patterns and an attitude survey on matters affecting employers of office staff.

Contents & Tables per issue: 32. Own research 100%
Origin of
Statistics

Response   1983
Availability General
Cost   £48
Address   ADIA House, 84-86 Regent St, London W1R 5PA
Telephone   01 437 7855; Telex: 298240
Contact   Beverley Howard, Statistical Services Division

654

Originator MARKS, ALFRED BUREAU LTD

Title   WORD PROCESSING SALARY SURVEY, bi-annual
Coverage   Covers salaries and conditions of employment of personnel in the U.K. together with types and locations of installations, staff turnover and training. Each issue contains a subsidiary report on matters relating to the employment of W.P. staff.

Contents & Tables per issue: Own research 100%
Origin of
Statistics

Response   1983
Availability General
Cost   £40, £16 to participating companies
Address   ADIA House, 84-86 Regent St, London W1R 5PA
Telephone   01 437 7855; Telex: 298240
Contact   Beverley Howard, Statistical Services Division

655

Originator MCARDLE, JAMES AND ASSOCIATES

Title   AUTOTREND UK ANNUAL REVIEW, annual
Coverage   Review of the passenger car market and industry in UK. Covers suppliers' strengths and weaknesses in the British Market; market share implications of recent and imminent model launches; model pricing strategies; domestic producers' sourcing policies and production plans; trends in the company car market; residual values of cars; Japanese producers' market shares in UK compared with those in other European markets.
Comments   This title now suspended but a revamped publication is due shortly.
Response   1983
Availability General

Cost	£65
Address	48 Grafton Way, London W1P 5LB
Telephone	01 388 4932
Contact	Above address

656

Originator	MCCARDLE, JAMES AND ASSOCIATES
Title	AUTOTREND UK FORECAST MODEL, quarterly
Coverage	Model for forecasting short term demand for passenger cars in the UK. Incorporates monthly registrations from January 1970. Generates forecasts of quarterly demand for one year ahead. Also analyses trends in car production and economic developments affecting demand for new cars.
Comments	This title now suspended but a revamped publication is due shortly.
Response	1983
Availability	General
Cost	£95
Address	48 Grafton Way, London W1P 5LB
Telephone	01 388 4932
Contact	Above address

657

Originator	MCCARTHY INFORMATION LTD
Title	FT STATS FICHE, twice a week
Coverage	Statistics from the Financial Times produced on fiche.
Contents & Origin of Statistics	Tables per issue: Varies. Non official source 100%
Currency	2 or 3 days
Response	1984
Availability	General
Cost	£253 + VAT
Address	Manor House, Ash Walk, Warminster, Wiltshire
Telephone	0985 215151
Contact	Above address

658

Originator	MEAT TRADES JOURNAL
Title	MARKETS SECTION, weekly in a weekly journal. 1965-
Coverage	Production and stock data on the meat trade plus live, wholesale and retail price trends.

Contents & Origin of Statistics	Tables per issue: 20-25. Own research 30%, Other non official source 30%, Government statistics 40%
Currency	7 days
Response	1984
Availability	General
Cost	£23 or 35p for a single issue
Address	International Thomson organisation, 93-99 Goswell Rd, London EC1
Telephone	01 253 9533; Telex: 894461
Contact	Clive Still, Markets Editor

659

Originator	MECHANICAL ENGINEERING NEWS
Title	SALARY SURVEY, annual in a monthly journal
Coverage	Salary survey of the members of the Institution of Mechanical Engineers with data by type of member, sector of work and location. Other data on fringe benefits, overtime, work abroad etc.
Contents & Origin of Statistics	Tables per issue: 23. Own research 100%
Comments	Not published every year up to 1983.
Currency	3-4 months
Response	1984
Availability	General
Cost	£19
ISSN	0306 9540
Address	Mechanical Engineering Publications, PO Box 24, Northgate Avenue, Bury St Edmunds, Suffolk IP32 6BW
Telephone	0284 63277; Telex: 817376
Contact	Above address

660

Originator	MEDIA EXPENDITURE ANALYSIS LTD (MEAL)
Title	ADVERTISEMENT ANALYSIS, monthly
Coverage	A detailed description of advertising giving a record of each advertisement placed in the media during the month. Includes total expenditure and sub totals for press and television for each brand and product group.
Contents & Origin of Statistics	Tables per issue: Own research 100%
Comments	Various specialised services and microfiche and on-line facilities also available. Expenditure by individual agencies also available.

Currency	Same month as publication month
Response	1984
Availability	General
Cost	£670 (reduced rates available for more than one subscription)
Address	63 St Martins Lane, London WC2N 4JT
Telephone	01 240 1903/6
Contact	Above address

661

Originator	MEDIA EXPENDITURE ANALYSIS LTD (MEAL)
Title	BRAND EXPENDITURE BY AREA, monthly
Coverage	Data on the attribution of brand expenditure by area for TV, press and total expenditure. It provides a guide to the amount of advertising weight in each area. The areas are defined by TV regions and the allocation of press expenditure is according to JICNARS readership profiles.
Contents & Origin of Statistics	Tables per issue: Own research 100%
Comments	Various specialised services and microfiche and on-line facilities also available. Expenditure by individual agencies also available.
Currency	Same month as month of publication
Response	1984
Availability	General
Cost	£670 (reduced rates for more than one subscription)
Address	63 St Martins Lane, London WC2R 1HH
Telephone	01 240 1903/6
Contact	Above address

662

Originator	MEDIA EXPENDITURE ANALYSIS LTD (MEAL)
Title	BRAND EXPENDITURE BY MEDIA GROUP (PRESS), monthly
Coverage	Data on the allocation of brand expenditure across the various media groups in the press. Data for each brand on the latest month and the last 12 months.
Contents & Origin of Statistics	Tables per issue: Own research 100%
Comments	Various other specialised service and microfiche and on-line facilities also available. Expenditure by individual agencies also available.
Currency	Same month as publication month
Response	1984
Availability	General

Cost	£670 (reduced rates for more than one subscription)
Address	63 St Martins Lane, London WC2N 4JT
Telephone	01 240 1903/6
Contact	Above address

663

Originator	MEDIA EXPENDITURE ANALYSIS LTD (MEAL)
Title	BRAND EXPENDITURE BY MEDIA GROUP (TV), monthly
Coverage	Gives a detailed analysis of television expenditure and total press expenditure. Data for each brand on latest month and previous 12 months for each television area with a profile as a percentage of the television total.
Contents & Origin of Statistics	Tables per issue: Own research 100%
Comments	Various other specialised services and microfiche and on-line facilities available. Expenditure by individual agencies also available.
Currency	Same month as publication month
Response	1984
Availability	General
Cost	£670 (reduced rates for more than one subscription)
Address	63 St Martins Lane, London WC2N 4JT
Telephone	01 240 1903/6
Contact	Above address

664

Originator	MEDIA EXPENDITURE ANALYSIS LTD (MEAL)
Title	BRAND EXPENDITURE BY MEDIUM, monthly
Coverage	Standard monthly product group reports showing expenditure for each of the latest 12 months and total for the period. Expenditure in television and the press is broken down and a percentage profile gives the distribution of expenditure during the period.
Contents & Origin of Statistics	Tables per issue: Own research 100%
Comments	Various specialised services and microfiche and on-line facilities also available. Expenditure by individual agencies also available.
Currency	Same month as publication month
Response	1984
Availability	General
Cost	£670 (reduced rates for more than one subscription)
Address	63 St Martins Lane, London WC2N 4JT

Telephone	01 240 1903/6
Contact	Above address

665

Originator	MEDIA EXPENDITURE ANALYSIS LTD (MEAL)
Title	MEAL QUARTERLY DIGEST OF ADVERTISING EXPEND-ITURE, quarterly
Coverage	Advertising expenditure by brand within product groups. Each brand is attributed to one of 350 product groups which in turn are classified in 22 categories. Each year 2 million advertisements are analysed and all brands spending at least £2,500 a month are included. A list of the media coverage is given in each issue.
Contents & Origin of Statistics	Tables per issue: 113pgs. Own research 100%.
Comments	Various specialised services and microfiche and on-line services also available. Expenditure by individual agencies also available.
Currency	Same quarter as publication quarter
Response	1984
Availability	General
Cost	£350
Address	63 St Martins Lane, London WC2N 4JT
Telephone	01 240 1903/6
Contact	Above address

666

Originator	MEDIA EXPENDITURE ANALYSIS LTD (MEAL)
Title	SPECIALIST MARKET MONITORS, monthly
Coverage	Data on advertising expenditures by medium in 8 areas: advertising trade press, agricultural products, commercial vehicles, computers and business equipment, equestrian publications, licensed trade, telecommunications, boats and yachting.
Contents & Origin of Statistics	Tables per issue: Own research 100%
Comments	Various specialised services and microfiche and on-line services also available.
Currency	Same month as month of publication
Response	1984
Availability	General
Cost	£670 for a single product group (reduced rates for more than one subscription)
Address	63 St Martins Lane, London WC2N 4JT

Telephone	01 240 1903/6
Contact	Above address

667

Originator	MEDICAL MARKET INVESTIGATIONS LTD
Title	AUDIT OF THE USE OF DIAGNOSTIC KITS AND REAGENTS IN HOSPITAL LABORATORIES, bi-annual
Coverage	Monitors use of kits, reagents and associated equipment
Contents & Origin of Statistics	Own research 100%. Supporting text 20%
Response	1983
Availability	On subscription
Address	25A Hockerill St, Bishop's Stortford Herts CM23 2DH
Contact	Mr. M.J.G. Allan

668

Originator	MERSEYSIDE CHAMBER OF COMMERCE AND INDUSTRY
Title	MCCI QUARTERLY ECONOMIC SURVEY, quarterly. March 1978-
Coverage	Survey of members, issued as a news release. Economic conditions such as orders, production, stocks, cashflow, labour and investment. Data for 5 quarters given.
Contents & Origin of Statistics	Tables per issue: 8. Own research 100%.
Comments	Details of statistical techniques used.
Currency	4 weeks
Response	1984
Availability	General
Cost	Free
Address	Number One Old Hall St, Liverpool L3 9HG
Telephone	051 227 1234 ; Telex: 627110
Contact	Alison Fisher, Administrative Officer

669

Originator	MERSEYSIDE PASSENGER TRANSPORT EXECUTIVE
Title	ANNUAL REPORT, annual
Coverage	Section of statistics: passenger journeys, vehicle miles, number of vehicles, operating costs. Also data included with text on organisations' activities.

Contents & Origin of Statistics	Tables per issue: 7. Own research 100%. Supporting text 80%

Response	1984
Availability	General
Cost	Free
Address	24 Hatton Garden, Liverpool L3 2AN
Telephone	051 227 5181
Contact	Mark P. White, Marketing Manager

670

Originator	METAL PACKAGING MANUFACTURERS ASSOCIATION

Title	UK METAL PACKAGING INDUSTRY STATISTICS, annual
Coverage	Sales, number of employees, sales per employee, sales in units. 3 years data given.

Contents & Origin of Statistics	Tables per issue: 5. Own research 100%. Supporting text 10%

Comments	Data also given in bulletin 'Metapack Business'
Response	1984
Availability	General
Cost	Free
Address	Castle Chambers, 3-9 Sheet St, Windsor Berks SL4 1BN
Telephone	07535 56012; Telex: 849731
Contact	Mandy Wright, Administrative Secretary

671

Originator	METAL SINK MANUFACTURERS ASSOCIATION

Title	UNTITLED, monthly
Coverage	Production and sales data.

Contents & Origin of Statistics	Tables per issue: Own research 100%

Comments	Data also released on activities of Boiler and Radiator Manufacturer Association, British Bath Manufacturers Association and Plasti Bath Manufacturers Association
Response	1983
Availability	Members
Address	Fleming House, Renfrew St, Glasgow G3 6TG
Telephone	041 332 0826
Contact	Mr. Clark

672

Originator	METALWORKING PRODUCTION
Title	SURVEY OF MACHINE TOOLS AND PRODUCTION EQUIPMMENT IN THE UK,every 5 years published separately from monthly journal
Coverage	Trends in sales and use of different types of machine tools with an industrial sector and regional analysis. Some international data and data on future planning requirements. Based on returns from over 3,000 manufacturing units.
Contents & Origin of Statistics	Tables per issue: 65. Own research 100%. Supporting text 10%
Comments	Latest survey - 1983, (5th edition)
Response	1984
Availability	General
Cost	Cost (pa):
Address	Morgan-Grampian Ltd, 30 Calderwood St, Woolwich, London SE18 6QH
Telephone	01 855 7777
Contact	E.D. Holland, Editor

673

Originator	METROPOLITAN PENSIONS ASSOCIATION LTD
Title	MPA MONTHLY DIGEST OF STATISTICS, monthly. 1975-
Coverage	Movements in RPI, average weekly earnings, state basic pension, competitive immediate annuity rate, FT industrial ordinary share index, London clearing banks base lending rate and indices of particular interest to pension scheme managers.
Contents & Origin of Statistics	Tables per issue: 1. Own research 12.5%, Other non official source 25%, Government statistics 62.5%.
Currency	1 month
Response	1984
Availability	Pension scheme managers
Address	MPA Ltd, Metropolitan House, Northgate, Chichester, PO19 1BE
Telephone	0243 785151; Telex: 86717
Contact	Elisabeth Bailey, Librarian

674

Originator	MEW RESEARCH
Title	SURVEY OF UK GOLF EQUIPMENT AND HOLIDAYS MARKET, irregular

Coverage	Golf clubs, balls, bags, trolleys, gloves, clothing, shoes. Golfing holidays data. Golfer profile data. Golfer readership.
Contents & Origin of Statistics	Tables per issue: Own research 100%
Comments	Interviews with sample
Response	1983
Availability	General
Cost	£2,200, £50 per section
Address	7 Layer Gardens, London W3 9PR
Telephone	01 992 6294
Contact	Marion E. Wertheim

675

Originator	MID GLAMORGAN COUNTY COUNCIL
Title	MID GLAMORGAN IN FIGURES, annual. 1975-
Coverage	Summary data on the county covering population, households housing, employment, unemployment, education, socio-economi groups etc.
Contents & Origin of Statistics	Tables per issue: 30.
Currency	Varies
Response	1984
Availability	General
Cost	Free
Address	Room 520, 5th Floor, Mid Glamorgan County Council, Greyfriar Rd, Cardiff CF1 3LG
Telephone	0222 28033, Ext 478
Contact	Janice Grindle, Economic Policy and Research Unit

676

Originator	MILK MARKETING BOARD
Title	ANNUAL REPORT AND ACCOUNTS, annual
Coverage	Includes a statistics section covering producer numbers, milk qualit realisation for manufactured milk, prices, consumption, utilisatio UK self-sufficiency ratios, transport, milk records, sales, yields ar cow numbers.
Contents & Origin of Statistics	Tables per issue: 13. Unstated 100%
Currency	Varies
Response	1984

Availability	General
Cost	Free
Address	Thames Ditton, Surrey KT7 0EL
Telephone	01 398 4101; Telex: 8956671
Contact	Above address

677

Originator	MILK MARKETING BOARD
Title	DAIRY FACTS AND FIGURES, annual. 1962-
Coverage	Data on producers, dairy farming, milk supplies, utilisation, prices, advertising, transport, expenditure, consumption and trade. Also some figures for the EEC. Figures cover all the UK, and historical figures are given in most tables.
Contents & Origin of Statistics	Tables per issue: 175. Own research 75%, Government statistics 25%. Supporting text 15%
Comments	The publication is jointly produced by all the UK Milk Marketing Boards.
Currency	Varies
Response	1984
Availability	General
Cost	Free to registered milk producers, £6 to others
Address	Thames Ditton, Surrey KT7 0EL
Telephone	01 398 4101; Telex: 8956671
Contact	Above address

678

Originator	MILK MARKETING BOARD
Title	KEY MILK FIGURES IN ENGLAND AND WALES, annual
Coverage	Basic figures for sales by region, consumption, utilisation, regional prices, realisation for milk manufactured, EEC prices, number of producers, livestock numbers, transport and milk quality.
Contents & Origin of Statistics	Tables per issue: 25. Unstated 100%.
Comments	Produced in card format
Currency	Varies
Response	1984
Availability	General
Cost	Free
Address	Thames Ditton, Surrey KT7 0EL

Telephone	01 398 4101; Telex: 8956671
Contact	Above address

679

Originator	MILK MARKETING BOARD
Title	MILK PRODUCER, monthly
Coverage	Producer prices, supplies, sales by region.
Contents & Origin of Statistics	Tables per issue: 8.
Comments	Journal produced by Jackson Rudd on 01 405 3611.
Currency	1 month
Response	1984
Availability	General
Cost	Free to milk producers, £7.50 to others
Address	Thames Ditton, Surrey KT7 0EL
Telephone	01 398 4101; Telex: 8956671
Contact	Heather Rogers, Editor

680

Originator	MILK MARKETING BOARD
Title	NATIONAL MILK RECORDS: AREA REPORTS BOOKS, annual
Coverage	Milk production and quality by leading cows and herds in 4 different areas of England and Wales: North, Midlands and Wales, East and South East, West. The reports are produced in 4 volumes.
Contents & Origin of Statistics	Tables per issue: Unstated 100%
Response	1984
Availability	General
Cost	£10 or £3 for a single volume
Address	Thames Ditton, Surrey KT7 0EL
Telephone	01 398 4101; Telex: 8956671
Contact	Janet McClellan

681

Originator	MILK MARKETING BOARD
Title	PRODUCERS' PRICES FOR MILK, monthly

Coverage	Forecasts basic prices payable to wholesale producers for the coming year by month and by region. Also includes 'table of monthly gallonages of milk sold off farms'
Contents & Origin of Statistics	Tables per issue: 1. Own research 100%
Comments	Produced in the form of a press release
Currency	1 month
Response	1984
Availability	General
Cost	£15
Address	Thames Ditton, Surrey KT7 0EL
Telephone	01 398 4101; Telex: 8956671
Contact	Above address

682

Originator	MILK MARKETING BOARD FOR NORTHERN IRELAND
Title	ANNUAL REPORT, annual. 1956-
Coverage	Statistical section covering number of registered milk producers, production, prices size of herds, yields, and sales.
Contents & Origin of Statistics	Tables per issue: 8-10. Supporting text 80%
Currency	6 months
Response	1984
Availability	General
Cost	Free
Address	456 Antrim Rd, Belfast BT15 5GD
Telephone	0232 770123; Telex: 747136
Contact	Library

683

Originator	MILK MARKETING BOARD FOR NORTHERN IRELAND
Title	KEY MILK FIGURES IN NORTHERN IRELAND, annual. 1978-
Coverage	Statistics on milk production, utilisation, producer prices, dairy herd, milk quality, EEC institutional prices.
Contents & Origin of Statistics	Tables per issue: 5pgs. Own research 90%, Government statistics 10%.
Comments	Statistics published in folding card format.
Currency	3-4 months
Response	1984

Availability	General
Cost	Free
Address	456 Antrim Rd, Belfast BT15 5GD
Telephone	0232 770123; Telex: 7747136
Contact	Library

684

Originator	MILK MARKETING BOARD FOR NORTHERN IRELAND

Title	TOPICS, monthly
Coverage	General review of milk trends in Northern Ireland. Mainly articles and news items, but some regular statistics on milk production, utilisation, prices and quality.
Contents & Origin of Statistics	Tables per issue: 8-10. Supporting text 90%.
Currency	2 months
Response	1984
Availability	Primarily for milk producers but available generally on request.
Cost	Free
Address	456 Antrim Rd, Belfast BT15 5GD
Telephone	0232 770123; Telex: 747136
Contact	Library

685

Originator	MILLING FEED AND FARM SUPPLIES

Title	PROTEIN PRICES AND FERTILIZER PRICES, monthly in a monthly journal
Coverage	General changes in prices of proteins and fertilizers.
Contents & Origin of Statistics	Tables per issue: 2
Currency	1 month
Response	1984
Availability	General
Cost	£40.90
ISSN	0140 4059
Address	Turret-Wheatland Ltd, 886 High Rd, Finchley, London N12
Telephone	01 446 2411; Telex: 268207
Contact	T. Tebbatt, Publisher

686

Originator	MILPRO LTD
Title	PRESCRIBING TRENDS, monthly. October 1975-
Coverage	Monitor of trends in general practitioners' prescribing. Data available for 14 therapeutic groups and 300 specific products within these.
Contents & Origin of Statistics	Tables per issue: c30pgs. Own research 100%.
Currency	2 weeks
Response	1984
Availability	Subscribers only
Cost	Varies
Address	1-2 Berners St, London W1
Telephone	01 637 1444 ; Telex: 25206
Contact	A. Scott, Senior Research Executive

687

Originator	MINING JOURNAL
Title	METAL ORE MARKETS, weekly in a weekly journal
Coverage	Brief tabulation of London Metal Exchange prices, stocks, turnovers and monthly average prices. Tabulation of selection of main non-ferrous metals and ore prices.
Contents & Origin of Statistics	Tables per issue: 3. Own research + other non official source 100%
Currency	1 day
Response	1984
Availability	General
Cost	£80 or £1.25 for a single issue
ISSN	0026 5225
Address	Mining Journal Ltd, 15 Wilson St, London EC2
Telephone	01 606 2567
Contact	Ron Marshman, Editor

688

Originator	MIRROR GROUP NEWSPAPERS LTD
Title	MGN MARKETING MANUAL OF THE UK, biennial
Coverage	Comprehensive consumer marketing data including social and economic, market-place data over 100 product fields, media and advertising.

Contents & Origin of Statistics	Tables per issue: 442. Non official source 25%, Government statistics 75%

Comments	Latest issue at time of writing - 1979.
Response	1983
Availability	General
Cost	£6) approx
Address	33 Holborn, London EC1
Telephone	01 353 0246
Contact	Above address

689

Originator	MM CORPORATE SERVICES LTD

Title	CONFECTIONERY DIGEST, frequency varies. 1982-
Coverage	Market sizes for chocolate and sugar confectionery by product type. Also prices, retailing trends, manufacturers and brands and marketing trends.

Contents & Origin of Statistics	Tables per issue: 39. Own research 25%, Other non official source 60%, Government statistics 15%. Supporting text 60%

Currency	6 months
Response	1984
Availability	General
Cost	£80
Address	38-40 Featherstone St, London EC1Y 8RN
Telephone	01 251 6504
Contact	A.T. Lowry, Director

690

Originator	MM CORPORATE SERVICES LTD

Title	OFFICE EQUIPMENT DIGEST, annual. 1983-
Coverage	Market sizes for office furniture, office machines, stationery and computers. Some forecasts for certain products

Contents & Origin of Statistics	Tables per issue: 27. Own research 50%, Other non official source 10%, Government statistics 40%. Supporting text 60%

Currency	10 months
Response	1984
Availability	General
Cost	£75
Address	38-40 Featherstone St, London EC1Y 8RN

| Telephone | 01 251 6504 |
| Contact | A.T. Lowry, Director |

691

| Originator | MONKS PUBLICATIONS |

Title	TOP MANAGEMENT REMUNERATION, bi-annual. 1978-
Coverage	Pay and benefits of directors and senior managers in all industries and sectors.
Contents & Origin of Statistics	Tables per issue: 180pgs. Own research 100%. Supporting text 10%
Comments	Special analyses of database on request. Data held on 1200 mainly quoted companies.
Currency	Varies
Response	1984
Availability	General
Cost	£105 (reduced rates for participants)
Address	Debden Green, Saffron Walden, Essex, CB11 3LX
Telephone	0371 830939
Contact	Tony Harcourt, Editor

692

| Originator | MONTAGU, SAMUEL AND CO LTD |

Title	THE SAMUEL MONTAGU NEW ISSUE STATISTICS, monthly. 1919-
Coverage	Monthly figures for the latest year for new capital issues by type of security, geographical origination and market origination.
Contents & Origin of Statistics	Tables per issue: 4. Own research 100%. Supporting text 30%
Comments	These statistics were published by the Midland Bank from 1919 to April 1983.
Currency	1 month
Response	1984
Availability	General
Cost	Free
Address	114 Old Broad St, London EC2P 2HY
Telephone	01 588 6464; Telex: 887213
Contact	Mr A.J. Catmull, Manager, Corporate Finance Division

693

Originator	MORRELL, JAMES AND ASSOCIATES
Title	BUSINESS FORECASTS, quarterly. 1980-
Coverage	Summary forecasts of the main economic variables plus output in 15 sectors, consumer spending in 11 sectors, property trends, regional information and population and life-style trends. Up to 10 years ahead.
Contents & Origin of Statistics	Tables per issue: 23. Own research 100%. Supporting text 50%
Currency	1 month
Response	1984
Availability	General
Cost	Cost (pa):£106
Address	1 Paternoster Row, St Paul's, London EC4M 7DH
Telephone	01 236 6950/ 01 248 3999
Contact	M.H. Morrell, Company Secretary

694

Originator	MOTOR CYCLE ASSOCIATION OF GREAT BRITAIN LTD
Title	ESTIMATED RUNNING COSTS, annual
Coverage	Running costs for powered two wheelers.
Contents & Origin of Statistics	Tables per issue: 1. Own research 100%
Comments	More detailed figures available to members only.
Currency	6 months
Response	1984
Availability	General
Cost	Free
Address	Starley House, Eaton Rd, Coventry CV1 2FH
Telephone	0203 27427
Contact	C.H. Smart, Statistics/Information Officer

695

Originator	MOTOR CYCLE ASSOCIATION OF GREAT BRITAIN LTD
Title	FIRST REGISTRATIONS OF POWERED TWO AND THREE WHEELED VEHICLES IN THE UK, monthly
Coverage	Data by make, model and geographical area. Divided into mopeds, scooters and motor cycles.

Contents & Origin of Statistics	Tables per issue: 2. Own research 100%

Comments	More detailed information available to members.
Currency	1 month
Response	1984
Availability	General
Cost	Free
Address	Starley House, Eaton Rd, Coventry CV1 2FH
Telephone	0203 27427
Contact	C.H. Smart, Statistics/Information Officer

696

Originator	MOTOR CYCLE ASSOCIATION OF GREAT BRITAIN LTD

Title	IMPORT/EXPORT OF POWERED TWO-WHEELERS, monthly
Coverage	Imports and exports of motor cycles, mopeds, scooters and sidecars.

Contents & Origin of Statistics	Tables per issue: 3. Government statistics 100%.

Comments	More detailed information available to members only
Currency	1 month
Response	1984
Availability	General
Cost	Free
Address	Starley House, Eaton Rd, Coventry CV1 2FH
Telephone	0203 27427
Contact	C.H. Smart, Statistics/Information Officer

697

Originator	MOTOR CYCLE ASSOCIATION OF GREAT BRITAIN LTD

Title	UK MOTOR CYCLE INDUSTRY IN A NUTSHELL, annual
Coverage	Summary of production, imports, exports, vehicles in use and sales.

Contents & Origin of Statistics	Tables per issue: 9. Own research 60%, Government statistics 40%

Comments	More detailed figures available to members only.
Currency	6 months
Response	1984
Availability	General
Cost	Free
Address	Starley House, Eaton Rd, Coventry CV1 2FH

Telephone	0203 27427
Contact	C.H. Smart, Statistics/Information Officer

698

Originator	MOTOR TRADER

Title	REGISTRATIONS AND DATACHECK, monthly in a weekly journal
Coverage	Breakdown of new car registrations in the UK and trends in market shares of car manufacturers and importers.
Contents & Origin of Statistics	Tables per issue: 1. Non official source 100%
Currency	1 month
Response	1984
Availability	General
Cost	£14
Address	Business Press International, Quadrant House, The Quadrant, Sutton, Surrey SM2 5AS
Telephone	01 661 3500; Telex: 892084
Contact	N.A. Brown, Editor

699

Originator	MOTOR TRANSPORT

Title	COST TABLES, quarterly in weekly journal, 1965 -
Coverage	Costs of running commercial vehicles in a range of weight categories giving standing costs and costs for a range of annual mileage.
Contents & Origin of Statistics	Tables per issue: 20. Own research 90%, Government statistics 10%
Currency	2-3 weeks
Response	1984
Availability	General
Cost	45p for a single copy
ISSN	0027 206X
Address	Business Press International, Quadrant House, The Quadrant, Sutton, Surrey SM2 5AS
Telephone	01 661 3719, Telex: 892084
Contact	Mike Forbes, Assistant Features Editor

700

Originator	MUSHROOM GROWERS ASSOCIATION
Title	MUSHROOM GROWERS ASSOCIATION INDUSTRY SURVEY, annual. 1979-
Coverage	Production and manpower figures for the sector plus a cost analysis, methods of growing, and industry yield figures. Based on a survey of members.
Contents & Origin of Statistics	Tables per issue: 11. Own research 100%. Supporting text 50%
Currency	1-2 months
Response	1984
Availability	Members
Address	Agriculture House, Knightsbridge, London SW1X 7NJ
Telephone	01 235 5077, ext 329; Telex: 919669
Contact	D.N. Locke, Director

701

Originator	MUSIC PUBLISHERS' ASSOCIATION LTD
Title	SUMMARY OF PRINTED MUSIC SALES, bi-annual
Coverage	UK and overseas sales of printed music. Previous year's data for comparison.
Contents & Origin of Statistics	Tables per issue: 1. Own research 100%. Supporting text 20%
Currency	4-5 months
Response	1984
Availability	General
Cost	Free
Address	103 Kingsway, London WC2B 6QX
Telephone	01 831 7591/2/3
Contact	P.J. Dadswell

702

Originator	NATIONAL AND LOCAL GOVERNMENT OFFICERS ASSOCIATION
Title	STATISTICAL INFORMATION, monthly. May 1982-
Coverage	Unemployment, retail price index, tax and price index, index of average earnings, recent public sector pay settlements.

Contents & Origin of Statistics	Tables per issue: 6. Non official source 20%, Government statistics 80%. Supporting text 10%
Currency Response	1 month
Response	1984
Availability	Members and some others
Cost	Free
Address	1 Mabledon Place, London WCLH 9AJ
Telephone	01 388 2366, ext 377
Contact	Hugh Robertson, Research Assistant

703

Originator	NATIONAL ASSOCIATION OF DROP FORGERS AND STAMPERS
Title	ECONOMIC AND STATISTICAL REVIEW, 3 or 4 times per year
Coverage	Current statistical information on the drop forging industry, economic analysis, forecasts, market developments, prices and deliveries
Contents & Origin of Statistics	Tables per issue: 5. Own research 100%
Response	1983
Availability	General
Cost	£20
Address	Grove Hill House, 245 Grove Lane, Handsworth, Birmingham B20 2HB
Telephone	021 554 3311
Contact	D.A.T. Powis, Director

704

Originator	NATIONAL ASSOCIATION OF PENSION FUNDS LTD
Title	ANNUAL SURVEY OF OCCUPATIONAL PENSION SCHEMES, annual. 1975-
Coverage	Public and private sector schemes. Covers income and expenditure and size of fund, nature of schemes, benefits provided and Social Security Pensions Act 1975.
Contents & Origin of Statistics	Tables per issue: 116. Own research 100%. Supporting text 50%
Comments	Covers 100 public sector schemes and 1023 private sector schemes.
Currency	1 year
Response	1984
Availability	General

Cost	£28 (£14 for members)
ISSN	0309 0078
Address	Sunley House, Bedford Park, Croydon, Surrey CR0 0XF
Telephone	01 681 2017
Contact	Mrs. B.I. Walker, Assistant Secretary

705

Originator	NATIONAL ASSOCIATION OF SOFT DRINKS MANUFAC-TURERS
Title	FACTSHEETS, annual
Coverage	Information sheets containing statistics on various aspects of the industry, eg sales, consumption, packaging.
Contents & Origin of Statistics	Tables per issue: 16 sheets. Own research 90%, Government statistics 10%. Supporting text 80%
Currency	1 year
Response	1984
Availability	General
Cost	Free
Address	The Gatehouse, 2 Holly Rd, Twickenham TW1 4EF
Telephone	01 892 8082
Contact	Janette Gledhill, Information Officer

706

Originator	NATIONAL ASSOCIATION OF STEEL STOCK HOLDERS
Title	BUSINESS TRENDS, monthly
Coverage	Summary of executive opinion on a range of topics eg economy, sales trends, stock levels, buying and selling prices, processing and credit. Trends surveys carried out for a range of products.
Contents & Origin of Statistics	Tables per issue: 8 (per product group). Own research 100%. Supporting text 10%
Response	1984
Availability	Members
Cost	Free
Address	Gateway House, High St, Birmingham B4 75Y
Telephone	021 632 5821 ; Telex: 335908
Contact	R.E. Cash, Secretary

707

Originator	NATIONAL ASSOCIATION OF STEEL STOCKHOLDERS
Title	ANNUAL REPORT, annual

Coverage	Statistical appendix gives domestic supplies, deliveries to stockholders from UK, production, imports and share of imported steel products in the domestic markets of the ECSC countries.
Contents & Origin of Statistics	Tables per issue: 3. Own research 65%, Government statistics 35%. Supporting text 80%
Response	1984
Availability	General
Cost	Free
Address	Gateway House, High St, Birmingham B4 75Y
Telephone	021 632 5821 ; Telex: 335908
Contact	R.E. Cash, Secretary

708

Originator	NATIONAL ASSOCIATION OF STEEL STOCKHOLDERS
Title	STOCKHOLDER TRADING SUMMARIES, monthly
Coverage	Opening stock, gross receipts, gross despatches and intertrading included in despatches for a range of products eg general steels, strip mill, engineering steels, stainless steels, bright steels and tube and hollow sections.
Contents & Origin of Statistics	Tables per issue: c 6. Own research 100%.
Response	1984
Availability	Members
Cost	Free
Address	Gateway House, High St, Birmingham B4 7SY
Telephone	021 632 5821; Telex: 335908
Contact	R.E. Cash, Secretary

709

Originator	NATIONAL BEDDING FEDERATION
Title	UNTITLED
Coverage	Statistics on bedding
Response	1983
Availability	Members
Address	251 Brompton Rd, London SW3 2EZ
Telephone	01 589 4888
Contact	Peter Llewellyn, Director

710

Originator	NATIONAL BOOK COMMITTEE
Title	PUBLIC LIBRARY SPENDING IN ENGLAND AND WALES, annual
Coverage	Expenditure, estimated and actual, per head of population by counties for a number of years.
Contents & Origin of Statistics	Tables per issue: 3. Non official source 100%. Supporting text 20%.
Comments	Publication sponsored by various organisations including the Publishers Association, Library Association, Society of Authors.
Response	1984
Availability	General
Cost	Free
Address	c/o The National Book League, 45 East Hill, London SW18 2QZ
Telephone	01 870 9055
Contact	Publications Officer

711

Originator	NATIONAL BOOK LEAGUE
Title	LIBRARY BOOK SPENDING IN UNIVERSITIES, POLYTECHNICS AND COLLEGES, biennial. 1982-
Coverage	University expenditure on books as %, whole expenditure on books per full-time equivalent student in polytechnics and as % of total expenditure and expenditure on books in further education by local authority.
Contents & Origin of Statistics	Tables per issue: 8. Non official source 75%, Government statistics 25%. Supporting text 30%
Comments	Also produced one-off 'Books for Schools' in 1979, giving expenditure data
Currency	Varies
Response	1984
Availability	General
Cost	Free
Address	Book House, 45 East Hill, London SW18 2QZ
Telephone	01 870 9055
Contact	Andy Patterson, Head of Touring Exhibitions

712

Originator	NATIONAL BOOK LEAGUE
Title	PUBLIC LIBRARY SPENDING IN ENGLAND AND WALES, annual. 1981-
Coverage	Actual and estimated expenditure per head of population for public Library books by county and metropolitan district, publishers turnover.
Contents & Origin of Statistics	Tables per issue: 4. Non official source 50%, Unstated 50%. Supporting text 30%
Response	1984
Availability	General
Cost	Free
Address	Book House, 45 East Hill, London SW18 2WWZ
Telephone	01 870 9055
Contact	Andy Patterson, Head of Touring Exhibitions

713

Originator	NATIONAL BUS COMPANY
Title	ANNUAL REPORT, annual. 1969-
Coverage	Contains a section of statistics, including number of journeys, miles, employees and fares.
Contents & Origin of Statistics	Tables per issue: 4. Own research 100%. Supporting text 50%
Currency	6 months
Response	1984
Availability	General
Cost	£2.50
Address	Canterbury House, 393 Cowley Rd, Oxford OX4
Telephone	0865 774611
Contact	R.B. Medley, Planning and Research

714

Originator	NATIONAL CARAVAN COUNCIL LTD
Title	BRITISH CARAVAN INDUSTRY STATISTICS, annual
Coverage	Members' production, caravans in use, caravan parks, imports and exports. Also production data for Europe.
Contents & Origin of Statistics	Tables per issue: 5. Own research 100%

Response	1983
Availability	General
Cost	Free
Address	43-45 High St, Weybridge, Surrey KT13 8BT
Telephone	0932 51376/9
Contact	Director General

715

Originator	NATIONAL CAVITY INSULATION ASSOCIATION
Title	UNTITLED, annual
Coverage	Surveys of members' activities.
Contents & Origin of Statistics	Tables per issue: Own research 100%
Response	1983
Availability	Members
Address	178/202 Great Portland St, London W1N 6AQ
Telephone	01 637 7481
Contact	Above address

716

Originator	NATIONAL CHAMBER OF TRADE
Title	ELECTRICITY BOARD - SAMPLE CHARGES (NON-DOM-ESTIC), annual. 1976-
Coverage	Standing/fixed charge, rates for unit for various areas and schemes. Also gives charges for gas.
Contents & Origin of Statistics	Tables per issue: 2pgs. Own research 100%. Supporting text 25%
Response	1984
Availability	Members and researchers
Cost	Free
Address	Enterprise House, Henley-on-Thames, Oxfordshire RG9 1TU
Telephone	0491 576161
Contact	Mr. B. Tennant, Secretary

717

Originator	NATIONAL CHAMBER OF TRADE
Title	WATER CHARGING OPTIONS, annual. 1976-
Coverage	For each water authority gives standing charge, volume charge and rate in the £.

Contents & Origin of Statistics	Tables per issue: 1. Own research 100%. Supporting text 50%
Response	1984
Availability	Members and researchers
Cost	Free
Address	Enterprise House, Henley-on-Thames, Oxfordshire RG9 1TU
Telephone	0491 576161
Contact	Mr. B. Tennant, Secretary

718

Originator	NATIONAL COAL BOARD
Title	REPORT AND ACCOUNTS, annual. 1947-
Coverage	Report of year's activities and supporting statistics on aspects of the coal industry.
Contents & Origin of Statistics	Tables per issue: 20. Supporting text 75%
Currency	3 months
Response	1984
Availability	General
Cost	£2.50
Address	Hobart House, Grosvenor Place, London SW1X 7AE
Telephone	01 235 2020
Contact	P.G. Toms, Librarian

719

Originator	NATIONAL COMPUTING CENTRE
Title	SALARIES AND FRINGE BENEFITS IN COMPUTING, annual
Coverage	18 major job categories analysed. Employee and installations analyses. Salaries and benefits including holidays analysed by region, value of computer, SIC, system used, and size of organisation. Section on employment trends.
Contents & Origin of Statistics	Tables per issue: 88. Own research 100%
Comments	Random sample of qualifying computer installations from NCC'S National Computer Index
Response	1983
Availability	General
Cost	£84
Address	Oxford Rd, Manchester M1 7ED

| **Telephone** | 061 228 6333 |
| **Contact** | R. Brody |

720

Originator	NATIONAL COUNCIL OF BUILDING MATERIAL PRODU-CERS
Title	BMP FORECASTS, 3 times per year
Coverage	Forecasts 3 years ahead for housing starts and completions, other new work and repair, maintenance and improvement.
Contents & Origin of Statistics	Tables per issue: 4. Own research 100%. Supporting text 80%
Currency	1 month
Response	1984
Availability	General
Cost	£16
ISSN	0144 9060
Address	33 Alfred Place, London WC1E 7EN
Telephone	01 580 3344
Contact	Miss E.Hurn, Administrator

721

Originator	NATIONAL COUNCIL OF BUILDING MATERIAL PRODU-CERS
Title	BMP STATISTICAL BULLETIN, monthly
Coverage	Housebuilding starts and completions, renovations, prices, mortgages, architects' workload, value of new orders and output, fixed capital expenditure, building material production, prices and trade.
Contents & Origin of Statistics	Tables per issue: 22. Non official source 50%, Government statistics 50%. Supporting text 7%
Comments	Also contains summary forecasts from 'BMP Forecasts'.
Currency	2 months
Response	1984
Availability	General
Cost	Cost (pa):£21.50
ISSN	0144 9036
Address	33 Alfred Place, London WC1E 7EN
Telephone	01 580 3344
Contact	Miss E. Hurn, Administrator

722

Originator	NATIONAL DOCK LABOUR BOARD
Title	ANNUAL REPORT AND ACCOUNTS, annual
Coverage	Includes a section of statistical tables. Report covers labour force, registers, training, education, welfare, pensions, premises and staff as well as usual financial accounts.
Contents & Origin of Statistics	Tables per issue: Own research 100%. Supporting text 50%
Response	1983
Availability	General
Cost	£1
Address	22-26 Albert Embankment, London SE1 7TE
Telephone	01 735 7271/9
Contact	J. Russell, Executive Officer

723

Originator	NATIONAL FARMERS' UNION
Title	AGRICULTURE - SOME BASIC STATISTICS, annual
Coverage	Data on crop production and area, meat production, size of holdings, employment, farmland, incomes, total output and the degree of self-sufficiency.
Contents & Origin of Statistics	Tables per issue: 15. Unstated 100%.
Comments	Produced in card format.
Currency	Latest year
Response	1984
Availability	General
Cost	Free
Address	Agriculture House, Knightsbridge, London, SW1X 7NJ
Telephone	01 235 5077
Contact	The Librarian

724

Originator	NATIONAL FARMERS' UNION
Title	AGRICULTURE'S PLACE IN THE NATIONAL ECONOMY, biennial
Coverage	Includes data on factors of production, agricultural output, technical and economic efficiency, self-sufficiency, and trends in ancillary industries. Also contains international comparisons.

Contents &	Tables per issue: 7-9. Unstated 100%. Supporting text 40%.
Origin of	
Statistics	
Comments	Produced in card format.
Currency	12 months
Response	1984
Availability	Members
Cost	Free
Address	Agriculture House, Knightsbridge, London, SW1X 7NJ
Telephone	01 235 5077
Contact	The Librarian

725

Originator	NATIONAL FEDERATION OF SITE OPERATORS LTD
Title	UNTITLED
Coverage	Compile statistics for tourist board and ministerial use. Some data circulated in bi-monthly journal for members.
Contents &	Tables per issue: Own research 100%
Origin of	
Statistics	
Response	1983
Availability	Members
Address	Chichester House, 31 Park Rd, Gloucester GL1 1LH
Telephone	0452 26911 and 413041
Contact	J. Finn, Executive Administrator

726

Originator	NATIONAL GAS CONSUMERS' COUNCIL
Title	ANNUAL REPORT, annual. 1974-
Coverage	Analysis of the performance of the gas industry, as measured by survey research and by complaint statistics.
Contents &	Tables per issue: 3. Own research 100%. Supporting text 85%
Origin of	
Statistics	
Comments	Produced one-off reports - 'Family expenditure survey - expenditure on fuels' and 'Gas consumers and gas appliances'.
Currency	3 months
Response	1984
Availability	General
Cost	Free
Address	4th Floor, 162 Regent St, London W1R 5TB

Telephone	01 439 0012
Contact	John Winward, Public Affairs

727

Originator	NATIONAL HOUSE-BUILDING COUNCIL
Title	PRIVATE HOUSE-BUILDING STATISTICS, quarterly. 1981-
Coverage	Dwelling starts and completions, prices, market share of timber frame, first time buyers ability to buy, some regional data.
Contents & Origin of Statistics	Tables per issue: 12. Own research 90%, Government statistics 10%. Supporting text 5%
Currency	2 weeks
Response	1984
Availability	General
Cost	£10
Address	Chiltern Avenue, Amersham, Bucks HP6 5AP
Telephone	024 03 4477
Contact	Mr. C.J. Brett, Computer Manager

728

Originator	NATIONAL HOUSING AND TOWN PLANNING COUNCIL
Title	HOUSING AND PLANNING REVIEW, 6 times per year
Coverage	Includes a regular statistical section with variety of data on housing and town planning.
Contents & Origin of Statistics	Tables per issue: 5. Own research 40%, Government statistics 20%, Unstated 40%
Response	1983
Availability	General
Cost	£10
Address	Norvin House, 45-55 Commercial St, London E1 6BA
Telephone	01 247 5732/3
Contact	Ray Walker, Director

729

Originator	NATIONAL INSTITUTE OF ECONOMIC AND SOCIAL RESEARCH
Title	NATIONAL INSTITUTE ECONOMIC REVIEW, quarterly
Coverage	General trends in the home and world economy with forecasts usually up to 18 months ahead and special articles on relevant topics.

Contents & **Origin of** **Statistics**	Tables per issue: 25. Supporting text 80%
Comments	Microfilm copies of back numbers available.
Currency	Curreny of data: Varies
Response	1984
Availability	General
Cost	£30 (Students, £12)
ISSN	0027 9501
Address	2 Dean Trench St, Smith Square, London SW1P 3HE
Telephone	01 222 7665
Contact	Mrs K Jones, Secretary

730

Originator	NATIONAL SULPHURIC ACID ASSOCIATION LTD
Title	QUARTERLY SUMMARY OF MONTHLY RETURNS, quarterly
Coverage	Summary of production and consumption of sulphuric acid, oleum and sulphur raw materials.
Contents & **Origin of** **Statistics**	Tables per issue: 2. Own research 100%.
Comments	Consists of one sheet of data.
Currency	1-2 months
Response	1984
Availability	Primarily members but generally available on request
Cost	Free
Address	Picadilly House, 33/37 Regent St, London SW1Y 4NF
Telephone	01 734 3561; Telex: 21724
Contact	B.D.C. Shields, Deputy Director

731

Originator	NATIONAL SULPHURIC ACID ASSOCIATION LTD.
Title	ANNUAL REPORT AND FINANCIAL STATEMENTS, annual
Coverage	A statistical section covers the production of sulphuric acid in the UK and Eire, the import of sulphur and the usage of raw materials. Other tables cover the consumption of the acid by major industries in the UK and trade uses of the acid.
Contents & **Origin of** **Statistics**	Tables per issue: 10. Unstated 100%. Supporting text 40%.
Comments	Annual accounts of the Association also included.
Currency	10 months
Response	1984

Availability	Primarily members but generally available on request
Cost	Free
Address	Piccadilly House, 33/37 Regent St, London SW1Y 4NF
Telephone	01 734 3561; Telex: 21724
Contact	B.D.C. Shields, Deputy Director

732

Originator	NATIONAL SULPHURIC ACID ASSOCIATION LTD.

Title	ANNUAL SUMMARY OF MONTHLY RETURNS, annual
Coverage	Summary of production and consumption of sulphuric acid, oleum and sulphur raw materials.

Contents & Origin of Statistics	Tables per issue: 3. Own research 100%.

Comments	Consists of one sheet of data.
Currency	2-3 months
Response	1984
Availability	Primarly members but generally available on request
Cost	Free
Address	Piccadilly House, 33/37 Regent St, London SW1Y 4NF
Telephone	01 734 3561; Telex: 21724
Contact	B.D.C. Shields, Deputy Director

733

Originator	NATIONAL SUPERVISORY COUNCIL FOR INTRUDER ALARMS

Title	BACKGROUND INFORMATION, updated as required. 1979-
Coverage	Annual installations of new intruder alarms by type of alarm and by type of premises.

Contents & Origin of Statistics	Tables per issue: 3. Own research 100%. Supporting text 50%

Response	1984
Availability	General
Cost	Free
Address	1st floor, St. Ives House, St. Ives Rd, Maidenhead, Berks SL6 1RD
Telephone	0628 37512
Contact	Brigadier Needham, Director General

734

Originator	NATIONAL UTILITY SERVICES LTD
Title	UTILITY NEWSBRIEFS, quarterly
Coverage	Essentially a newsletter on energy and telecommunications, containing a regular section on costs of energy, water and telecommunications by industrial sector and region.
Contents &	Tables per issue: 4pgs. Own research 100%
Origin of	
Statistics	
Response	1984
Availability	Clients and special organisations
Cost	Free
Address	Carolyn House, Dingwall Rd, Croydon CR9 3LX
Telephone	01 681 2500; Telex: 917363
Contact	Sir Milton Sharp, Director

735

Originator	NATIONAL WESTMINSTER BANK PLC
Title	ECONOMIC AND FINANCIAL OUTLOOK, monthly
Coverage	General items on economy and contains a statistical appendix. Covers commodities, interest rates, currencies and money supply. Forecast 5 years ahead. Some international data.
Contents &	Tables per issue: 22. Own research 50%, Other non official source
Origin of	20%, Unstated 30%. Supporting text 50%
Statistics	
Comments	Issued 'Interest and exchange rate update'.
Currency	1 month
Response	1984
Availability	Bank customers
Cost	Free
Address	Market Intelligence Dept, 41 Lothbury, London EC2P 2BP
Telephone	01 726 1118
Contact	Mr. D. Kern, Chief Economist

736

Originator	NATIONWIDE BUILDING SOCIETY
Title	HOUSE PRICES, quarterly. 1955-
Coverage	House prices by region and by type of house. Also general indices of house prices, housebuilding costs, retail prices and earnings. Other data on the relationship between house prices, mortgage advances, incomes and repayments and previous owner occupiers.

Contents & Origin of Statistics	Tables per issue: 17. Own research 90%, Government statistics 10%. Supporting text 10%

Currency	2-3 weeks
Response	1984
Availability	General
Cost	Free
ISSN	0263 3639
Address	New Oxford House, High Holborn, London WC1V 6PW
Telephone	01 242 8822
Contact	Mr B. Bissett, Planning Officer

737

Originator	NEW CIVIL ENGINEER

Title	CONSTRUCTION INDICES, monthly in a weekly journal
Coverage	Prices of labour, materials and building work in the civil engineering sector. Latest month available plus the previous 3 months.

Contents & Origin of Statistics	Tables per issue: 2. Government statistics 100%

Comments	The magazine of the Institution of Civil Engineers
Currency	1 month
Response	1985
Availability	General
Cost	£56
ISSN	0307 7683
Address	Thomas Telford Ltd, Gt. George St, London SW1
Telephone	01 222 7722; Telex: 298105
Contact	Above address

738

Originator	NEW CIVIL ENGINEER

Title	ICE SALARY SURVEY, every 2/3 years in a weekly journal
Coverage	Analysis of salaries by employer, age, type of work, location size of firm etc.

Contents & Origin of Statistics	Tables per issue: 23. Own research 100%

Comments	Survey based on 10,000 members of the Institution of Civil Engineers and is carried out by Peter Peregrinus Ltd, 1 Station House, Nightingale Rd, Hitchin, Herts. Telephone - 0462 53331.
Response	1984
Availability	General
Cost	£56

ISSN	0307 7683
Address	Thomas Telford Ltd, Gt George St, London SW1
Telephone	01 222 7722; Telex: 298105
Contact	Above address

739

Originator	NEWCASTLE UNDER LYME BOROUGH COUNCIL
Title	HOUSING DEVELOPMENT MONITORING REPORTS, bi-annual. 1982-
Coverage	Examination of recent housebuilding activity in the borough, progress being made towards satisfying housing needs and land supply for private sector housebuilding.
Contents & Origin of Statistics	Tables per issue: 17. Own research 90%, Other non official source 10%. Supporting text 60%
Comments	Also produce a number of reports on the census.
Currency	6 weeks
Response	1984
Availability	General
Cost	£1
Address	Civic Offices, Merrial St, Newcastle-under-Lyme, Staffs ST5 2AG
Telephone	0782 610161, ext 377
Contact	Eric Kelsall, Senior Planning Assistant

740

Originator	NEWCASTLE UNDER LYME BOROUGH COUNCIL
Title	UNEMPLOYMENT REVIEW, bi-annual. 1980-
Coverage	Comparison of umemployment in North Staffordshire, the Borough and Great Britain as a whole. Includes. redundancies, vacancies and age and duration statistics.
Contents & Origin of Statistics	Tables per issue: 4. Own research 10%, Government statistics 90%. Supporting text 50%
Comments	Until March 1983 the review was prepared quarterly.
Currency	1-3 months
Response	1984
Availability	General
Cost	Free
Address	Civic Offices, Merrial St, Newcastle-under-Lyme, Staffs ST5 2AG
Telephone	0782 610161, ext 394
Contact	Steven Burrows, Planning Assistant

741

Originator	NEWPORT BOROUGH COUNCIL
Title	INDUSTRIAL AND EMPLOYMENT MONITOR, quarterly. 1980-
Coverage	Review of industrial and commercial developments in the Borough, planning permissions and local/national employment trends.
Contents & Origin of Statistics	Tables per issue: 18. Government statistics 15%, Unstated 85%. Supporting text 50%
Currency	Varies
Response	1984
Availability	General
Cost	Free
Address	Civic Centre, Newport, Gwent NPT 4UR
Telephone	0633 65491
Contact	J.M. Wignall, Director of Technical Services

742

Originator	NIELSEN RESEARCHER
Title	GROCERY TRADING REVIEW, annual in a journal published 3 or 4 times per year
Coverage	General review of grocery trading based on a survey of 700 units providing details of over 50,000 retail shops. Gives 10 year trends in general and by region.
Contents & Origin of Statistics	Tables per issue: Own research 100%
Comments	Journal contains various reviews of grocery and retail trading and products. See also entries headed A.C. Nielsen Co Ltd.
Response	1984
Availability	General
Cost	Free
Address	A.C. Nielsen Co Ltd, Nielsen House, Headington, Oxford OX3 9BR
Telephone	0865 64851; Telex: 83136
Contact	Above address

743

Originator	NIELSEN, A.C. CO LTD
Title	CASH AND CARRY TRADING IN 19--, annual

Coverage	Results of 3000 interviews with cash and carry users in various depots throughout Great Britain. Data on customer profiles, depot number and turnover trends, distribution by region, location and size, concentration of turnover etc.
Contents & Origin of Statistics	Tables per issue: Own research 100%
Comments	Report based on the Nielsen Cash and Carry Index. Various other specialised services available such as the Nielsen Retail Indexes, Nielsen Consumer Research, Compumark, CMIS, Dataquest and Nielsen Clearing House. See also entry headed 'Nielsen Researcher'.
Response	1984
Availability	On application
Cost	£150 plus £20 for each additional copy +VAT
Address	Nielsen House, Headington, Oxford OX3 9BR
Telephone	0865 64851; Telex: 83136
Contact	Above address

744

Originator	NIELSEN, A.C. CO LTD
Title	FOOD TRADES REPORT, biennial
Coverage	A review of trading for all grocery outlets with details of superstores, multiples, cooperatives, independents etc.
Contents & Origin of Statistics	Tables per issue: Own research 100%
Comments	Various other specialised services such as Nielsen Retail Indexes, Nielsen Consumer Research, Compumark, CMIS, Dataquest and Nielsen Clearing House. See also separate entry headed 'Nielsen Researcher'.
Response	1984
Availability	General
Cost	£150 plus £20 for each additional copy +VAT
Address	Nielsen House, Headington, Oxford OX3 9BR
Telephone	0865 64851; Telex: 83136
Contact	Above address

745

Originator	NIELSEN, A.C. CO LTD
Title	NIELSEN MARKET INFORMATION MANUAL, annual
Coverage	Data on over 250 markets covering products sold in grocers, off-licences, pharmacies, confectioners and cash and carry outlets. Also contains general economic, demographic and advertising data.

Contents &	Tables per issue: Own research 95%, Non official statistics + govern-
Origin of	ment statistics 5%
Statistics	

Comments Various other specialised services available such as Nielsen Retail Indexes, Nielsen Consumer Research, Compumark, CMIS, Dataquest and Nielsen Clearing House. See also separate entry headed 'Nielsen Researcher'

Response 1984
Availability On application
Cost £600 plus £60 for additional copies, (£100 discount for previous purchasers)
Address Nielsen House, Headington, Oxford OX3 9BR
Telephone 0865 64851; Telex: 83136
Contact Above address

746

Originator NIELSEN, A.C. CO LTD

Title OFF LICENCE TRADING IN 19.., biennial
Coverage General review of the off-licence trade including numbers and turnover trends by region and shop type, licensing trends in grocers, licensed multiple grocers by region and county, economic data and general market trend data.

Contents &	Tables per issue: Own research 100%
Origin of	
Statistics	

Comments Various other specialised services such as the Nielsen Retail Indexes, Nielsen Consumer Research, Compumark, CMIS, Dataquest and Nielsen Clearing House. See also separate entry headed 'Nielsen Researcher'.

Response 1984
Availability General
Cost £150 plus £20 for additional copies +VAT
Address Nielsen House, Headington, Oxford OX3 9BR
Telephone 0865 64851; Telex: 83136
Contact Above address

747

Originator NOP MARKET RESEARCH LTD

Title ALCOHOLIC DRINKS SURVEY, annual
Coverage Drinking habits of a sample of approximately 2000 adults analysed by social class, TV area, sex and age. Covers wine, spirits and cocktails giving awareness of brands, source of purchase, frequency of drinks etc.

Contents & Origin of Statistics	Tables per issue: Own research 100%

Comments	Exclusive questions and analysis available by negotiation. Omnibus surveys also carried out on a weekly basis.
Response	1984
Availability	General
Cost	£1175 (single section - £500)
Address	Tower House, Southampton St, London WC2E 7HN
Telephone	01 836 1511
Contact	Tony Lees or Maureen Amar

748

Originator	NOP MARKET RESEARCH LTD

Title	EATING OUT, annual
Coverage	Covers consumer requirements and behaviour when taking friends to restaurants, hotels, steakhouses, pubs, winebars etc.

Contents & Origin of Statistics	Tables per issue: Own research 100%

Comments	Special analysis available and omnibus surveys also carried out on a weekly basis.
Response	1984
Availability	General
Cost	On request
Address	Tower House, Southampton St, London WC2E 7HN
Telephone	01 836 1511
Contact	Tony Lees or Maureen Amar

749

Originator	NOP MARKET RESEARCH LTD

Title	FINANCIAL RESEARCH SURVEY, bi-annual
Coverage	Trend data on the personal financial and savings markets based on a sample of approximately 5,500 people. Monitors movements and trends in bank account holdings, usage of various savings media and credit methods.

Contents & Origin of Statistics	Tables per issue: Own research 100%

Comments	Confidential questions can be added to survey by negotiation. Omnibus surveys also carried out on a weekly basis.
Response	1984
Availability	General
Cost	On request

Address	Tower House, Southampton St, London WC2E 7HN
Telephone	01 836 1511
Contact	Tony Lees or Maureen Amar

750

Originator	NOP MARKET RESEARCH LTD
Title	PUBS IN GREAT BRITAIN SURVEY, regular
Coverage	Data on pub customers' eating habits and pub visiting and drinking habits. Also covers attitude to pub facilities, features and atmosphere. Survey based on a sample of 1200 adults.
Contents & Origin of Statistics	Tables per issue: Own research 100%
Comments	Special analysis available and omnibus surveys also carried out on a weekly basis.
Response	1984
Availability	General
Cost	£1,250
Address	Tower House, Southampton St, London WC2E 7HN
Telephone	01 836 1511
Contact	Tony Lees or Maureen Amar

751

Originator	NORTH CORNWALL DISTRICT COUNCIL
Title	HOUSING AND INDUSTRIAL LAND AVAILABILITY REPORT, annual
Coverage	Residential land available, outstanding planning permissions, new sites, dwellings complete and under construction, structure plan balance, allocated residential land and industrial land available.
Contents & Origin of Statistics	Tables per issue: 5. Own research 100%. Supporting text 25%
Response	1984
Availability	General
Cost	£1
Address	Planning and Development Department, 3-5 Barn Lane, Bodmin Cornwall
Telephone	0208 4121
Contact	Mr W.M. Burden, Planning Technician

752

Originator	NORTH OF SCOTLAND MILK MARKETING BOARD
Title	ANNUAL REPORT, annual. 1935-
Coverage	Producer and market trends over a 10 year period. The remainder is made up of financial and general information.
Contents & Origin of Statistics	Tables per issue: 4. Own research 100%. Supporting text 20%
Currency	3 months
Response	1984
Availability	General
Cost	Free
Address	Claymore House, 29 Ardconnel Terrace, Inverness IV2 3AF
Telephone	0463 232611 ; Telex: 75254
Contact	Mr A. Mackintosh, Market Development Officer

753

Originator	NORTH OF SCOTLAND MILK MARKETING BOARD
Title	MILK TOPICS, monthly. 1957-
Coverage	Current prices paid to milk producers, milk supplies and utilisation.
Contents & Origin of Statistics	Tables per issue: 16pgs. Own research 100%. Supporting text 60%
Currency	2 weeks
Response	1984
Availability	General
Cost	Free
Address	Claymore House, 29 Ardconnel Terrace, Inverness IV2 3AF
Telephone	0463 232611 ; Telex: 75254
Contact	Mr A. Mackintosh, Market Development Officer

754

Originator	NORTH WEST INDUSTRIAL DEVELOPMENT ASSOCIATION
Title	NORWIDA NEWSLETTER, quarterly. 1960-
Coverage	Economic situation, developments and closures in the North West.
Contents & Origin of Statistics	Tables per issue: 3. Own research 20%, Government statistics 80%. Supporting text 90%
Currency	1-2 months
Response	1984

Availability	General
Cost	£3
Address	Brazennose House, Brazennose St, Manchester M2 5AZ
Telephone	061 834 6778; Telex: 667822
Contact	Mr R.J. Tyler, Research Officer

755

Originator	NORTH WEST WATER AUTHORITY
Title	SUMMARY OF FISHERIES STATISTICS, annual. 1974-
Coverage	Catch data, fish culture and hatchery operations, restocking with trout and freshwater fish, fish movement recorded at authority fish counters, counts of salmon, fish mortalities, number of fishing licenses issued.
Contents & Origin of Statistics	Tables per issue: 40. Own research 100%.
Currency	6 months
Response	1984
Availability	General
Cost	£2
ISBN	0144 9141
Address	Rivers Division, P.O. Box 12, New Town House, Buttermarket St, Warrington, Cheshire, WA1 2QG
Telephone	0925 53999; Telex: 628425
Contact	D. Cragg-Hine, Fisheries Liaison Officer

756

Originator	NORTHAMPTONSHIRE CHAMBER OF COMMERCE AND INDUSTRY
Title	QUARTERLY ECONOMIC SURVEY, quarterly
Coverage	Data on labour, production capacity, confidence, orders, stocks investment etc.
Contents & Origin of Statistics	Tables per issue: 12. Own research 100%
Comments	Sample survey of members.
Response	1983
Availability	Members, other chambers
Cost	Not for sale
Address	The Avenue, Cliftonville, Northampton NN1 5BG
Telephone	0604 22422
Contact	Above address

757

Originator	NORTHAMPTONSHIRE COUNTY COUNCIL
Title	POPULATION BULLETIN, annual
Coverage	Consists of 4 sections : estimate of population, births and deaths, population migration and population projections to 1992.
Contents & Origin of Statistics	Tables per issue: 36. Own research 40%, Government statistics 30%, Unstated 30%. Supporting text 5%
Comments	Contains map of district and parish boundaries.
Currency	1 year
Response	1984
Availability	General
Cost	Free
Address	George Row, Northampton
Telephone	0604 34833, ext 5217
Contact	J. Andelin, Principal Research Officer

758

Originator	NORTHERN IRELAND TOURIST BOARD
Title	HOTEL OCCUPANCY SURVEY, monthly. 1972-
Coverage	Room and bedspace occupancy by grade and by region.
Contents & Origin of Statistics	Tables per issue: 2. Own research 100%. Supporting text 25%
Currency	1 month
Response	1984
Availability	General
Cost	Free
Address	River House, 48 High St, Belfast, BT1 2DS
Telephone	0232 231221/7 ; Telex: 748087
Contact	Mr C. Mullaghan, Research Department

759

Originator	NORTHERN IRELAND TOURIST BOARD
Title	TOURISM FACTS, annual. 1978-
Coverage	Information card giving summary of all the major volume and expenditure figures relating to the various categories of visitors to Northern Ireland and the holidaying habits of N.I. residents.
Contents & Origin of Statistics	Tables per issue: 31. Unstated 100%. Supporting text 20%

Currency	1 year
Response	1984
Availability	General
Cost	Free
Address	River House, 48 High St, Belfast, BT1 2DS
Telephone	0232 231221/7 ; Telex: 748087
Contact	Mr C. Mullaghan, Research Department

760

Originator	NORTHERN IRELAND TOURIST BOARD
Title	TOURISM IN NORTHERN IRELAND, annual. 1980-
Coverage	Covers all aspects of tourism in the area. Divides into 3 sections: incoming tourism, holiday-taking by Northern Ireland residents and accommodation survey.
Contents & Origin of Statistics	Tables per issue: c90. Own research 100%. Supporting text 25%
Response	1984
Availability	General
Cost	Free
Address	River House, 48 High St, Belfast, BT1 2DS
Telephone	0232 231221/7 ; Telex: 748087
Contact	Mr C. Mullaghan, Research Department

761

Originator	NORTHUMBERLAND COUNTY COUNCIL
Title	FACTS CARD, annual
Coverage	Data for the county on rates, gross revenue and capital spending, income and grants, staffing and general areas, eg population and education.
Contents & Origin of Statistics	Tables per issue: 12. Unstated 100%.
Currency	Varies
Response	1984
Availability	General
Cost	Free
Address	County Hall, Morpeth, Northumberland NE61 2EF
Telephone	0670 514343 ; Telex: 537048
Contact	Treasurer's Department

762

Originator	NORWICH AND NORFOLK CHAMBER OF COMMERCE AND INDUSTRY
Title	QUARTERLY MANUFACTURING SURVEY, quarterly. October 1981-
Coverage	Survey of members and non-members, issued as a press release. Economic conditions such as orders, exports, stocks, labour, production, investment and confidence for the next quarter. Data for 4 quarters given.
Contents & Origin of Statistics	Tables per issue: 8. Own research 100%. Supporting text 30%
Comments	Available on Sirius disc.
Currency	1 month
Response	1984
Availability	Members and press
Cost	Free
Address	112 Barrack St, Norwich, NR3 1UB
Telephone	0603 25977/25992 ; Telex: 975247
Contact	Margaret Camina, Assistant Secretary (Research)

763

Originator	NOTTINGHAMSHIRE CHAMBER OF COMMERCE AND INDUSTRY
Title	QUARTERLY ECONOMIC SURVEY, quarterly. 1978-
Coverage	Survey of firms in the Nottinghamshire and East Midlands area covering deliveries, orders, production, stocks, cashflow, labour, investment, confidence and business factors.
Contents & Origin of Statistics	Tables per issue: 2pgs. Own research 100%.
Comments	Results of survey are consolidated with results from other chambers in the East Midlands.
Currency	1-2 weeks
Response	1984
Availability	Chamber members (general results issued as a press release)
Cost	Free
Address	395 Mansfield Rd, Nottingham NG5 2DL
Telephone	0602 624624; Telex: 37605
Contact	M. Brosch, Committee Executive

764

Originator	NURSERY TRADER
Title	NEWSDESK, approximately bi-annually in a quarterly journal
Coverage	Market size for the industry with breakdowns of market and brand shares.
Response	1984
Availability	Bona fide retailers and manufacturers
Cost	£10.50
Address	Wheatland Journals Ltd, Penn House, Penn Place, Rickmansworth, Hertfordshire WD3 1SN
Telephone	0923 777000; Telex: 888095
Contact	Alison Davis

765

Originator	ORKNEY ISLANDS COUNCIL
Title	ORKNEY ECONOMIC REVIEW, annual. 1980-
Coverage	General review, weather, agriculture, fishing, manufacturing, tourism, oil, transport, population and gross output in primary and manufacturing sectors
Contents & Origin of Statistics	Tables per issue: 21. Non official source 25%, Government statistics 75%. Supporting text 30%
Currency	Varies
Response	1984
Availability	General
Cost	Free
Address	School Place, Kirkwall, Orkney
Telephone	0856 3535
Contact	J. Baster, Economist, Chief Executive's Department

766

Originator	OXFORD ECONOMIC FORECASTING LTD
Title	QUARTERLY ECONOMIC FORECAST, quarterly. 1981-
Coverage	Forecast of macro-economy. Industry detail and disaggregated consumer spending.
Contents & Origin of Statistics	Tables per issue: 40. Own research 10%, Other non official source 10%, Government statistics 80%. Supporting text 50%
Currency	1-2 days
Response	1984
Availability	General
Cost	£100 + VAT

Address	Oxford Centre for Management Studies, Kennington, Oxford, OX1 5NY
Telephone	0865 735422 ; Telex: 83147
Contact	Mr. J. Walker, Managing Director

767

Originator	OXFORDSHIRE COUNTY COUNCIL
Title	ANNUAL POPULATION FORECASTS FOR OXFORDSHIRE, annual. 1975-
Coverage	Population forecasts up to 8 years ahead in total, by district, age, households, and school pupil forecasts.
Contents & Origin of Statistics	Tables per issue: 4. Supporting text 30%
Comments	Appendices to the report issued as separate reports.
Currency	2-3 months
Response	1984
Availability	General
Cost	Free
Address	County Hall, New Rd, Oxford OX1 1ND
Telephone	0865 815268
Contact	Mrs J. Naccache, Research and Intelligence Unit

768

Originator	OXFORDSHIRE COUNTY COUNCIL/OXFORDSHIRE JOINT DISTRICT HOUSING GROUP
Title	OXFORDSHIRE HOUSING STATISTICS, annual. 1975-
Coverage	Statistics on housing provision, management, maintenance, and finance, housing conditions and the private sector.
Contents & Origin of Statistics	Tables per issue: 19. Own research 100%.
Currency	9 months
Response	1984
Availability	Members and Officers plus generally available locally
Address	County Hall, New Rd, Oxford 0X1 1ND
Telephone	0865 815268
Contact	Mr D. R. Spark, Research and Intelligence Unit

769

Originator	PA PERSONNEL SERVICES LTD
Title	TOP MANAGEMENT PAY SURVEY, continuous update
Coverage	Salary survey covering 45 senior management posts prepared for the individual. As part of service receive an annual report on salary administration and fringe benefit practices and trends and various club surveys.
Contents & Origin of Statistics	Tables per issue: Own research 100%.
Comments	Also issue an annual 'International Pay and Benefits Survey' free.
Currency	1-2 months
Response	1984
Availability	Participants only
Cost	£300 (+ VAT)
Address	Hyde Park House, 60A Knightsbridge, London, SW1X 7LE
Telephone	01 235 6060; Telex: 27874
Contact	Miss Sheila M. Smith, Manager, Pay Research

770

Originator	PACKAGING REVIEW
Title	INDUSTRY REVIEW, annual in the January issue of a monthly journal. 1971 -
Coverage	Review of the packaging materials, containers and machinery industries.
Contents & Origin of Statistics	Tables per issue: 30. Own research + other non official source 90%, Government statistics 10%
Currency	1 month
Response	1984
Availability	General
Cost	£28 or £2.80 for a single issue
ISSN	0048 2684
Address	Business Press International, Quadrant House, The Quadrant, Sutton, Surrey SM2 5AS
Telephone	01 661 3193; Telex: 892084
Contact	Ms. P. Covell, Editor

771

Originator	PAINTMAKERS ASSOCIATION OF GREAT BRITAIN LTD
Title	ANNUAL STATISTICAL REVIEW SUMMARY, annual

Coverage	General summary data from the 'Annual Statistical Review' - see next entry.
Contents & Origin of Statistics	Tables per issue: Own research 100%
Response	1984
Availability	Selected organisations and individuals
Cost	Free
Address	Alembic House, 93 Albert Embankment, London SE1 7TY
Telephone	01 582 1185
Contact	M.J. Levete, Director

772

Originator	PAINTMAKERS ASSOCIATION OF GREAT BRITAIN LTD
Title	ANNUAL STATISTICAL REVIEW, annual
Coverage	Trends in the industry based on a survey of members.
Contents & Origin of Statistics	Tables per issue: Own research 100%
Response	1984
Availability	Members
Cost	Free
Address	Alembic House, 93 Albert Embankment, London SE1 7TY
Telephone	01 582 1185
Contact	M.J. Levete, Director

773

Originator	PAINTMAKERS ASSOCIATION OF GREAT BRITAIN LTD
Title	MIDYEAR STATISTICAL REVIEW, annual
Coverage	Trends in the industry based on a survey of members
Contents & Origin of Statistics	Tables per issue: Own research 100%
Response	1984
Availability	Members
Cost	Free
Address	Alembic House, 93 Albert Embankment, London SE1 7TY
Telephone	01 582 1185
Contact	M.J. Levete, Director

774

Originator	PAINTMAKERS ASSOCIATION OF GREAT BRITAIN LTD
Title	QUARTERLY SALES BULLETIN, quarterly
Coverage	Sales for the quarter compared with the sales of the year. Also has selling prices indices and covers the last 3 years. Based on a survey of 40 member companies.
Contents & Origin of Statistics	Tables per issue: 5. Own research 100%. Supporting text 60%
Response	1984
Availability	General
Address	Alembic House, 93 Albert Embankment, London SE1 7TY
Telephone	01 582 1185
Contact	M.J. Levete, Director

775

Originator	PALMER MARKET RESEARCH
Title	CONTRACT FLOORCOVERING MARKET IN GREAT BRITAIN, biennial
Coverage	Analysed by main type of carpet, resilient floorcovering, industrial and other floorcoverings. Attitudes to floorcoverings and major manufacturers.Includes a 4 year forecast.
Contents & Origin of Statistics	Tables per issue: 50. Own research 90%, Government statistics 10%. Supporting text 50%
Currency	9 months
Response	1984
Availability	General
Cost	£2200 + VAT
Address	Isabel House, 46-47 Victoria Rd, Surbiton, Surrey KT6 4JL
Telephone	01 390 5348; Telex: 291561
Contact	Robert Palmer, Proprietor

776

Originator	PALMER MARKET RESEARCH
Title	TRADE PAINT MARKET IN GREAT BRITAIN, triennial
Coverage	Decorative paint market analysed by type of paint, sector and distribution. Attitudes to major paint manufacturers. Protective coatings market analysed by type of coating and end use. Includes forecast four years ahead.

Contents &	Tables per issue: 30. Own research 90%, Government statistics 10%.
Origin of	Supporting text 50%
Statistics	

Comments	Latest edition published April 1984.
Currency	6 months
Response	1984
Availability	General
Cost	£1750 + VAT
Address	Isabel House, 46-47 Victoria Rd, Surbiton, Surrey KT6 4JL
Telephone	01 390 5348; Telex: 291561
Contact	Robert Palmer, Proprietor

777

Originator	PALMER MARKET RESEARCH

Title	WINDOW FRAME AND DOMESTIC DOOR MARKETS IN GREAT BRITAIN, biennial
Coverage	Market analysed by material and by sector. Covers new buildings, domestic renovations, home improvements. Patio and residential (entrance) doors are also included. Forecast given 4 years ahead.

Contents &	Tables per issue: 30. Own research 90%, Government statistics 10%.
Origin of	Supporting text 50%
Statistics	

Comments	Latest edition published June 1984.
Currency	6 months
Response	1984
Availability	General
Cost	£1900 + VAT
Address	Isabel House, 46-47 Victoria Rd, Surbiton, Surrey KT6 4JL
Telephone	01 390 5348; Telex: 291561
Contact	Robert Palmer, Proprietor

778

Originator	PANEL ON TAKE-OVERS AND MERGERS

Title	ANNUAL REPORT, annual. 1969-
Coverage	Numbers of take-overs and mergers during a year.

Contents &	Tables per issue: 1. Own research 100%. Supporting text 85%
Origin of	
Statistics	

Currency	2 months
Response	1984
Availability	General
Cost	Free
Address	P.O. Box 226, The Stock Exchange Building, London EC2P 2JX

Telephone	01 628 2318
Contact	Mrs J.H. O'Neill, Assistant to the Secretary

779

Originator	PANNELL KERR FORSTER ASSOCIATES
Title	MONTHLY BULLETIN OF TRENDS IN LONDON HOTELS, monthly. 1973-
Coverage	Performance trends by volume and revenue of London hotels based on a sample survey of London hotels. Hotels are grouped according to average achieved room rate and food and beverage costs.
Contents & Origin of Statistics	Tables per issue: 6. Own research 100%.
Comments	Also publish international volume.
Currency	6 weeks
Response	1984
Availability	Contributors only
Cost	Free
Address	78 Hatton Garden, London EC1N 8JA
Telephone	01 831 7393; Telex: 295928
Contact	J.A. Goldsmith, Administrator of Statistical Services

780

Originator	PANNELL KERR FORSTER ASSOCIATES
Title	OUTLOOK IN THE HOTEL AND TOURISM INDUSTRY - LONDON TRENDS, annual
Coverage	Summary of the performance of a sample of London hotels. Details of occupancy levels, achieved room rate, and sales and the cost of sales of food and beverage departments.
Contents & Origin of Statistics	Tables per issue: 11. Own research 75%, Government statistics 25%. Supporting text 50%
Comments	Also publish international volume.
Currency	3 months
Response	1984
Availability	General
Cost	Free
Address	78 Hatton Garden, London EC1N 8JA
Telephone	01 831 7393; Telex: 295928
Contact	J. Goldsmith, Administrator of Statistical Services

781

Originator	PANNELL KERR FORSTER ASSOCIATES
Title	OUTLOOK IN THE HOTEL AND TOURISM INDUSTRY - UK TRENDS, annual
Coverage	Review of the operating and financial characteristics of a sample of hotels throughout the UK. Details of room occupancy rates, revenues, departmental costs and expenses, income, and the ratio of departmental expenses to income.
Contents & Origin of Statistics	Tables per issue: 11. Own research 75%, Government statistics 25%. Supporting text 50%
Comments	Also publish international volume
Currency	6 months
Response	1984
Availability	General
Cost	Free
Address	78 Hatton Garden, London EC1N 8JA
Telephone	01 831 7393; Telex: 295928
Contact	J. Goldsmith, Administrator of Statistical Services

782

Originator	PANNELL KERR FORSTER ASSOCIATES
Title	QUARTERLY BULLETIN OF TRENDS IN PROVINCIAL HOTELS, quarterly. 1983-
Coverage	Analysis of operating performance, in volume and revenue terms, of a sample of hotels grouped by English Tourist Board region, and Scotland and Wales. Also details of food and beverage costs and % of revenue paid through credit card companies.
Contents & Origin of Statistics	Tables per issue: 36. Own research 100%.
Comments	Also publish international volume.
Currency	2-3 months
Response	1984
Availability	Contributors only
Cost	Free
Address	78 Hatton Garden, London EC1N 8JA
Telephone	01 831 7393; Telex: 295928
Contact	J.A. Goldsmith, Adminstrator of Statistical Services

783

Originator	PAPER FACTS AND FIGURES
Title	PAPER AND BOARD INDICES, 6 times a year in a journal published 6 times a year. October 1983-
Coverage	Index of price changes of coated and uncoated wood-free and mechanical papers.
Contents & Origin of Statistics	Tables per issue: 5. Own research 100%
Currency	2 weeks
Response	1984
Availability	General
Cost	£34
ISSN	0031 112X
Address	Benn Business Information Services Ltd, Union House, Eridge Rd, Tunbridge Wells, Kent
Telephone	0892 38991
Contact	Martin White, Manager

784

Originator	PAPER INDUSTRIES RESEARCH ASSOCIATION
Title	ECONOMICS AND MARKET INTELLIGENCE, 3 times per year
Coverage	Covers total printing and publishing industry, national and regional newspapers, books, periodicals and general printing and publishing Data on imports and exports, economic indicators, market and forecasts.
Response	1983
Availability	Members, others by arrangement
Cost	£2,500 + VAT first sector, second and subsequent £250 + VAT each
Address	Randalls Rd, Leatherhead, Surrey KT22 7RU
Telephone	03723 76161
Contact	Above address

785

Originator	PAPER INDUSTRIES RESEARCH ASSOCIATION
Title	STATISTICAL REVIEW OF PACKAGING, annual

Coverage	One year a full economic and statistical review, the next updates of statistical tables. (Over 5 year period.) Detailed review of the market for pacaging materials and packs, including sales, production and prices. Sections analysing in detail the end- use of the different packaging media by the following industries - food and drink, tobacco, pharmaceutical products, toiletries and cosmetics. Also data on machinery and plastics end-use applications.
Response	1983
Availability	General
Cost	£130, £100 to members
Address	Randalls Rd, Leatherhead, Surrey, KT22 7RU
Telephone	03723 76161
Contact	Above address

786

Originator	PAR (AGRICULTURAL RESEARCH)
Title	CEREAL GROWERS' USE OF CROP PROTECTION CHEM-ICALS, annual
Coverage	Data on growers' use of and attitudes to crop protection chemicals based on a sample survey of 240 to 800 farmers.
Contents & Origin of Statistics	Tables per issue: Own research 100%. Supporting text 20%
Comments	Specialised services available on request.
Response	1984
Availability	General
Cost	£6,000 ('off the shelf data' available at negotiated price)
Address	Elm Cottage, Mil Rd, Shiplake, Henley-on-Thames, Oxfordshire
Contact	John Hamilton Russell, Chief Executive

787

Originator	PAR (AGRICULTURAL RESEARCH)
Title	OILSEED RAPE GROWERS' USE OF CROP PROTECTION CHEMICALS, annual
Coverage	Data on growers' use of and attitudes to crop protection chemicals based on a sample survey of 240 to 800 farmers.
Contents & Origin of Statistics	Tables per issue: Own research 100%. Supporting text 20%
Comments	Specialised services available on request.
Response	1984
Availability	General
Cost	£2,500 ('off the shelf' data at negotiated price)

Address	Elm Cottage, Mil Rd, Shiplake, Henley-on-Thames, Oxfordshire
Contact	John Hamilton Russell, Chief Executive

788

Originator	PAR (AGRICULTURAL RESEARCH)
Title	POTATO GROWERS' USE OF CROP PROTECTION CHEM-ICALS, annual
Coverage	Data on growers' use of and attitudes to crop protection chemicals based on a sample survey of 240 to 800 farmers.
Contents & Origin of Statistics	Tables per issue: Own research 100%. Supporting text 20%
Comments	Specialised services available on request
Response	1984
Availability	General
Cost	£4,500 ('off the shelf' data at negotiated prices)
Address	Elm Cottage, Mil Rd, Shiplake, Henley-on-Thames, Oxfordshire
Contact	John Hamilton Russell, Chief Executive

789

Originator	PAR (AGRICULTURAL RESEARCH)
Title	SUGAR BEET GROWERS' USE OF CROP PROTECTION CHEMICALS, annual
Coverage	Data on growers' use of and attitudes to crop protection chemicals based on a sample survey of 240 to 800 farmers.
Contents & Origin of Statistics	Tables per issue: Own research 100%. Supporting text 20%
Comments	Specialised services available on request
Response	1984
Availability	General
Cost	£4,500 ('off the shelf' data at negotiated price)
Address	Elm Cottage, Mil Rd, Shiplake, Henley-on-Thames, Oxfordshire
Contact	John Hamilton Russell, Chief Executive

790

Originator	PERSONNEL MANAGEMENT
Title	GUARDIAN RECRUITMENT MONITOR, monthly in monthly journal. August 1983-
Coverage	Number of columns devoted to recruitment advertising for latest month in 'quality' newspapers plus % change on previous month.

Contents & Origin of Statistics	Tables per issue: 2. Non official source 100%

Currency	2 months
Response	1984
Availability	General
Cost	£25, or £2.20 for single copy
Address	Personnel Publications Ltd, 1 Hills Place, London W1
Telephone	01 734 1773
Contact	News Editor

791

Originator	PET FOOD MANUFACTURERS' ASSOCIATION

Title	PFMA MARKETING INFORMATION, annual
Coverage	Data on market size and value for prepared pet food products with % change from previous year. Also a general commmentary on the figures and details of how the figures are prepared.

Contents & Origin of Statistics	Tables per issue: 1. Own research 100%. Supporting text 60%

Currency	3 months
Response	1984
Availability	Members and general
Cost	Free
Address	6 Catherine St, London WC2B 5JJ
Telephone	01 836 2460; Telex: 299388
Contact	Elizabeth Archer, Executive Secretary

792

Originator	PET FOOD MANUFACTURERS' ASSOCIATION

Title	PFMA PROFILE, annual
Coverage	Data on pet ownership, cost of pet foods, and the market size and value of prepared pet foods. Also general information on the industry, PFMA's views and current legislation.

Contents & Origin of Statistics	Tables per issue: 5. Own research 100%. Supporting text 80%

Currency	3 months
Response	1984
Availability	Members and general
Cost	Free
Address	6 Catherine St, London WC2B 5JJ

Telephone	01 836 2460; Telex: 299388
Contact	Elizabeth Archer, Executive Secretary

793

Originator	PETROLEUM TIMES
Title	PETROLEUM TIMES PRICE REPORT, twice monthly in a monthly journal
Coverage	UK pump prices of petrol in major towns and UK product prices charged by major companies.
Contents & Origin of Statistics	Tables per issue: 2. Own research 100%. Supporting text 50%
Comments	Subscribers to Petroleum Times receive the twice- monthly Price Report as a separate document. It also contains overseas price information
Currency	1 week
Response	1985
Availability	General
Cost	£65 or £3 for a single issue
ISSN	0263 3590
Address	Business Press International Ltd, Quadrant House, The Quadrant, Sutton, Surrey, SM2 5AS
Telephone	01 661 3500; Telex: 982084
Contact	Bart Collins, Editor

794

Originator	PHARMACEUTICAL JOURNAL
Title	INDEPENDENT PHARMACIES, NHS TURNOVER AND CASH TURNOVER, monthly in a weekly journal
Coverage	Turnover of pharmacies in Great Britain
Contents & Origin of Statistics	Tables per issue: Non official source 100%
Comments	Also publish other statistics - see other entries
Response	1984
Availability	General
Cost	Free to members, £33.50 to other organisations
Address	Pharmaceutical Society of Great Britain, 1 Lambeth High St, London SE1 7JN
Telephone	01 735 9141
Contact	Jocelyn Luxon

795

Originator	PHARMACEUTICAL JOURNAL
Title	PHARMACY NUMBERS, PHARMACY STUDENT NUMBERS, PHARMACIST NUMBERS annual in a weekly journal
Coverage	Pharmacist numbers gives details of employment of pharmacists by principal occupation and age. Pharmacy number covers Great Britain and students numbers analyses students attending pharmacy coleges.
Contents & Origin of Statistics	Tables per issue: Own research 100%
Comments	Also publish prescription statistics - see other entry
Currency	Varies
Response	1984
Availability	General
Cost	Free to members, £33.50 to other organisations
Address	Pharmaceutical Society of Great Britain, 1 Lambeth High St, London SE1 7JN
Telephone	01 735 9141
Contact	Jocelyn Luxon

796

Originator	PHARMACEUTICAL JOURNAL
Title	PRESCRIPTION STATISTICS FOR ENGLAND AND WALES, monthly and annual in a weekly journal
Coverage	Data on number and types of prescriptions.
Contents & Origin of Statistics	Tables per issue: Non official source 100%
Comments	Also publish other statistics - see other entries
Response	1984
Availability	General
Cost	Free to members, £33.50 to other organisations
Address	Pharmaceutical Society of Great Britain, 1 Lambeth High St, London SE1 7JN
Telephone	01 735 9141
Contact	Jocelyn Luxon

797

Originator	PHARMACEUTICAL JOURNAL
Title	RETAIL SALES INDEX FOR CHEMISTS, monthly in a weekly journal
Coverage	Sales trends for chemists.

Contents &	Tables per issue: Government statistics 100%
Origin of	
Statistics	
Comments	Also publish other statistics - see other entries
Response	1984
Availability	General
Cost	Free to members, £33.50 to other organisations
Address	Pharmaceutical Society of Great Britain, 1 Lambeth High St, London SE1 7JN
Telephone	01 735 9141
Contact	Jocelyn Luxon

798

Originator	PHILLIPS AND DREW
Title	ECONOMIC FORECASTS, monthly
Coverage	Short term forecasts and forecasts for 2 and 5 years ahead for the major economic variables plus an assessment of economic policy, economic assumptions and a summary of UK forecasts.
Contents &	Tables per issue: Own research + government statistics 100%
Origin of	
Statistics	
Comments	Also produce 'one-off' sector reports and international publications.
Response	1984
Availability	Private circulation
Cost	£350 or £35 for a single issue
Address	120 Moorgate, London EC2M 6XP
Telephone	01 628 4444; Telex: 291163
Contact	Above address

799

Originator	PHILLIPS AND DREW
Title	EQUITY MARKET INDICATORS, 6 issues per year
Coverage	General equity trends.
Comments	Also produce 'one-off' reports on particular sectors and international publications.
Response	1984
Availability	General
Cost	Free to clients, £170 to others or £35 for a single issue.
Address	120 Moorgate, London EC2M 6XP
Telephone	01 628 4444; Telex: 291163
Contact	Above address

800

Originator	PHILLIPS AND DREW
Title	GILTS - THE MONTH AHEAD, monthly
Coverage	General trends for gilts and bonds.
Comments	Also produce 'one-off' sector reports and international publications.
Response	1984
Availability	General
Cost	Free to clients, £225 to others or £25 for a single issue
Address	120 Moorgate, London EC2M 6XP
Telephone	01 628 4444; Telex: 291163
Contact	Above address

801

Originator	PHILLIPS AND DREW
Title	MARKET REVIEW, monthly
Coverage	General review of economic and market trends.
Comments	Also produce 'one-off' sector reports and international publications.
Currency	Varies
Response	1984
Availability	General
Cost	Free to clients, £65 to others or £7 for a single issue
Address	120 Moorgate, London EC2M 6XP
Telephone	01 628 4444; Telex: 291163
Contact	Above address

802

Originator	PIGS MARKETING BOARD (NORTHERN IRELAND)
Title	ANNUAL REPORT AND ACCOUNTS, annual
Coverage	Pig population figures, bacon prices, market supplies, prices and feed costs, produce grading etc.
Contents & Origin of Statistics	Tables per issue: 6. Government statistics 15%, Unstated 85%. Supporting text 50%
Response	1984
Availability	General
Cost	Free
Address	New Forge Lane, Belfast BT9 5NX
Telephone	0232 669431
Contact	H.D. Ritchie, Senior Economist

803

Originator	PIZZA ASSOCIATION
Title	PIZZA PRESS, quarterly. Autumn 1984-
Coverage	General data on the pizza industry.
Contents & Origin of Statistics	Tables per issue: Varies
Currency	Varies
Response	1984
Address	29 Market Place, Wantage, Oxfordshire
Telephone	02357 66339
Contact	Jim Winship, Editor

804

Originator	PLUNKETT FOUNDATION
Title	PRESS RELEASE, annual
Coverage	Summary data in aggregate on 600 co-operatives in the UK.
Contents & Origin of Statistics	Tables per issue: 1. Supporting text 50%
Currency	12 months
Response	1984
Availability	General
Address	31 St Giles, Oxford OX1 3LF
Telephone	0865 53960/1
Contact	T.F. Riordan, Statistics Officer

805

Originator	PLUNKETT FOUNDATION
Title	STATISTICS OF AGRICULTURAL CO-OPERATIVES IN THE UK, annual. 1969-
Coverage	Aggregate data on 600 co-operatives in the UK. Data on sales, profits, share interest and bonus payments, membership and staff numbers.
Contents & Origin of Statistics	Tables per issue: 30-35.
Currency	12 months
Response	1984
Availability	General
Cost	£4.12

ISSN	0266 0091
Address	31 St Giles, Oxford OX1 3LF
Telephone	0865 53960/1
Contact	T.F. Riordan, Statistics Officer

806

Originator	PORTSMOUTH DISTRICT COUNCIL
Title	PORTSMOUTH INDICATORS, quarterly
Coverage	Quarterly reports on unemployment, housing, council house sales and general statistics.
Contents & Origin of Statistics	Tables per issue: 14. Own research 35%, Government statistics 65%. Supporting text 40%
Currency	Varies
Response	1983
Availability	General
Address	Civic Offices, Guildhall Square, Portsmouth PO1 2AU
Telephone	0705 22251
Contact	City Planning Officer

807

Originator	PORTSMOUTH DISTRICT COUNCIL
Title	PORTSMOUTH POINTERS, annual
Coverage	General data on population, housing, tourism, employment/ unemployment etc.
Contents & Origin of Statistics	Tables per issue: 8. Own research 40%, Government statistics 60%.
Comments	Produced in pocket card format.
Currency	Varies
Response	1983
Availability	General
Cost	Free
Address	Civic Offices, Guildhall Square, Portsmouth PO1 2AU
Telephone	0705 22251
Contact	City Planning Officer

808

| Originator | POTATO MARKETING BOARD |
| Title | FLOW CHART FOR POTATOES IN GREAT BRITAIN, annual |

Contents &	Tables per issue: 1. Own research 50%, Government statistics 50%.
Origin of	
Statistics	

Response	1984
Availability	General
Cost	Free
Address	Broadfield House, 4 Between Towns Rd, Cowley, Oxford
Telephone	0865 714455
Contact	J. Pearson, Statistics

809

Originator	POTATO MARKETING BOARD

Title	POTATO PROCESSING IN GREAT BRITAIN, annual
Coverage	Consumption figures, exports and imports of processed potatoes, raw potatoes used for processing in the UK and information on varieties of potatoes used for processing purposes.

Contents &	Tables per issue: 6. Own research 90%, Government statistics 10%.
Origin of	Supporting text 50%
Statistics	

Response	1984
Availability	General
Cost	Free
ISSN	0140 9557
Address	50 Hans Crescent, London SW1X 0WB
Telephone	01 589 4874; Telex: 912193
Contact	J. Pearson, Statistics

810

Originator	POTATO MARKETING BOARD

Title	POTATO STATISTICS BULLETIN, annual
Coverage	Monthly rate of human consumption and planting by variety by registered producers.

Contents &	Tables per issue: 7. Own research 85%, Government statistics 15%.
Origin of	
Statistics	

Response	1984
Availability	General
Cost	Free
Address	50 Hans Crescent, Knightsbridge, London SW1X 0NB
Telephone	01 589 4874; Telex: 912193
Contact	J. Pearson, Statistics

811

Originator	POWER RESEARCH ASSOCIATES
Title	MARKET INFORMATION REQUIREMENTS OF UK COMPANIES, every 2-3 years
Coverage	Covers the marketing information needs of UK marketing management.
Contents & Origin of Statistics	Tables per issue: Own research 100%. Supporting text 10%
Response	1983
Availability	General
Cost	£50 + VAT
Address	17 Wigmore St, London W1H 9LA
Telephone	01 580 5816
Contact	M.C. Power

812

Originator	POWER RESEARCH ASSOCIATES
Title	PIZZA MARKET IN THE UK, annual/biennial
Coverage	Covers UK fast food market, especially pizzas.
Contents & Origin of Statistics	Tables per issue: Own research 100%. Supporting text 25%
Response	1983
Availability	General
Cost	£275 + VAT
Address	17 Wigmore St, London W1H 9LA
Telephone	01 580 5816
Contact	M.C. Power

813

Originator	PRESS COUNCIL
Title	THE PRESS AND THE PEOPLE, annual. 1953-
Coverage	Ownership, circulation of British press with radio and television interests.
Contents & Origin of Statistics	Tables per issue: 10. Own research 100%. Supporting text 75%
Currency	4-6 months
Response	1984
Availability	General

Cost	£4.50
Address	1 Salisbury Square, London EC4Y 8AE
Telephone	01 353 1248
Contact	R.J.P. Swingler, Secretary

814

Originator	PRESSURE SENSITIVE MANUFACTURERS ASSOCIATION
Title	UNTITLED
Coverage	Regular sales statistics, business trends and raw material trend surveys of members are circulated.
Contents & Origin of Statistics	Tables per issue: Own research 100%
Response	1983
Availability	Members
Address	35 New Bridge St, London EC4V 6BH
Telephone	01 248 5271
Contact	E.G.C. Bing, Secretary

815

Originator	PRINTING INDUSTRIES
Title	ECONOMIC TRENDS, monthly in a monthly journal
Coverage	General economic data covering the retail price index, industrial trends, employment etc.
Contents & Origin of Statistics	Tables per issue: 12. Non official source 10%. Own research 90%
Comments	The Federation publishes various other regular surveys - see entries headed 'British Printing Industries Federation'.
Response	1984
Availability	General
Cost	Free to members, £3.50 to others
Address	British Printing Industries Federation, 11 Bedford Row, London WC1R 4DX
Telephone	01 242 6904

816

Originator	PRINTING WORLD
Title	PRICES PERISCOPE AND PAPER PRICES INDEX, quarterl in a weekly journal. 1980-
Coverage	Prices of types of paper and material/fuel costs.

Contents &	Tables per issue: 1. Own research 100%
Origin of	
Statistics	

Currency	1-2 months
Response	1984
Availability	General
Cost	£37 or 70p for a single issue
ISSN	0032 8715
Address	Benn Publications Ltd, Benn House, Sovereign Way, Tonbridge, Kent TN9 1RW
Telephone	0732 364422; Telex: 95132
Contact	Roy Coxhead, Editor

817

| **Originator** | PROCUREMENT WEEKLY |

| **Title** | PRICES GUIDE, weekly in a weekly journal |
| **Coverage** | Prices of various commodities including metals, soft commodities, paper, fuel, plastics, chemicals, fish, meat and vegetables. Current prices plus 6 months and 12 months |

Contents &	Tables per issue: 1. Own research 100%
Origin of	
Statistics	

Currency	2-3 days
Response	1984
Availability	General
Cost	£27
Address	Institute of Purchasing and Supply, IPS House, High St, Ascot, Berkshire
Contact	B. Wyllie, IPS

818

| **Originator** | PROFESSIONAL PUBLISHING LTD |

| **Title** | BUSINESS CARS SURVEY, biennial. 1979- |
| **Coverage** | Survey of company car fleets using sample from British Institute of Management. Data on allocation, acquisition and fundings, cost control, depreciation, replacement and disposal and taxation. |

Contents &	Tables per issue: 16. Own research 90%, Government statistics 10%.
Origin of	Supporting text 70%
Statistics	

Comments	Data also available on magnetic tape
Currency	6 months
Response	1984
Availability	General
Cost	£31.25

ISBN	O946559 01 5
Address	Alhambra House, 27-31 Charing Cross Rd, London WC2H 0AU
Telephone	01 930 3951
Contact	M. Woodmansey, Editor

819

Originator	PROFESSIONAL PUBLISHING LTD
Title	MOTOR INDUSTRY HANDBOOK, continuously updated. July 1984-
Coverage	Data on car numbers, patterns of ownership, consumer and business use, trade, overseas markets, energy, fuel and retailing, taxation and the law regarding the motor industry.
Contents & Origin of Statistics	Tables per issue: 500 per year. Own research 20%, Other non official source 60%, Government statistics 20%. Supporting text 20%.
Currency	6 months
Response	1984
Availability	General
Cost	£30, first year, then £25 for updates.
ISBN	O 946559 05 8
Address	Alhambra House, 27-31 Charing Cross Rd, London WC2H 0AU
Telephone	01 930 3951
Contact	M. Woodmansey, Editor

820

Originator	PUBLIC ATTITUDE SURVEYS RESEARCH LTD
Title	BEER MARKET, quarterly
Coverage	Syndicated sample survey of drinkers' consumption and behaviour. Sample of 20,000 adults a year, by face-to-face interviewing.
Contents & Origin of Statistics	Tables per issue: Own research 100%.
Response	1983
Availability	General
Cost	£15,000
Address	P.O. Box 91, Rye Park House, London Rd, High Wycombe, Bucks HP11 1EF
Telephone	0494 32771
Contact	A.E.C. Eastaugh, Managing Director

821

Originator	PUBLIC ATTITUDE SURVEYS RESEARCH LTD
Title	WINE MARKET, quarterly
Coverage	Syndicated sample survey of drinkers' consumption and behaviour. Sample of 14,400 adults a year, by face-to-face interviewing.
Contents & Origin of Statistics	Tables per issue: Own research 100%.
Response	1983
Availability	General
Cost	£8,750
Address	P.O. Box 91, Rye Park House, London Rd, High Wycombe, Bucks HP11 1EF
Telephone	0494 32771
Contact	A.E.C. Eastaugh, Managing Director

822

Originator	PUBLICAN
Title	READERS' PANEL SURVEY, quarterly in a fortnightly journal
Coverage	Survey of approximately 42 pubs giving information on alcohol prices by region and by type of pub, e.g. tenanted/free house/managed and urban or rural.
Contents & Origin of Statistics	Tables per issue: 5. Own research 100%. Supporting text 40%
Response	1984
Availability	Controlled circulation to publicans
Cost	Free
Address	Maclaren Publishers Ltd, Maclaren House, Scarbrook Rd, Croydon CR9 1QH
Telephone	01 688 7788; Telex: 946665
Contact	Brian Gorton

823

Originator	PUBLISHERS ASSOCIATION
Title	QUARTERLY STATISTICS, quarterly
Coverage	Covers the performance of UK publishing industry over 1 year. Statistics cover turnover, by book type, exports, book prices, student buying and expenditure forecasts. Each issue contains news items on special topics.

Contents &	Tables per issue: 40-50. Supporting text 40%
Origin of	
Statistics	
Comments	Various occasional publications also produced
Currency	1 month
Response	1984
Availability	General
Cost	Free to members, £12.50 to non-members
ISSN	0260 5198
Address	19 Bedford Square, London WC1B 3HJ
Telephone	01 580 6321; Telex: 21792
Contact	Philip Flamank

824

Originator	PUBLISHERS ASSOCIATION
Title	SCHOOL BOOK SPENDING SERIES 2, 3 issues per year
Coverage	Schoolbook spending figures by local education authority area. Individual reports for each area.
Contents &	Tables per issue: 7-10. Own research 100%. Supporting text 30%
Origin of	
Statistics	
Comments	Various occasional publications also produced.
Response	1984
Availability	General
Address	19 Bedford Square, London WC1B 3HJ
Telephone	01 580 6321; Telex: 21792
Contact	Philip Flamank

825

Originator	PURCHASING
Title	DATAFILE, monthly in a monthly journal
Coverage	Prices of chemicals, plastics, metals, and basic materials plus exchange rates.
Currency	1 month
Response	1984
Availability	Controlled circulation but generally available on subscription
Cost	Free on controlled circulation to purchasing industry £30 to others
Address	Morgan-Grampian (Publishers) plc, 30 Calderwood St, Woolwich London SE18 6QH
Telephone	01 855 7777
Contact	A. Barry, Editor

826

Originator	RADIO CITY
Title	JICRAR BOOKLET, annual
Coverage	Survey conducted according to JICRAR specifications. Includes cumulative weekly audience reach and in half-hour divisions, audience profile, reach by different radio stations, reach for Liverpool Echo. Reach and frequency analysis for typical advertising campaigns. Lancashire radio audience.
Contents & Origin of Statistics	Tables per issue: 15. Own research 100%
Response	1983
Availability	General
Cost	£1,000 per thousand
Address	8-10 Stanley St, Liverpool L1 6AF
Telephone	051 227 5100
Contact	Miss R. Garbett Edwards, Sales Promotion Executive

827

Originator	RADIO TEES
Title	GREAT NORTHERN RADIO MARKET, annual
Coverage	Contains demographic profiles, Acorn profile, industrial profile retail structure and living standards, including food, holidays leisure activities, toiletries, consumer durables and household goods. Also contains listening figures and circulation figures for local papers.
Contents & Origin of Statistics	Tables per issue: 24. Own research 60%, Government statistics 10%, Unstated 30%
Comments	Produced in association with Metro Radio under joint name of Tyne Tees Radio
Currency	Varies
Response	1983
Availability	General
Cost	Free
Address	74 Dovecot St, Stockton-on-Tees, Cleveland TS18 1HB
Telephone	0642 615111
Contact	Paul Beach

828

Originator	RADIO TEES
Title	SURVEY OF THE RADIO AUDIENCE, 3 issues per year

Coverage	Results of a survey of radio listening. Information gathered via diary technique. Gives data for cumulative weekly audience (reach) and average half-hour audience. Covers ILR, Radio Luxembourg and BBC. Also includes information on Rate Card Segment audiences, Results of special reach and frequency package analyses, by sex, age and social class.
Contents & Origin of Statistics	Tables per issue: 8. Non official source 100%
Comments	Survey conducted by Research Surveys of Great Britain
Response	1983
Availability	General
Cost	Free
Address	74 Dovecot St, Stockton-on-Tees, Cleveland TS18 1HB
Telephone	0642 615111
Contact	Paul Beach

829

Originator	RATING AND VALUATION ASSOCIATION
Title	GENERAL RATE POUNDAGES AND PRODUCTS, annual
Coverage	Local authority rate poundages in England, Wales and Scotland. Gives total rate product, total domestic rateable value, total other rateable value, % increase over previous year and number of rating assessments and population.
Contents & Origin of Statistics	Tables per issue: 70pgs. Own research 100%.
Currency	1-2 months
Response	1984
Availability	General
Cost	£4
Address	115 Ebury St, London SW1W 9QT
Telephone	01 730 7258
Contact	Mr J. Price, Assistant Secretary

830

Originator	REDDITCH DEVELOPMENT CORPORATION
Title	EMPLOYMENT SURVEY, annual. 1974-
Coverage	Number of firms and employment trends in Redditch by SIC business size, and location. Also examines changes and trends in the employment structure over the last ten years. Based on a survey of all known firms in the area.

Contents & **Origin of** **Statistics**	Tables per issue: 35. Own research 85%, Government statistics 15%. Supporting text 45%
Comments	Details of survey method and questionnaire used given. Corporation winding up in 1985 - subsequent inquiries to Borough of Redditch Planning Department.
Currency	3-4 months
Response	1984
Availability	General
Cost	Free
ISBN	0 947591 01 X
Address	Holmwood, Plymouth Rd North, Southcrest, Redditch, Worcestershire B97 4PD
Telephone	0527 64200 ; Telex: 335201
Contact	M.S. McNidder, Chief Planner

831

Originator	REMUNERATION ECONOMICS LTD
Title	BIM NATIONAL MANAGEMENT SALARY SURVEY, annual. 1974-
Coverage	The survey analyses the earnings, fringe benefits and bonuses of over 24000 individuals, employed by 340 organisations at 9 levels of responsibility within a variety of company profiles eg sales turnover, industry, number of employees.
Contents & **Origin of** **Statistics**	Tables per issue: 360. Own research 100%.
Comments	Published in association with the BIM.
Currency	3 months
Response	1984
Availability	General
Cost	Cost (pa):£150 (£110 main report, £70 small business)
Address	Survey House, 51 Portland Rd, Kingston-upon-Thames, Surrey KT1 2SH
Telephone	01 549 8726
Contact	Peter Stevens, Director

832

Originator	REMUNERATION ECONOMICS LTD
Title	PERSONNEL MANAGEMENT SALARY SURVEY, annual. 1975-
Coverage	Salary survey covering 6 levels of responsibility, broken down by size of company, industry groups, location, age, qualification etc. Additional data on fringe benefits, recruitment.

Contents &	Tables per issue: 55. Own research 100%. Supporting text 50%
Origin of	
Statistics	
Comments	Published in association with the Institute of Personnel Management.
	Formerly published by Computer Economics Ltd.
Currency	1 month
Response	1984
Availability	General
Cost	£50 (£35 to participants)
Address	Survey House, 51 Portland Rd, Kingston-upon-Thames, Surrey KT1 2SH
Telephone	01 549 8726
Contact	Peter Stevens, Director

833

Originator	REMUNERATION ECONOMICS LTD
Title	SALARY SURVEY OF ENGINEERING FUNCTIONS, annual. 1981-
Coverage	Salary survey covering 8 zones of responsibility, broken down by size of company, industry group, activities, areas of work, location. Additional data on fringe benefits, overtime etc.
Contents &	Tables per issue: 70. Own research 100%. Supporting text 50%
Origin of	
Statistics	
Comments	Published in association with the Engineering Council.
Currency	2 months
Response	1984
Availability	General
Cost	£75 (£50 to participants)
Address	Survey House, 51 Portland Rd, Kingston-upon-Thames, Surrey KT1 2SH
Telephone	01 549 8726
Contact	Peter Stevens, Director

834

Originator	REMUNERATION ECONOMICS LTD
Title	SALARY SURVEY OF FINANCIAL FUNCTIONS, annual. 1975-
Coverage	Salary survey for 9 levels of responsibility, broken down by size of company, industry group, location, age and qualifications etc. Additional data on fringe benefits and recruitment.
Contents &	Tables per issue: 65. Own research 100%. Supporting text 50%
Origin of	
Statistics	

Comments	Formerly published by Computer Economics Ltd.
Currency	1 month
Response	1984
Availability	General
Cost	£50
Address	Survey House, 51 Portland Rd, Kingston-upon-Thames, Surrey KT1 2SH
Telephone	01 549 8726
Contact	Peter Stevens, Director

835

Originator	RESEARCH SURVEYS OF GREAT BRITAIN
Title	BABY OMNIBUS, 3 or 4 times per year
Coverage	Data on purchasing trends for baby products plus frequency of purchase, price paid, source of purchase and brand share. Also details of pre- and post advertising awareness, awareness and attitudes to new or existing products and images of products, services and companies. Based on a sample of 700 young mothers in 44 urban administrative areas. Analysis by 7 age groups, social class and incidence of birth.
Contents & Origin of Statistics	Tables per issue: Own research 100%
Comments	Also produce 'ad hoc' surveys
Currency	2-3 months
Response	1984
Availability	General
Address	Research Centre, West Gate, London W5 1EL
Telephone	01 997 5555
Contact	Above address

836

Originator	RESEARCH SURVEYS OF GREAT BRITAIN
Title	CATERING OMNIBUS SURVEY, 3 times a year
Coverage	Usage and consumption data for all product types in catering plus data on purchasing source, brand awareness, attitudes to products and brands, ownership of catering equipment, advertising recall and awareness, manufacturer images and reactions to new product concepts. Based on personal interviews with staff in approximately 600 catering establishments in Great Britain.
Contents & Origin of Statistics	Tables per issue: Own research 100%
Comments	Also perform 'ad hoc' surveys.

Currency	2 months
Response	1984
Availability	General
Cost	£200 entry fee plus prices for questions
Address	Research Centre, West Gate, London W5 1EL
Telephone	01 997 5555
Contact	Above address

837

Originator	RESEARCH SURVEYS OF GREAT BRITAIN
Title	GENERAL OMNIBUS SURVEY, weekly
Coverage	Data on product purchase, brand shares, purchase source, pre- and post advertising awareness, attitudes towards new and existing products and images of products, services and companies. Interviews carried out by random location and analysis by age, social class, sex and region.
Contents & Origin of Statistics	Tables per issue: Own research 100%
Comments	Also carry out 'ad hoc' surveys.
Currency	1 week
Response	1984
Availability	General
Cost	£112 entry fee plus fees for questions
Address	Research Centre, West Gate, London W5 1EL
Telephone	01 997 5555
Contact	Above address

838

Originator	RESEARCH SURVEYS OF GREAT BRITAIN
Title	MOTORISTS OMNIBUS SURVEY, monthly
Coverage	Data on products purchased, source of purchase, brand share, frequency of purchase, price paid, pre- and post advertising awareness and attitudes to new or existing products, services and companies. The survey interviews 1000 motorists per month and analysis available by age, social class and region.
Contents & Origin of Statistics	Tables per issue: Own research 100%
Comments	Also produce 'ad hoc' surveys
Currency	1 month
Response	1984
Availability	General
Cost	£120 entry fee plus fees for questions

Address	Research Centre, West Gate, London W5 1EL
Telephone	01 997 5555
Contact	Above address

839

Originator	RETAIL JEWELLER
Title	PRECIOUS METAL PRICES, weekly in a weekly journal
Coverage	Selling, scrap and market prices of precious metals.
Contents & Origin of Statistics	Tables per issue: 1. Non official source 100%
Currency	1 week
Response	1985
Availability	Controlled circulation to jewellery trade (free) but available to others on subscription
Cost	£20 or 90p for a single issue
Address	Thomson Publishing Ltd, Knightway House, 20 Soho Square, London W1V 6DT
Telephone	01 734 1255
Contact	Above address

840

Originator	REWARD REGIONAL SURVEYS LTD
Title	CLERICAL AND OPERATIVE REWARDS, bi-annual
Coverage	Analysis of basic pay and average earnings for all main clerical and operative positions. Analysis by size of company, area and industry.
Contents & Origin of Statistics	Tables per issue: Own research 100%
Comments	Special reports prepared to order and a 'Salary Advice and Data Bank Enquiry Service' and 'Relocation Information Packs' also available. Above publication produced in January and July.
Response	1984
Availability	General
Cost	£55 (£27 to participants), or £35 for a single copy (£17 to participants)
Address	1 Mill St, Stone, Staffordshire ST15 8BA
Telephone	0785 814554/815365
Contact	Above address

841

Originator	REWARD REGIONAL SURVEYS LTD
Title	COMPUTER SALARIES AND BENEFITS, annual
Coverage	Data on salaries paid to computing staff by various job categories.
Contents & Origin of Statistics	Tables per issue: Own research 100%
Comments	Produced in association with the National Computing Centre and published every January. Special reports prepared to order and a 'Salary Advice and Data Bank Enquiry Service' and 'Relocation Information Packs' also available.
Response	1984
Availability	General
Cost	£75
Address	1 Mill St, Stone, Staffordshire ST15 8BA
Telephone	0785 814554/815365
Contact	Above address

842

Originator	REWARD REGIONAL SURVEYS LTD
Title	DIRECTORS' REWARDS, annual
Coverage	Total remuneration and basic salary analysis overall, by appointment and industry. Fees, bonuses and other cash benefits are also included.
Contents & Origin of Statistics	Tables per issue: Own research 100%
Comments	Produced in association with the Institute of Directors. Special reports prepared to order and a 'Salary Advice and Data Bank Enquiry Service' and 'Relocation Information Packs' also available. Above publication produced every November.
Response	1984
Availability	General
Cost	£100 (£60 to participants)
Address	1 Mill St, Stone, Staffordshire ST15 8BA
Telephone	0785 814554/815365
Contact	Above address

843

Originator	REWARD REGIONAL SURVEYS LTD
Title	LONDON WEIGHTING, annual

Coverage	Payments trends for the private sector in London and other large towns based on data provided by over 80 organisations.
Contents & Origin of Statistics	Tables per issue: Own research 100%
Comments	The above report is published every August. Special reports prepared to order and a 'Salary Advice and Data Bank Enquiry Service' and 'Relocation Information Packs' also available.
Response	1984
Availability	General
Cost	£40 (£20 to participants)
Address	1 Mill St, Stone, Staffordshire ST15 8BA
Telephone	0785 814554/815365
Contact	Above address

844

Originator	REWARD REGIONAL SURVEYS LTD
Title	RESEARCH AND DEVELOPMENT SALARIES, annual
Coverage	Data on basic salaries and total remuneration in the R&D field.
Contents & Origin of Statistics	Tables per issue: Own research 100%
Comments	Above report published in July. Special reports prepared to order and a 'Salary Advice and Data Bank Enquiry Service' and 'Relocation Information Packs' also available.
Response	1984
Availability	General
Cost	£75 (£45 to participants)
Address	1 Mill St, Stone, Staffordshire ST15 8BA
Telephone	0785 814554/815365
Contact	Above address

845

Originator	REWARD REGIONAL SURVEYS LTD
Title	REWARD, bi-annual
Coverage	Management salary report covering over 140 job occupations and including advice, forecasts and comment on salary movements. Analysis by job for basic salary and total renumeration, by size of company, industry, location, qualifications and age.
Contents & Origin of Statistics	Tables per issue: 40. Own research 100%

Comments	Special reports prepared to order and a 'Salary Advice and Data Bank Enquiry Service' and 'Relocation Information Pack' are also available.
Response	1984
Availability	General
Cost	£105 or £70 for a single issue
Address	1 Mill St, Stone, Staffordshire ST15 8BA
Telephone	0785 814554/815365
Contact	Above address

846

Originator	REWARD REGIONAL SURVEYS LTD
Title	SALARY, WAGE AND CONDITIONS OF SERVICE REPORTS, bi-annual
Coverage	Data on actual payments and analysis of salaries, wages and conditions of service in 17 regional and county areas of England and Scotland.
Contents & Origin of Statistics	Tables per issue: Own research 100%
Comments	Special reports prepared to order. A 'Salary Advice and Data Bank Enquiry Service' and 'Relocation Information Packs' also available.
Response	1984
Availability	General
Cost	£60 (£40 to participants)
Address	1 Mill St, Stone, Staffordshire ST15 8BA
Telephone	0785 814554/815365
Contact	Above address

847

Originator	REWARD REGIONAL SURVEYS LTD
Title	SALES AND MARKETING REWARDS, annual
Coverage	Survey of salaries and benefits for Marketing and Sales positions giving basic salary, bonus and commission, company cars and other benefits analysed by job.
Contents & Origin of Statistics	Tables per issue: Own research 100%
Comments	Produced in association with the Institute of Marketing and published every November. Special reports prepared to order and a 'Salary Advice and Data Bank Enquiry Service' and 'Relocation Information Packs' also available.
Response	1984
Availability	General

Cost	£60 (£50 to Institute of Marketing members)
Address	1 Mill St, Stone, Staffordshire ST15 8BA
Telephone	0785 814554/815365
Contact	Above address

848

Originator	ROWE AND PITMAN
Title	KEY STATISTICS, monthly
Coverage	Statistics on the gilts market
Contents & Origin of Statistics	Tables per issue: Own research + government statistics 100%
Currency	Varies
Response	1983
Availability	Clients
Address	City Gate House, 39-45 Finsbury Square, London EC2A 1JA
Telephone	01 606 1066
Contact	Above address

849

Originator	ROYAL BANK OF SCOTLAND GROUP
Title	MONTHLY SUMMARY OF BUSINESS CONDITIONS IN THE UK, monthly
Coverage	Covers production, employment, overseas transations, prices, wages, industrial investment, banking, short-term money rates, and the Stock Exchange.
Contents & Origin of Statistics	Tables per issue: 14. Own research 10%, Government statistics 40%, Unstated 50%
Currency	Varies
Response	1983
Availability	General
Cost	Free
Address	P.O. Box 31, 42 St. Andrew Square, Edinburgh EH2 2YE
Telephone	031 556 8555
Contact	Public Relations Office

850

Originator	ROYAL INSTITUTE OF BRITISH ARCHITECTS
Title	EMPLOYMENT AND EARNINGS SURVEY, annual. 1976-

Coverage	Employment, earnings and RIBA membership figures for public and private architects. Earnings data gives a range of figures for various job categories.
Contents & Origin of Statistics	Tables per issue: 36. Own research 100%. Supporting text 10%
Currency	6 months
Response	1984
Availability	General
Cost	£9.50 (plus 50p p&p)
Address	66 Portland Place, London W1N 4AD
Telephone	01 580 5533
Contact	Mrs Jarman, Research Officer, Statistics Section

851

Originator	ROYAL INSTITUTE OF BRITISH ARCHITECTS
Title	RIBA QUARTERLY STATISTICAL BULLETIN, quarterly. 1960s-
Coverage	Data on workload of private architects only. Includes value of new commissions and production drawings by building types and information by region for different building types. Also details of rehabilitation work.
Contents & Origin of Statistics	Tables per issue: 11. Own research 100%. Supporting text 15%
Currency	3 months
Response	1984
Availability	General
Cost	£15
Address	66 Portland Place, London W1N 4AD
Telephone	01 580 5533
Contact	Mrs Jarman, Research Officer, Statistics Section

852

Originator	ROYAL INSTITUTION OF CHARTERED SURVEYORS
Title	HOUSING MARKET SURVEY, monthly
Coverage	Based on a survey of estate agents with approximately 202 contributing. Gives national figures and figures for the East Midlands for various types and ages of property. Gives latest prices and prices for 3 months ago.
Contents & Origin of Statistics	Tables per issue: 1. Own research 100%

Comments	Also carry out a survey of property market indicators in conjunction with the Financial Times. Above publication issued in the form of a press release.
Response	1984
Availability	General
Cost	Free
Address	12 Great George St, Parliament Square, London SW1P 3AD
Telephone	01 222 7000
Contact	Margaret Cox

853

Originator	ROYAL INSTITUTION OF CHARTERED SURVEYORS
Title	OFFICE RENT SURVEYS, quarterly
Coverage	Surveys rents in the City of London, the West End, Liverpool and Newcastle. Figures are quarterly for a 5 year period and properties are divided into pre-war, refurbished, post-war centrally heated, air-conditioned and all building types.
Contents & Origin of Statistics	Tables per issue: 4. Own research 100%
Comments	The survey is carried out in conjunction with the Institute of Actuaries.
Response	1984
Availability	General
Cost	Free
Address	12 Great George St, Parliament Square, London SW1P 3AD
Telephone	01 222 7000
Contact	Margaret Cox

854

Originator	ROYAL INSTITUTION OF CHARTERED SURVEYORS - BUILDING COST INFORMATION SERVICE
Title	BCIS QUARTERLY REVIEW OF BUILDING PRICES, quarterly
Coverage	A survey of building prices by type of building and by region based on a survey of subscribers to BCIS.
Contents & Origin of Statistics	Tables per issue: 7. Own research 100%
Response	1984
Availability	General
Cost	£60 or £25 for a single issue
Address	85-87 Clarence St, Kingston-upon-Thames, Surrey KT1 1RB

Telephone   01 546 7554
Contact   Above address

855

Originator   ROYAL INSTITUTION OF CHARTERED SURVEYORS -
                  BUILDING COST INFORMATION SERVICE

Title   BUILDING COST INFORMATION SERVICE, monthly
Coverage   Data on various building costs including tenders, labour and materials
                  and based on information supplied by members of BCIS.

Contents &   Tables per issue: Own research 100%
Origin of
Statistics

Comments   Produced in the form of a loose-leaf publication.
Response   1984
Availability Members who are willing to exchange information
Cost   £85
Address   85-87 Clarence St, Kingston-upon-Thames, Surrey KT1 1RB
Telephone   01 546 7554
Contact   Above address

856

Originator   ROYAL INSTITUTION OF CHARTERED SURVEYORS -
                  BUILDING COST INFORMATION SERVICE

Title   GUIDE TO HOUSE REBUILDING COSTS FOR INSURANCE
                  VALUATION, annual
Coverage   Data on house rebuilding costs by area and condition and type of
                  building. Based on a survey of members of BCIS.

Contents &   Tables per issue: 45. Own research 100%
Origin of
Statistics

Comments   Updated every quarter by the 'House Rebuilding Cost Index'
Response   1984
Availability General
Cost   £4
Address   85-87 Clarence St, Kingston-upon-Thames, Surrey KT1 1RB
Telephone   01 546 7554
Contact   Above address

857

Originator   ROYAL SOCIETY FOR THE PREVENTION OF ACCIDENTS

Title   CARE IN THE HOME, quarterly

Coverage	Home and leisure safety. Data broken down by sex, age and cause of accident.
Contents & Origin of Statistics	Tables per issue: Government statistics 80%
Currency	1-2 years
Response	1984
Availability	General
Cost	£4.80
Address	Cannon House, The Priory Queensway, Birmingham B4 6BS
Telephone	021 233 2461 ; Telex: 336546
Contact	Derek J. Hirst, Statistical Officer

858

Originator	ROYAL SOCIETY FOR THE PREVENTION OF ACCIDENTS
Title	CARE ON THE ROAD, monthly
Coverage	Contains 'Road accident statistical review', giving accidents and casualties by class of road users and severity of injury.
Contents & Origin of Statistics	Tables per issue: 2. Non official source 10%, Government statistics 90%.
Currency	6-8 months
Response	1984
Availability	General
Cost	On application
ISSN	0045 5768
Address	Cannon House, The Priory Queensway, Birmingham B4 6BS
Telephone	021 233 2461 ; Telex: 336546
Contact	Derek J. Hirst, Statistical Officer

859

Originator	ROYAL SOCIETY FOR THE PREVENTION OF ACCIDENTS
Title	THE FACTS ABOUT ACCIDENTS, annual
Coverage	Wide range of types of accidents covered, with emphasis on childhood ones.
Contents & Origin of Statistics	Tables per issue: 40. Non official source 10-20%, Government statistics 80-90%. Supporting text 50%
Currency	1-2 years
Response	1984
Availability	General
Cost	On application
Address	Cannon House, The Priory Queensway, Birmingham B4 6BS

Telephone	021 233 2461 ; Telex: 336546
Contact	Derek J. Hirst, Statistical Officer

860

Originator	ROYAL SOCIETY FOR THE PREVENTION OF ACCIDENTS
Title	ROAD ACCIDENT STATISTICS, annual
Coverage	Personal injury road accident data for police force areas, estimates of the cost to the nation of accidents, estimates of road traffic, casualty trends over the past ten years by class of road user.
Contents & Origin of Statistics	Tables per issue: 35-40. Government statistics 100%. Supporting text 15%
Currency	12-18 months
Response	1984
Availability	General
Cost	£3.15 (£2.10 members)
Address	Cannon House, The Priory Queensway, Birmingham B4 6BS
Telephone	021 233 2461 ; Telex: 336546
Contact	Derek J. Hirst,Statistical Officer

861

Originator	ROYAL SOCIETY OF CHEMISTRY
Title	ROYAL SOCIETY OF CHEMISTRY REMUNERATION SURVEY, biennial. 1913-
Coverage	Numbers employed and remuneration of professional chemists by age group for class of employment, field of employment, location of employment, type of work and qualification.
Contents & Origin of Statistics	Tables per issue: 25. Own research 99%, Government statistics 1%. Supporting text 2%
Comments	Conducted a survey of conditions of employment and fringe benefits in January 1984. Results to be published in instalments.
Currency	2 months
Response	1984
Availability	General
Cost	£40 (free to members)
ISBN	0851 86459 7
Address	30 Russell Square, London WC1B 5DT
Telephone	01 631 1355
Contact	D.M. Bartlett, Professional Affairs Department

862

Originator	RPA MANAGEMENT
Title	EXHIBITION AND CONFERENCE MONITOR, annual
Contents & Origin of Statistics	Tables per issue: Own research + other non official source 100%
Currency	Varies
Response	1983
Availability	General
Cost	Varies
Address	1-7 Albion Place, Britton St, London EC1M 5RE
Telephone	01 251 2535
Contact	Above address

863

Originator	RYDEN KENNETH AND PARTNERS
Title	SCOTTISH INDUSTRIAL AND COMMERCIAL PROPERTY REVIEW, bi-annual
Coverage	Forecast of future trends in the level of economic activity in Scotland, together with a guide to the commercial property market and a survey of new industrial and warehouse accommodation.
Contents & Origin of Statistics	Tables per issue: 23. Own research 50%, Other non official source 50%. Supporting text 25%
Currency	Varies
Response	1984
Availability	General
Cost	Free
Address	71 Hanover St Edinburgh, EH2 1EE
Telephone	031 225 6612
Contact	J.A.G. Fiddes

864

Originator	RYDEN, KENNETH AND PARTNERS
Title	SCOTTISH RESIDENTIAL PROPERTY REVIEW, bi-annual. July 1983-
Coverage	Measures changes in house prices, general behaviour of housing market during previous 6 months, and predicts likely developments in market over next 12 months. Analysis based primarily on Edinburgh, Glasgow, Aberdeen and Dundee

Contents & Origin of Statistics	Tables per issue: 5. Own research 100%
Comments	Produced in collaboration with the Halifax Building Society and Herriot Watt University.
Response	1983
Availability	General
Cost	Free
Address	71 Hanover St, Edinburgh EH2 1EE
Telephone	031 225 6612
Contact	Above address

865

Originator	SAUNDERS, RICHARD AND PARTNERS
Title	CITY FLOORSPACE SURVEY, monthly. 1974-
Coverage	Trends in the office letting market in the City of London and its fringes. Concentrates on the amount of floorspace let and the amount available for occupation. Breakdown by size, number, age, classification and postal districts.
Contents & Origin of Statistics	Tables per issue: 13. Own research 100%.
Currency	1 month
Response	1984
Availability	General
Cost	£25
Address	27-32 Old Jewry, London EC2R 8DQ
Telephone	01 606 7461 ; Telex: 886042
Contact	Hexell Lewis, Partner

866

Originator	SAVILLS
Title	AGRICULTURAL LAND MARKET REPORT, quarterly
Coverage	Covers growth of land acquisition by the financial institutions over 18 years and total return index of different land grades compared with the retail price index over same period.
Contents & Origin of Statistics	Tables per issue: 3. Own research 100%
Comments	Data extracted from Agricultural Performance Analysis - see next entry
Response	1983
Availability	General
Cost	Free

Address	20 Grosvenor Hill, Berkeley Square, London W1X 0HQ
Telephone	01 499 8644
Contact	Catherine Day

867

Originator	SAVILLS
Title	SAVILLS-RTP AGRICULTURAL PERFORMANCE ANALYSIS, bi-annual
Coverage	Chapters on ownership by financial institutions of let land and investment performance. Analysis of growth of institutional investment in farmland and of its performance in terms of rental capital growth, total return and yield. Gives regional distribution and land quality.
Contents & Origin of Statistics	Tables per issue: 26. Own research 100%
Response	1983
Availability	General
Address	20 Grosvenor Hill, Berkeley Square, London W1X 0HQ
Telephone	01 499 8644
Contact	Catherine Day

868

Originator	SCOTCH WHISKY ASSOCIATION
Title	STATISTICAL REPORT, annual
Coverage	Figures on the activities of the industry including production, exports, stocks, and duty paid. Figures for previous years also given.
Contents & Origin of Statistics	Tables per issue: 17. Own research 10%, Government statistics 90%.
Currency	6 months
Response	1984
Availability	Members
Address	17 Half Moon St, London, W1
Telephone	01 629 4384
Contact	Information and Development Office

869

Originator	SCOTTISH DEVELOPMENT AGENCY
Title	LABOR PERFORMANCE OF US PLANTS IN SCOTLAND, biennial. 1979-

Coverage   Results of a survey carried out by PEIDA, economic consultants, and covering 82% of manufacturing plants in Scotland. Examines industrial relations and labour performance. Plants are also analysed by industry grouping, size of employment, and year of establishment.

Contents &   Tables per issue: 16. Own research 100%. Supporting text 20%
Origin of
Statistics

Comments   Most figures are presented in graph form.
Response   1984
Availability   General
Cost   Free
Address   120 Bothwell St, Glasgow G2 7JP
Telephone   041 248 2700 ; Telex: 777600
Contact   E. Peters, Research Officer, Information Department

870

Originator   SCOTTISH DEVELOPMENT AGENCY

Title   LOCATE IN SCOTLAND - KEY INDICATORS, annual. 1979-
Coverage   Statistics on employment, earnings and land and factory costs. Employment figures by sector and earnings figures by occupation. General energy costs and a summary of financial assistance are also given.

Contents &   Tables per issue: 9. Non official source 10%, Government statistics
Origin of   90%. Supporting text 45%
Statistics

Currency   6-12 months
Response   1984
Availability   General
Cost   Free
Address   120 Bothwell St, Glasgow G2 7JP
Telephone   041 248 2700 ; Telex: 777600
Contact   E. Peters, Research Officer, Information Department

871

Originator   SCOTTISH DEVELOPMENT AGENCY

Title   SURVEY OF PAY AND CONDITIONS IN MAJOR MANU-
                      FACTURING COMPANIES, bi-annual. 1980-
Coverage   Survey of approximately 40-50 companies. Jobs surveyed in three categories - general production, clerical and administrative, and professional, technical and managerial. Covers wage levels (weighted and unweighted), length of working week, holidays, turnover rates and absenteeism categorised by job title.

Contents & Origin of Statistics	Tables per issue: 4. Own research 100%. Supporting text 60%
Comments	Copy of questionnaire used in publication plus definitions of all the job descriptions used.
Currency	1 month
Response	1984
Availability	Restricted to companies and researchers
Cost	Free
Address	120 Bothwell St, Glasgow G2 7JP
Telephone	041 248 2700; Telex: 777600
Contact	E. Peters, Research Officer, Information Department

872

Originator	SCOTTISH FARM BUILDINGS INVESTIGATION UNIT
Title	FARM BUILDING COST GUIDE, annual. 1975-
Coverage	Labour, plant, equipment, building cost analyses and measured rates. Gives historical data and predictions for the coming year.
Contents & Origin of Statistics	Tables per issue: 48 pgs. Own research 100%. Supporting text 40%
Currency	1 year
Response	1984
Availability	General
Cost	£4
ISSN	0309 4146
Address	North of Scotland College of Agriculture, Craibstone, Bucksburn, Aberdeen AB2 9TR
Telephone	0224 713622
Contact	John MacCormack, Information Officer

873

Originator	SCOTTISH LANDOWNERS FEDERATION
Title	LAND PRICE SURVEY FOR SCOTLAND, quarterly
Coverage	Rural land values in Scotland.
Contents & Origin of Statistics	Tables per issue: 1.
Comments	Published on one sheet.
Response	1984
Availability	General
Address	18 Abercromby Place, Edinburgh EH3 6TY

Telephone	031 556 4466
Contact	Above address

874

Originator	SCOTTISH MILK MARKETING BOARD
Title	ANNUAL REPORT AND ACCOUNTS, annual
Coverage	Includes statistics section with data on producer numbers, dairy herd and milk production, milk supply and utilisation, total sales off farms, milk sales analysis, income from milk, number of first inseminations, primary haulage cost, and production and producer distribution by regions and districts.
Contents & Origin of Statistics	Tables per issue: 15. Unstated 100%
Response	1983
Availability	General
Cost	Free
Address	Underwood Rd, Paisley, Renfrewshire PA3 1TJ
Telephone	041 887 1234
Contact	Above address

875

Originator	SCOTTISH MILK MARKETING BOARD
Title	KEY MILK FIGURES IN SCOTLAND, annual
Coverage	Basic data on milk production.
Contents & Origin of Statistics	Tables per issue: Own research 100%
Response	1983
Availability	General
Cost	£0.75
Address	Underwood Rd, Paisley, Renfrewshire PA3 1TJ
Telephone	041 887 1234
Contact	Above address

876

Originator	SCOTTISH MILK MARKETING BOARD
Title	MILK BULLETIN, monthly
Coverage	Trade journal containing statistics on milk supply, sales, prices utilisation, and composition. Data on bulls. Also world data in special report.

Contents &	Tables per issue: 14. Unstated 100%
Origin of	
Statistics	

Currency	Varies
Response	1984
Availability	General
Cost	Free to producers
Address	Underwood Rd, Paisley, Renfrewshire PA3 1TJ
Telephone	041 887 1234
Contact	M.J. Miller, Editor

877

Originator	SCOTTISH MILK MARKETING BOARD

Title	STRUCTURE OF SCOTTISH MILK PRODUCTION, triennial
Coverage	Detailed analysis of data from a dairy farm census.

Contents &	Tables per issue: Own research 100%
Origin of	
Statistics	

Response	1983
Availability	General
Cost	£3
Address	Underwood Rd, Paisley, Renfrewshire PA3 1TJ
Telephone	041 887 1234
Contact	Above address

878

Originator	SCOTTISH TOURIST BOARD

Title	RESEARCH AND PLANNING INFORMATION HAND-BOOK, updated quarterly. 1976-
Coverage	Reports of research studies carried out by the Board, eg annual monitoring studies, tourism market trends, social and economic data.

Contents &	Tables per issue: 25. Own research 90%, Other non official source
Origin of	10%. Supporting text 60%
Statistics	

Comments	In looseleaf format.
Currency	6 months to one year
Response	1984
Availability	General
Cost	£30 (after one year £15)
Address	23, Ravelston Terrace, Edinburgh EH4 3EU
Telephone	031 332 2433 ; Telex: 72272
Contact	T. Costley, Research Officer

879

Originator	SCOTTISH TOURIST BOARD
Title	SCOTTISH HOTEL OCCUPANCY SURVEY, monthly. 1974-
Coverage	Sample survey of Scottish hotel room and bed occupancy. By size and status of hotel, tariff, location and group membership.
Contents & Origin of Statistics	Tables per issue: 6. Own research 100%. Supporting text 5%
Currency	2 months
Response	1984
Availability	General
Cost	Free
Address	23 Ravelston Terrace, Edinburgh EH4 3EU
Telephone	031 332 2433 ; Telex: 72272
Contact	T. Costley, Research Officer

880

Originator	SCRIMGEOUR, KEMP-GEE AND CO
Title	BUILDING BULLETIN
Coverage	Contains some company information but also a large amount of sector information. Gives data and commentary on construction, house building, materials, timber and china clay.
Contents & Origin of Statistics	Tables per issue: 47. Non official source 10%, Government statistics 5%, Unstated 85%
Availability	Private circulation
Address	20 Copthall Avenue, London EC2R 7JS
Telephone	01 600 7595
Contact	Above address

881

Originator	SCRIMGEOUR, KEMP-GEE AND CO
Title	ELECTRICAL BULLETIN
Coverage	Contains some company information but also a large amount of sector information. General introduction gives investment review, earnings projections, sector price related graphs. Includes statistics on consumer electronics, domestic appliances, capital goods, components, and orders and sales. Final section on share price graphs. Figures cover a 5 year period.

Contents & Origin of Statistics	Tables per issue: 139. Unstated 100%

Response	1983
Availability	Private circulation
Address	20 Copthall Avenue, London EC2R 7JS
Telephone	01 600 7595
Contact	Above address

882

Originator	SCRIMGEOUR, KEMP-GEE AND CO

Title	QUARTERLY ECONOMIC FORECAST, quarterly
Coverage	Covers most aspects of UK economy for 2 years ahead.
Response	1983
Availability	Clients
Address	20 Copthall Avenue, London EC2R 7JS
Telephone	01 600 7595
Contact	Above address

883

Originator	SEA FISH INDUSTRY AUTHORITY

Title	ANNUAL REPORT, annual
Coverage	Contains statistical appendices on the fishing fleet, supplies and production, consumption, trade and grant and loan schemes.
Contents & Origin of Statistics	Tables per issue: 22. Non official source 15%, Government statistics 60%, Unstated 25%. Supporting text 70%

Currency	5 months
Response	1984
Availability	General
Cost	£2.50
ISBN	0903041 20 1
Address	Sea Fisheries House, 10 Young St, Edinburgh EH2 4JQ
Telephone	031 225 2515; Telex: 727225
Contact	Mr S. Young, Fishery Economics Research Unit

884

Originator	SEA FISH INDUSTRY AUTHORITY
Title	HOUSEHOLD FISH CONSUMPTION IN G.B., quarterly

Coverage	Analysis of the sales of fish by species for household consumption in Britain and in each of the major television regions. Divided into fish/chilled and frozen sales.
Contents & Origin of Statistics	Tables per issue: 25. Own research 100%. Supporting text 20%

Response	1984
Availability	General
Cost	£50
Address	Sea Fisheries House, 10 Young St, Edinburgh EH2 4JQ
Telephone	031 225 2515; Telex: 727225
Contact	Mr S. Young, Fishery Economics Research Unit

885

Originator	SEA FISH INDUSTRY AUTHORITY
Title	SUPPLIES BULLETIN, quarterly
Coverage	Catches by UK vessels for major fishing grounds, UK supplies of demersal food fish available for consumption, trade of fish and fish products, stocks of frozen white fish, performance and disposition of deep sea fleet.
Contents & Origin of Statistics	Tables per issue: 14. Government statistics 100%.

Currency	3 months
Response	1984
Availability	General
Cost	Free
ISSN	0309 5517
Address	Sea Fisheries House, 10 Young St, Edinburgh EH2 4JQ
Telephone	031 225 2515; Telex: 727225
Contact	Mr S. Young, Fishery Economics Research Unit

886

Originator	SEA FISH INDUSTRY AUTHORITY
Title	TRADE BULLETIN, monthly
Coverage	Quantity and value of imports and exports of fish intended for human consumption. Detail given for various forms of presentation and for major species.
Contents & Origin of Statistics	Tables per issue: 9. Government statistics 100%.
Comments	Also issue 'European Supplies Bulletin' quarterly for £80 pa
Response	1984

Availability	General
Cost	Free
ISSN	1044 9303
Address	Sea Fisheries House, 10 Young St, Edinburgh EH2 4JQ
Telephone	031 225 2515; Telex: 727225
Contact	Mr. S. Young, Fishery Economics Research Unit

887

Originator	SERVICE INDUSTRIES JOURNAL
Title	FORECASTS OF HOTEL AND CATERING UNEMPLOY-MENT AND EMPLOYMENT TRENDS, annual in a journal published three times a year
Coverage	Forecast for 2 years ahead of employment/unemployment trends.
Contents & Origin of Statistics	Tables per issue: Own research 100%
Response	1984
Availability	General
Cost	£25
Address	Frank Cass & Co, Gainsborough House, 11 Gainsborough Rd, London E11 1 RS
Telephone	01 530 4226
Contact	G.P. Akehurst, Editor

888

Originator	SEWELL, RONALD AND ASSOCIATES
Title	FRANCHISE NETWORKS, annual. 1977-
Coverage	Analysis of car, commercial vehicle and petrol retailing networks.
Comments	Their yearbook also contains some marketing data, eg supply and distribution.
Response	1984
Availability	Members
Cost	£3.95
Address	1 Queen Square, Bath, BA1 2HE
Telephone	0225 318500 ; Telex: 444648
Contact	Paul Evans, Managing Director

889

Originator	SHAWS PRICE GUIDES LTD
Title	SHAWS GUIDE TO FAIR RETAIL PRICES, monthly

Coverage	Fair selling prices for consumer goods either recommended by the manufacturers or suggested by the editors. Divided into groceries, household, patent medicines, cigarettes, tobacco, cigars, soft drinks - each alphabetical by product and trade name/manufacturer.
Contents & Origin of Statistics	Tables per issue: 78pgs. Own research 100%.

Response	1984
Availability	General
Cost	£13.50
ISSN	0265 2889
Address	P.O. Box 32, Abingdon, Oxfordshire OX14 3LJ
Telephone	0235 32882; Telex: 837316
Contact	Martina Spence, Editor

890

Originator	SHAWS PRICE GUIDES LTD

Title	SHAWS WINE GUIDE, bi-annual
Coverage	Recommended fair prices for wines, aperitifs, spirits, beers, cider and soft drinks. Divided by country within type.
Contents & Origin of Statistics	Tables per issue: 110pg. Own research 100%.

Response	1984
Availability	General
Cost	£12
ISSN	0307 1170
Address	P.O. Box 32, Abingdon, Oxfordshire, OX14 3LJ
Telephone	0235 32882; Telex: 837316
Contact	Martina Spence, Editor

891

Originator	SHETLAND ISLANDS COUNCIL

Title	SHETLAND IN STATISTICS, annual. 1974-
Coverage	Physical, economic, industry, transport, social and political data given.
Contents & Origin of Statistics	Tables per issue: 80. Unstated 100%.
Comments	More detailed data available to serious researchers. Floppy disk available.
Currency	Varies
Response	1984

Availability	General
Cost	£1
ISBN	0 904562 20 4
Address	Research and Development Dept, 93 St. Olay St, Lerwick, Shetland ZE1 0E5
Telephone	0595 3535; Telex: 75350
Contact	Mr. D.J. Holme, Principal Research Officer

892

Originator	SHIP AND BOAT BUILDERS NATIONAL FEDERATION
Title	SBBNF INDUSTRY STATISTICS, annual
Coverage	Data on production, sales and imports and exports of boats, inflatables and sailboards.
Response	1984
Address	Boating Industry House, Vale Rd, Oatlands, Weybridge, Surrey
Telephone	0932 54511
Contact	R.S.C. Bedforth

893

Originator	SHOE AND LEATHER NEWS
Title	LEATHER MARKET AND HIDE PRICES, weekly in a weekly journal
Coverage	Prices and trends in English hides and imported hide market.
Contents & Origin of Statistics	Tables per issue: 2
Currency	1 Week
Response	1985
Availability	General
Cost	£24
Address	84-88 Great Eastern St, London EC2A 3ED
Telephone	01 739 2071
Contact	Above address

894

Originator	SIEBERT/HEAD LTD
Title	SIEBERT/HEAD INDEX: MONTHLY REVIEW OF PACKAGING MATERIAL PRICES, monthly. 1977-
Coverage	Prices for raw materials and finished packaging products. Includes quarterly report on trade.

| Contents & Origin of Statistics | Tables per issue: 4-6. Own research 30%, Other non official source 20%, Government statistics 50%. |

Currency	4 weeks
Response	1984
Availability	Packaging industry
Cost	£40
Address	193 Regent St, London W1R 7WA
Telephone	01 734 4536
Contact	Mike Wilks, Technical Executive

895

Originator	SILK ASSOCIATION OF GREAT BRITAIN

Title	SERICA, monthly. 1970-
Coverage	Mainly news and comment on the silk industry but includes a statistical section.

| Contents & Origin of Statistics | Tables per issue: Varies |

Currency	Varies
Response	1984
Availability	Primarily Members but available to others interested in silk
Cost	On application
ISSN	0266 0822
Address	c/o Rheinbergs Ltd, Morley Rd, Tonbridge, Kent TN9 1RN
Telephone	0732 351357; Telex: 95311
Contact	L Rheinberg, Secretary

896

Originator	SKELMERSDALE DEVELOPMENT CORPORATION

Title	SKELMERSDALE: POPULATION AND SOCIAL SURVEY, annual. 1965-
Coverage	Sections on population, households, employment, children, previous residence, migration, housing, environment, shopping, health services, transport and leisure.

| Contents & Origin of Statistics | Tables per issue: 105. Supporting text 8% |

Currency	6 months
Response	1984
Availability	General
Cost	£3.50
Address	High St, Skelmersdale, Lancashire WN8 8AR

Telephone	0695 24242
Contact	Ms Liz Donnelly (content information), Brian Burke (sales)

897

Originator	SKINNER, THOMAS DIRECTORIES
Title	LAXATIONS BUILDING PRICE BOOK, annual
Coverage	Price of materials, work and labour in the building industry.
Contents & Origin of Statistics	Tables per issue: 726pp. Own research + other non official source 100%
Response	1984
Availability	General
Cost	£26
ISSN	0342 26972
Address	Windsor Court, East Grinstead House, East Grinstead, West Sussex RH19 1XE
Telephone	0342 26972
Contact	Above address

898

Originator	SOCIETY OF BUSINESS ECONOMISTS
Title	UK ECONOMIC FORECASTS, bi-annual
Coverage	Forecasts of UK economic trends for the next two years by quarter. Covers main GDP expenditure items by % and £million, inflation, earning and balance of payments.
Contents & Origin of Statistics	Tables per issue: 3. Own research 100%. Supporting text 25%
Comments	Issued as a press release.
Response	1984
Availability	Members
Cost	Free
Address	11 Bay Tree Walk, Watford, Herts WD1 3RX
Telephone	0923 37287
Contact	Mr D. Kern, Secretary

899

Originator	SOCIETY OF MOTOR MANUFACTURERS AND TRADERS LTD
Title	MONTHLY STATISTICAL REVIEW, monthly

Coverage	Production by manufacturer, registrations and trade in products of the motor industry.
Contents & Origin of Statistics	Tables per issue: 13. Own research 40%, Government statistics 60%. Supporting text 5%
Currency	2 months
Response	1984
Availability	General
Cost	£40 (£20 members)
Address	Forbes House, Halkin St, London SW1X 7DS
Telephone	01 235 7000; Telex: 21628
Contact	D. Dyster, Statistics Department

900

Originator	SOCIETY OF MOTOR MANUFACTURERS AND TRADERS LTD
Title	MOTORSTAT EXPRESS, fortnightly. 1977-
Coverage	Production, registrations and trade.
Response	1984
Availability	General
Cost	£19.25 (£14.30 members)
Address	Forbes House, Halkin St, London SW1X 7DS
Telephone	01 235 7000; Telex: 21628
Contact	H. Sharpe, Statistics Dept.

901

Originator	SOCIETY OF MOTOR MANUFACTURERS AND TRADERS LTD
Title	NR 2, monthly
Coverage	Registrations of motor vehicles. Analysis by make and model range.
Contents & Origin of Statistics	Tables per issue: 80pgs. Own research 100%.
Currency	5 days
Response	1984
Availability	General
Cost	£300
Address	Forbes House, Halkin St, London SW1X 7DS
Telephone	01 235 7000; Telex: 21628
Contact	M. Troy, MVRIS

902

Originator	SOFT DRINKS
Title	SOFT DRINKS STATISTICS, quarterly in a monthly journal
Coverage	Sales of soft drinks by quarter
Contents & Origin of Statistics	Tables per issue: 1. Government statistics 100%. Supporting text 50%
Currency	12 months
Response	1984
Availability	General
Cost	Free to members of the National Association of Soft Drinks Manufacturers Ltd, £15 to others
Address	The Gatehouse, 2 Holly Rd, Twickenham, TW1 4EF
Telephone	01 892 8082
Contact	Janette Gledhill

903

Originator	SOUTH TYNESIDE BOROUGH COUNCIL
Title	QUARTERLY INDUSTRIAL REVIEW, quarterly. 1975-
Coverage	Consists of 3 sections:- articles on local issues, review of local and national economy, statistical appendix on unemployment.
Contents & Origin of Statistics	Tables per issue: 10. Unstated 100%. Supporting text 70%
Currency	2 months
Response	1984
Availability	General
Address	Planning Dept, Central Library Building, Catherine St, South Shields, Tyne and Wear
Telephone	0632 567531
Contact	Mr. C.J. Clarke, Principal Assistant Planner

904

Originator	SOUTH YORKSHIRE COUNTY COUNCIL
Title	SOUTH YORKSHIRE STATISTICS, annual. 1975-
Coverage	Abstract of statistics for the area, including politics, population, employment, finance, housing, transport, education, social services, health, recreation, environment, police, fire and public utilities.
Contents & Origin of Statistics	Tables per issue: c.180. Own research 60%, Government statistics 40%. Supporting text 5%

Currency	Varies
Response	1984
Availability	General
Cost	£3 (Free to libraries, schools etc)
ISSN	0309 4685
Address	County Hall, Kendray St, Barnsley, South Yorkshire, S70 2TN
Telephone	0226 86141
Contact	M. Sanderson, R. & I. Officer

905

Originator	SOUTH YORKSHIRE PASSENGER TRANSPORT EXECU-TIVE
Title	ABBREVIATED ANNUAL ACCOUNTS, annual
Coverage	Includes a certain amount of non-financial statistical information such as journeys, vehicles, staff and operations.
Contents & Origin of Statistics	Tables per issue: 16. Own research 100%. Supporting text 10%
Response	1983
Availability	General
Cost	Free
Address	Exchange St, Sheffield S2 5SZ
Telephone	0742 78688
Contact	Bruce Hugman, Public Relations Officer

906

Originator	SPACE PLANNING SERVICES LTD
Title	FITTING OUT COST INDEX, bi annual
Coverage	Measures the cost of preparing a typical speculative office shell for occupation. It charts the price changes occurring in various building elements, provides a total cost figure, a cost per square metre, and forecasts these six months ahead.
Contents & Origin of Statistics	Tables per issue: Own research 100%. Supporting text 50%
Response	1984
Availability	General
Cost	Free
Address	Western House, Uxbridge Rd, Hillingdon, Middlesex UB10 0LY
Telephone	01 573 2271
Contact	Above address

907

Originator	SPENCER THORNTON AND CO
Title	INVESTMENT RECOMMENDATIONS AND COMPANY PROFIT ESTIMATES, monthly
Coverage	Recommendations for investment and estimates of company profits.
Contents & Origin of Statistics	Tables per issue: 18. Own research 50%, Other non official source 50%. Supporting text 50%
Currency	Varies
Response	1983
Availability	Clients, possibly others
Cost	Free to clients
Address	Spenthorn House, 22 Cousin Lane, London EC4R 3TE
Telephone	01 628 4411
Contact	Above address

908

Originator	SPON, E. & F.N.
Title	SPONS ARCHITECT AND BUILDERS PRICE BOOK, annual.
Coverage	Prices of materials, prices for measured work and rates of wages.
Contents & Origin of Statistics	Tables per issue: 697pp. Own research + other non official source 100%
Comments	Other publications produced - see other entries
Response	1984
Availability	General
Cost	£24.50
ISSN	0306 3046
Address	11 New Fetter Lane, London EC4P 4EE
Telephone	01 583 9855
Contact	Mr Read

909

Originator	SPON, E. & F.N.
Title	SPONS CIVIL ENGINEERING PRICE BOOK, annual. 1985-
Coverage	Prices and costs of building, services, engineering, external work, landscaping, etc.
Contents & Origin of Statistics	Tables per issue: Own research + other non official source 100%
Comments	Other publications produced - see other entries

Response	1984
Availability	General
Cost	£20
ISSN	0265 1025
Address	11 New Fetter Lane, London EC4P 4EE
Telephone	01 583 9855
Contact	Above address

910

Originator	SPON, E. & F.N.
Title	SPONS LANDSCAPE AND EXTERNAL WORKS PRICE BOOK, annual
Coverage	Prices and costs covering hard and soft landscapes and external works generally.
Comments	Other publications produced - see other entries
Response	1984
Availability	General
Cost	£19.50
ISBN	0419 13610X
Address	11 New Fetter Lane, London EC4P 4EE
Telephone	01 583 9855
Contact	Above address

911

Originator	SPON, E. & F.N.
Title	SPONS MECHANICAL AND ELECTRICAL SERVICES PRICE BOOK, annual. 1969-
Coverage	Prices and costs of heating, lighting, ventilation and air conditioning and other service items in industrial and commercial property. Only publication covering costs of chemical plants and other large scale projects.
Contents & Origin of Statistics	Tables per issue: 482pp. Own research + other non official source 100%
Comments	Other publications produced - see other entries
Response	1984
Availability	General
Cost	£24.50
ISSN	0305 4543
Address	11 New Fetter Lane, London EC4P 4EE
Telephone	01 583 9855
Contact	Mr Read

912

Originator	SPON, E. & F.N.
Title	SPONS PLANT AND EQUIPMENT PRICE GUIDE, monthly
Coverage	New and second hand prices and specification details for nearly 5,000 models of construction plant.
Contents & Origin of Statistics	Tables per issue: Own research 100%
Comments	Published in loose-leaf format, previously 'Plant and Equipment Guide'. Other publications produced - see other entries.
Currency	1 month
Response	1984
Availability	General
Cost	£69.50
Address	11 New Fetter Lane, London EC4P 4EE
Telephone	01 583 9855
Contact	Above address

913

Originator	SPON, E. & F.N.
Title	SPONS QUARTERLY PRICE BOOK UPDATE, quarterly
Coverage	Updates the prices in the annual 'Spon's Mechanical and Electrical Services Price Book'
Contents & Origin of Statistics	Tables per issue: Own research + other non official source 100%
Comments	Other publications produced - see other entries
Currency	3 months
Response	1984
Availability	General
Cost	£23
Address	11 New Fetter Lane, London EC4P 4EE
Telephone	01 583 9855
Contact	Above address

914

Originator	SPORTS COUNCIL
Title	DIGEST OF SPORTS STATISTICS, biennial
Coverage	Compendium of statistics about organised and casual sports participation during a ten year period, with some information about the facilities and purchase of equipment and magazines, mainly in England. General section and separate sections on specific sports.

Contents & Origin of Statistics	Tables per issue: 145. Non official source 95%, Government statistics 5%

Currency	Varies
Response	1983
Availability	General
Cost	£6
Address	16 Upper Woburn Place, London WC1H 0QP
Telephone	01 388 1277
Contact	Miss A. Lightfoot, Information Centre

915

Originator	SPORTS TRADER

Title	IMPORT/EXPORT FIGURES, twice a year in a fortnightly journal
Coverage	Imports of sports equipment by major countries with commentary on trends.

Contents & Origin of Statistics	Tables per issue: Varies

Currency	3 months
Response	1985
Availability	General
Cost	£25 or £1 for a single issue
ISSN	0038 8254
Address	Benn Publications Ltd, Sovereign Way, Tonbridge, Kent TN9 1RW
Telephone	0732 364422; Telex: 95132
Contact	Above address

916

Originator	ST. JAMES'S GROUP

Title	ST. JAMES'S GROUP FORECAST, quarterly
Coverage	Group consists of 20 forecasters representing leading industrial and financial companies, using the Treasury Model. Short and medium term forecasts of the UK economy.

Response	1983
Availability	Members
Address	Economist Intelligence Unit, 27 St. James's Place, London SW1A 1NT
Telephone	01 493 6711
Contact	Above address

917

Originator	STANILAND HALL ASSOCIATES LTD
Title	ECONOMIC INDICATORS - FORECASTS FOR COMPANY PLANNING, quarterly. 1977-
Coverage	Indicators for UK production and demand and for costs and prices. Also gives world background. Forecasts for between one and five years ahead.
Contents & Origin of Statistics	Tables per issue: 39. Supporting text 50%
Comments	£395 with 'Consumer Spending Forecasts'
Response	1984
Availability	General
Cost	£190
ISSN	0263 7065
Address	42 Colebrooke Row, London N1 8AF
Telephone	01 359 6054
Contact	L.S. Staniland, Chairman/Managing Director

918

Originator	STANILAND HALL ASSOCIATES LTD.
Title	CONSUMER SPENDING FORECASTS, quarterly. 1975-
Coverage	Economic environment, personal incomes and spending, individual sectors and a special topic eg housing/DIY. Forecast between one and five years ahead
Contents & Origin of Statistics	Tables per issue: 49. Supporting text 50%
Comments	Also includes 8 brief monthly supplements. Inclusive price of £395 with 'Economic Indicators'
Response	1984
Availability	General
Cost	£275
ISSN	0307 8248
Address	42 Colebrook Row, London N1 8AF
Telephone	01 359 6054
Contact	L.S. Staniland, Chairman/Managing Director

919

Originator	STATS (MR) LTD
Title	RETAIL AUDIT REPORTS, monthly or bi-monthly

Coverage	Individual reports covering markets within liquor, grocery, chemists and tobacconists.
Contents & Origin of Statistics	Tables per issue: Own research 100%.
Response	1983
Availability	General
Cost	Varies according to report required
Address	Gloucester House, Smallbrook Queensway, Birmingham B5 4HP
Telephone	021 643 5972
Contact	R.K. Landells, Client Service Directorr

920

Originator	STORAGE EQUIPMENT MANUFACTURERS' ASSOCIATION
Title	STORAGE EQUIPMENT SALES, quarterly. 1972-
Coverage	Orders and dispatches of 4 categories of storage equipment:- racking, shelving, containers and platforms.
Contents & Origin of Statistics	Tables per issue: 1. Own research 100%.
Currency	2 months
Response	1984
Availability	Members
Cost	Free
Address	South Bank House, 235-241 Blackfriars Rd, London, SE1 8NW
Telephone	01 248 1662 ; Telex: 8812908
Contact	Mr C.D Meynell, Secretary

921

Originator	STRATHCLYDE PASSENGER TRANSPORT EXECUTIVE
Title	ANNUAL REPORT AND ACCOUNTS, annual
Coverage	Mainly financial information on the Executive but a section at the end contains data on passenger journeys, number of vehicles etc.
Contents & Origin of Statistics	Tables per issue: 10. Own research 100%. Supporting text 70%
Currency	2-3 months
Response	1984
Availability	General
Cost	Unstated
Address	Consort House, 12 West George St, Glasgow G2 1HN

Telephone	041 332 6811; Telex: 779746
Contact	Press and Media Officer

922

Originator	SURREY COUNTY COUNCIL
Title	AT A GLANCE, annual
Coverage	General data on the county including population, finance, education, transport, environment, etc.
Contents & Origin of Statistics	Tables per issue: Varies
Comments	Various other reports primarily for internal use and an Annual Report published.
Currency	Varies
Response	1984
Availability	General
Cost	Free
Address	County Hall, Penrhyn Rd, Kingston-upon-Thames, Surrey KT1 2DT
Telephone	01 546 1050; Telex: 263312
Contact	Public Relations

923

Originator	SURREY COUNTY COUNCIL
Title	POPULATION REPORT, annual. 1981-
Coverage	General data on population, households, dwellings, amenities, economic activity and migration plus population forecasts for 3 and 8 years ahead. Figures by districts.
Contents & Origin of Statistics	Tables per issue: 30-40. Own research 60%, Government statistics 40%. Supporting text 40%
Comments	Various other reports primarily for internal use and an Annual Report published.
Currency	Varies
Response	1984
Availability	General
Cost	£3
Address	County Hall, Penrhyn Rd, Kingston-upon-Thames, Surrey KT1 2DT
Telephone	01 546 1050 ext 3050; Telex 263312
Contact	Tony Madge, Planning Officer

924

Originator	SURREY COUNTY COUNCIL
Title	STATISTICS OF THE EDUCATION SERVICE, annual
Coverage	Data on number of pupils at schools by type and classes taught, external examination results, school leavers, teachers, accomodation trends, special education and further education.
Contents & Origin of Statistics	Tables per issue: 69. Own research 100%. Supporting text 5%
Comments	Various other reports primarily for internal use and an Annual Report published by the Council
Currency	Varies
Response	1984
Availability	General
Cost	£3
Address	County Hall, Penrhyn Rd, Kingston-upon-Thames, Surrey KT1 2DT
Telephone	01 546 1050, ext 3209; Telex: 263312
Contact	Education Department

925

Originator	SURREY COUNTY COUNCIL
Title	UNEMPLOYMENT AND VACANCIES, monthly. 1981-
Coverage	Monthly unemployment and vacancy figures by local employment office.
Contents & Origin of Statistics	Tables per issue: 2. Government statistics 100%. Supporting text 45%
Comments	Various other reports primarily for internal use and an Annual Report published.
Currency	1 month
Response	1984
Availability	General
Cost	Free
Address	County Hall, Penrhyn Rd, Kingston-upon-Thames, Surrey KT1 2D'
Telephone	01 546 1050 ext 3518; Telex: 263312
Contact	Sue Janota, Planning Officer

926

Originator	SWANSEA CITY DISTRICT COUNCIL
Title	SWANSEA ENTERPRISE PARK MONITORING REPOR' quarterly

Coverage	Enquiries, construction, firms and employment at Swansea Enterprise Park.
Contents & Origin of Statistics	Tables per issue: 35. Own research 100%
Currency	1 month
Response	1983
Availability	General
Cost	£2
Address	The Guildhall, Swansea SA1 4NL
Telephone	0792 50821
Contact	Planning Department

927

Originator	SYSTEM THREE SCOTLAND
Title	SCOTTISH CARRY-OUT MARKET FOR BEER AND LAGER, annual
Coverage	Covers frequency of purchase, consumption, brand awareness and usage.
Contents & Origin of Statistics	Tables per issue: Own research 100%
Response	1983
Availability	General
Cost	£180
Address	16 York Place, Edinburgh EH1 3EP
Telephone	031 556 9462
Contact	Above address

928

Originator	SYSTEM THREE SCOTLAND
Title	SCOTTISH SPIRITS REPORT - WHISKY, quarterly
Coverage	Covers frequency of purchase, consumption, brand awareness and usage
Contents & Origin of Statistics	Tables per issue: Own research 100%
Response	1984
Availability	General
Cost	£600
Address	16 York Place, Edinburgh EH1 3EP

| Telephone | 031 556 9462 |
| Contact | Above address |

929

Originator	SYSTEM THREE SCOTLAND
Title	SCOTTISH SPIRITS REPORTS - SHERRY, VODKA, WHITE RUM, DARK RUM, BRANDY, GIN, annual
Coverage	Covers frequency of purchase, consumption, brand awareness and usage.
Contents & Origin of Statistics	Tables per issue: Own research 100%
Response	1983
Availability	General
Cost	£150 each
Address	16 York Place, Edinburgh EH1 3EP
Telephone	031 556 9462
Contact	Above address

930

Originator	TACK RESEARCH LTD
Title	SALESMEN'S PAY AND EXPENSES, biennial. 1968-
Coverage	Gross pay and pay breakdown plus additional incentives offered to salesmen in the following categories: repeat consumer goods, durable consumer goods, repeat industrial, capital equipment and services.
Contents & Origin of Statistics	Tables per issue: 58. Own research 99%, Government statistics 1%.
Currency	4 months
Response	1984
Availability	General
Cost	£60 (£30 to providers of data)
Address	1-5 Longmoore St, London SW1V 1JJ
Telephone	01 834 5001
Contact	W. Benzie, Managing Director

931

Originator	TAYLOR NELSON AND ASSOCIATES
Title	FAMILY FOOD PANEL, bi-annual. 1974-
Coverage	Continuous monitor of consumption and usage of all foods and drink consumed in the home based upon a sample of 2100 households.

Contents & Origin of Statistics	Tables per issue: 70. Own research 100%. Supporting text 50%
Comments	Data available on magnetic tape and special analysis of data also available. Price above represents full subscription but cheaper packages are available.
Currency	4 weeks after data collection
Response	1984
Availability	General
Cost	£14,000
Address	457 Kingston Rd, Ewell, Epsom, Surrey KT19 0DH
Telephone	01 394 0191
Contact	Micheal A. Watson, Manager

932

Originator	TAYLOR NELSON AND ASSOCIATES
Title	MONITOR SOCIAL CHANGE RESEARCH PROGRAMME, annual. 1972-
Coverage	Changes in British attitudes and behaviour patterns and the implications for public and commercial bodies. Particular emphasis on health, food, retailing, consumerism, work, family life, leisure and socio-political involvement. Based on a sample of 2000.
Contents & Origin of Statistics	Tables per issue: 100pgs. Own research 100%. Supporting text 80%
Comments	Data is available in machine readable form and specific data analysis and consultancy work available. Price above represents full subscription but cheaper packages are available.
Currency	3 months after data collection
Response	1984
Availability	General
Cost	£16,000
Address	457 Kingston Rd, Ewell, Epsom, Surrey KT19 0DH
Telephone	01 394 0191
Contact	Caroline Corry, Manager

933

Originator	TAYSIDE REGIONAL COUNCIL
Title	QUARTERLY ECONOMIC REVIEW, quarterly. 1981-
Coverage	Review of local economic trends by sectoral activity and employment/unemployment trends. Also examines local economic initiatives.

Contents &	Tables per issue: Varies. Own research 50%, Other non official source
Origin of	25%, Government statistics 25%. Supporting text 70%
Statistics	

Currency	2-3 months
Response	1984
Availability	General
Cost	£2
Address	28 Crichton St, Dundee, Tayside
Telephone	0382 23281, ext 3281; Telex: 76518
Contact	R. Butler, Planning Department

934

Originator	TECHNOLOGY

Title	FIGURES OF THE MONTH, monthly in a weekly journal. 1977-
Coverage	General figures on the engineering industry.

Contents &	Tables per issue: Varies. Non official source 25%, Government
Origin of	statistics 75%
Statistics	

Comments	Journal previously called 'Engineering Today'.
Currency	Varies
Response	1984
Availability	General
Cost	£30 or 50p for a single copy
Address	Engineering Today Ltd, 55-57 Great Marlborough St, London W1V 1DP
Telephone	01 439 9606
Contact	Michael Orme, Editor

935

Originator	TELEVISION ADVERTISING BUREAU (SURVEYS) LTD. (TABS)

Title	TRACKING ADVERTISING AND BRAND STRENGTH/ HEALTH, monthly. Aug 1981-
Coverage	Monitors brand goodwill, advertising awareness, price image, brand awareness, claimed levels of buying/usage and brand image attributes. Based on a sample of 2000 adults and covers all TV areas except NE Scotland, Border, Channel Islands and Ulster.

Contents &	Tables per issue: 14. Own research 100%. Supporting text 5%
Origin of	
Statistics	

Currency	4-5 weeks
Response	1984
Availability	General

Cost	£2,500 - £4,000 depending on the number of brands and target market covered.
Address	18 Maddox St, London W1R 9PL
Telephone	01 629 0424
Contact	Mr A. Fawley, Marketing Director

936

Originator	TEXTILE MARKET STUDIES
Title	CLOTHING SURVEY, annual. 1970-
Coverage	Survey of 40,000 adults each year covering details of their purchasing of clothing and footwear. The information collected is kept on a databank and individual reports are prepared for individual clients.
Contents & Origin of Statistics	Tables per issue: Varies
Currency	8-10 weeks from survey
Response	1984
Availability	General (on subscription)
Cost	Varies according to information required
Address	Oxford House, 182 Upper Richmond Rd, London SW15 2SH
Telephone	01 785 2302; Telex: 24224
Contact	J.I. Harrison, Director

937

Originator	TEXTILE MARKET STUDIES
Title	DOMESTIC TEXTILE AND POTTERY SURVEY, quarterly
Coverage	Survey of purchasing habits of textiles and pottery. Information collected is held on a databank and individual reports prepared for individual clients.
Contents & Origin of Statistics	Tables per issue: Varies
Currency	8-10 weeks from survey
Response	1984
Availability	General (on subscription)
Cost	Varies according to information required
Address	Oxford House, 182 Upper Richmond Rd, London SW15 2SH
Telephone	01 785 2302; Telex: 24224
Contact	J.I. Harrison, Director

938

Originator	TEXTILE STATISTICS BUREAU
Title	POCKET FACTS ABOUT THE UK TEXTILE INDUSTRY, annual
Coverage	Covers employment, production, fibre consumption, exports, imports, trade balance. EEC data for comparison.
Contents & Origin of Statistics	Tables per issue: 13. Government statistics 100%.
Currency	Varies
Response	1984
Availability	General
Cost	Free
Address	2nd Floor, Royal Exchange, Manchester M2 7ER
Telephone	061 834 7871
Contact	Above address

939

Originator	TEXTILE STATISTICS BUREAU
Title	QUARTERLY STATISTICAL REVIEW, quarterly
Coverage	Includes data on emmployment in the textile industry, production, imports and exports. Covers cotton, man-made fibres, wool, woven and knitted fabrics, carpets and rugs, and household textiles. Some international statistics on yarn and fabrics.
Contents & Origin of Statistics	Tables per issue: 25. Non official source 10%, Government statistics 90%. Supporting text 2%
Currency	Varies
Response	1984
Availability	General
Cost	£16
Address	2nd Floor, Royal Exchange, Manchester M2 7ER
Telephone	061 834 7871
Contact	Above address

940

Originator	THAMES TELEVISION
Title	THAMES TELEVISION'S LONDON, varies
Coverage	Demographics, income/expenditure, retail structure and trade, holidays and tourism.

Contents & Origin of Statistics	Tables per issue: 65. Non official source 80%, Government statistics 20%. Supporting text 20%

Currency	1 year
Response	1984
Availability	Members and clients
Cost	Free
Address	149 Tottenham Court Rd, London W1
Telephone	01 388 5199
Contact	Sue Peacock, Research Department

941

Originator	THAMES WATER AUTHORITY

| Title | ANNUAL REPORT AND ACCOUNTS, annual. 1974- |
| Coverage | Contains a section entitled 'Facts and Figures', covering water supply, sewage treatment and disposal, river flows, rainfall and population. |

Contents & Origin of Statistics	Tables per issue: 8. Own research 80%, Government statistics 20%. Supporting text 85%

Response	1984
Availability	General
Cost	£3.50
Address	New River Head, 173 Rosebery Ave, London EC1R 4TP
Telephone	01 837 3307; Telex: 24439
Contact	Manager, Public Relations

942

Originator	THAMES WATER AUTHORITY

| Title | THAMES WATER STATISTICS, annual. 1976- |
| Coverage | Personnel, operating statistics, river and effluent quality and potable water quality. |

Contents & Origin of Statistics	Tables per issue: 48. Own research 100%.

Response	1984
Availability	Limited circulation
Cost	Free
ISSN	0309 8877
Address	New River Head, 173 Rosebery Ave, London EC1R 4TP
Telephone	01 837 3300; Telex: 24439

943

Originator	THAMESDOWN BOROUGH COUNCIL
Title	EMPLOYMENT SURVEY, annual
Coverage	Data on employment structure, the business environment, recruitment and training, small firms employment structure and computer personnel.
Contents & Origin of Statistics	Tables per issue: 18-20. Own research 100%
Comments	Also publish occasional publications titled 'Employment Information Report' and 'Housing Information Report'.
Currency	Varies
Response	1984
Availability	General
Cost	Unstated
Address	Civic Offices, Evelid St, Swindon, Wiltshire
Telephone	0793 26161
Contact	C.J. Moreton, Corporate Planning Unit.

944

Originator	THORPE, BERNARD AND PARTNERS
Title	PROPERTY REVIEW, 3 issues per year
Coverage	Largely commentary and articles on property trends throughout the UK but contains regular statistics on office and industrial rents in approximately 45 cities and towns, and occasional statistics on residential prices in the regions.
Contents & Origin of Statistics	Tables per issue: 4. Own research 100%. Supporting text 75%
Currency	2-3 months
Response	1984
Availability	General
Cost	Free
Address	1 Hanover Square, London W1R 0PT
Telephone	01 499 6353; Telex: 8813389
Contact	D. Enion, Marketing

945

Originator	TIMBER GROWER
Title	PRICE INDICES AND SALES CONTRACTS FOR TIMBER IN THE UK, quarterly in a quarterly journal

Coverage	Prices for homegrown timber and sales contracts from forestry commission areas in each county of the UK.
Contents & Origin of Statistics	Tables per issue: 2
Comments	The publication is the journal of Timber Growers Great Britain Ltd, Timber Growers England and Wales Ltd and Timber Growers Scotland Ltd.
Currency	2-3 months
Response	1984
Availability	General
Cost	£6 or £1.50 for a single issue. Free to members of the associations listed under the 'comments' heading.
Address	Sidmouth Printing Group, Alexandria Industrial Estate, Sidmouth, Devon EX10 9HL
Telephone	03955 2345
Contact	Timber Growers England and Wales Ltd, Agriculture House, Knightsbridge, London SW1

946

Originator	TIMBER TRADE FEDERATION
Title	UK YEARBOOK OF TIMBER STATISTICS, irregular
Coverage	Imports, exports, stocks, production and consumption of various types of timber, also wood products.
Contents & Origin of Statistics	Tables per issue: 40. Government statistics 100%
Comments	Although titled 'Yearbook' it has not been published on a yearly basis.
Currency	Varies
Response	1983
Availability	General
Cost	Free
Address	Clareville House, Whitcomb St, London WC2H 7DL
Telephone	01 839 1891
Contact	C.K. Norman, Statistician

947

Originator	TIMBER TRADES JOURNAL
Title	MARKET STATISTICS, monthly in a weekly journal
Coverage	Consumption, stocks, imports, exports, contracts etc for softwoods, hardwoods and panel products. Also details on housing starts, completions, producer prices and average earnings.

Contents &	Tables per issue: 6. Non official source 30%, Government statistics
Origin of	70%
Statistics	

Currency	2 months
Response	1984
Availability	General
Cost	£48 or £1 for a single issue
ISSN	0262 6071
Address	Benn Publications Ltd, Sovereign Houe, Sovereign Way, Tonbridge, Kent
Telephone	0732 362468; Telex: 95132
Contact	Neil Herbert Smith, Editor

948

Originator	TIN INTERNATIONAL
Title	STATISTICAL SUPPLEMENT AND LME PRICES, STOCKS AND TURNOVER, monthly in a monthly journal. 1928-
Coverage	Prices and stocks of tin on the London Metal Exchange.
Comments	Other statistics produced include an annual World Tinplate Survey.
Response	1984
Availability	General
Cost	£21 or £2.50 for a single issue
ISBN	ISSN 0040 795X
Address	Tin Publications Ltd, 7 High Rd, London W4 2NE
Telephone	01 995 9277
Contact	R.A. Amlot, Editor

949

Originator	TOWN AND COUNTRY PLANNING
Title	ANNUAL STATISTICAL REVIEW OF BRITAIN'S NEW TOWNS, annual in a monthly journal. 1955-
Coverage	Data on land area, the economy, population, employment, and housing stock of each new town. Usually appears in the November issue of the journal.
Contents &	Tables per issue: 5. Non official statistics + government statistics
Origin of	100%
Statistics	
Comments	The review's format changes each year to focus on different topics, although the basic data remains the same.
Currency	6 months
Response	1984
Availability	General
Cost	£38.50 (£14 to TCPA members) or £3.50 for a single issue
ISBN	ISSN 0040 9960

Address	Town and Country Planning, 17 Carlton House Terrace, London SW1Y 5AS
Telephone	01 930 8903
Contact	Jim Dumsday, Editor

950

Originator	TRADE INDEMNITY PLC

Title	NEWS RELEASE - BUSINESS FAILURES, monthly
Coverage	Monthly business failures notified to Trade Indemnity by its policy holders, by main trade category.

Contents & Origin of Statistics	Tables per issue: 1. Own research 100%. Supporting text 50%

Currency	1-2 weeks
Response	1984
Availability	General
Cost	Free
Address	Trade Indemnity House, 13-24 Great Eastern St, London EC2A 3AX
Telephone	01 739 4311 ; Telex: 21227
Contact	Isabella Pissarides, Management Information Services

951

Originator	TRADE INDEMNITY PLC

Title	QUARTERLY ECONOMIC BULLETIN, quarterly
Coverage	A review of the UK economy and industrial performance by major sectors followed by annual and quarterly statistics on bad debtors and business failures by trade category notified to Trade Indemnity by its policy holders.

Contents & Origin of Statistics	Tables per issue: 8. Own research 70%; Government statistics 30%. Supporting text 50%

Currency	1 month
Response	1984
Availability	General
Cost	Free
Address	Trade Indemnity House, 13-24 Great Eastern St, London EC2A 3AX
Telephone	01 739 4311; Telex: 21227
Contact	Isabella Pissarides, Management Information Services.

952

Originator	TRANS PROMOTIONS LTD
Title	DISTRIBUTION MANAGEMENT SALARY SURVEY, annual.
Coverage	Survey of salary levels, employment, fringe benefits and company cars in the physical distribution industry.
Contents & Origin of Statistics	Tables per issue: Own research 100%
Currency	3-4 months
Response	1984
Availability	General
Cost	£14
Address	64 North St, Guildford, Surrey GU1 3AD
Telephone	0483 502525
Contact	R. Wileman, Director

953

Originator	TRANSPORT ENGINEER
Title	TRUCK OPERATING COSTS FOR THE COMING YEAR, annually in a monthly journal.1980-
Coverage	Standing and running costs of trucks, according to weight and number of axles, and broken down into rigid and articulated trucks.
Contents & Origin of Statistics	Tables per issue: 2. Unstated 100%. Supporting text 50%
Comments	Figures usually published in the January issue
Currency	1 month
Response	1984
Availability	General
Cost	£12 or £1 for a single issue
ISSN	0020 3122
Address	The Institute of Road Transport Engineers, 1 Cromwell Place, London SW7 2JF
Telephone	01 589 3744
Contact	P.J. Edmonds, Assistant Secretary

954

Originator	TRAVEL AND TOURISM RESEARCH
Title	AIRLINE TRADE IMAGE SURVEY, annual. 1983-
Coverage	Examines travel agents' images of 65 international airlines.

Contents &   Tables per issue: Own research 100%
Origin of
Statistics

Response   1984
Availability   General
Cost   £350
Address   151 Farringdon Rd, London EC1
Telephone   01 833 1797; Telex: 21792
Contact   Peter Hodgson, Principal

955

Originator   TRAVEL AND TOURISM RESEARCH

Title   HOTEL GROUPS AND SHORT BREAK OPERATORS IMAGE
                  SURVEY, 1978-
Coverage   Examines in very great detail travel agents' image and recommenda-
                  tions for hotel groups and short holiday tour operators in the UK
                  and abroad.
Response   1984
Availability   General
Cost   £1200-2000
Address   151 Farringdon Rd, London EC1
Telephone   01 833 1797; Telex: 21792
Contact   Peter Hodgson, Principal

956

Originator   TRAVEL AND TOURISM RESEARCH

Title   TRAVEL AGENTS READERSHIP SURVEY, biennial. 1980-
Coverage   Readership of travel trade media, using representative sample of 400
                  ABTA travel agents. Results by agency type, status, size, type of
                  business and region.

Contents &   Tables per issue: Own research 100%
Origin of
Statistics

Response   1984
Availability   General
Cost   £450
Address   151 Farringdon Rd, London EC1
Telephone   01 833 1797; Telex: 21792
Contact   Peter Hodgson, Principal

957

Originator	TRAVEL ASSOCIATIONS CONSULTATIVE COUNCIL
Title	ANATOMY OF UK TOURISM, biennial
Coverage	Divided into 3 sections - domestic, inbound and outbound. Covers 10 year period. Includes data on accommodation, employment, tourist attractions for UK. Inbound section covers market for overseas visitors, business, VFR (visiting friends and relatives) and holiday visitors. Outbound also covers business, VFR markets, inclusive tours and independent holidays.
Contents & Origin of Statistics	Tables per issue: 107. Non official source 40%, Government statistics 60%. Supporting text 5%
Currency	Varies
Response	1983
Availability	General
Cost	£25
Address	c/o 55-57 Newman St, London, W1P 4HH
Telephone	01 637 2444
Contact	Above address

958

Originator	TVS
Title	MARKETING HANDBOOK, biennial
Coverage	Includes population characteristics of TVS area, employment and industry, living standards, retail trade, television audience.
Contents & Origin of Statistics	Tables per issue: 72. Non official source 90%, Government statistics 10%.
Currency	Varies
Response	1983
Availability	General
Cost	Free
Address	Television Centre, Vinters Park, Maidstone ME14 5NZ
Telephone	0622 54945; Telex: 965911
Contact	Gordon Tucker, Senior Manager, Press and Public Relations

959

Originator	TYNE AND WEAR COUNTY COUNCIL
Title	ECONOMIC DEVELOPMENT BULLETIN, quarterly
Coverage	Review of county economy. Also variety of statistics on redundancies, unemployment, factory closures, earnings. Gives national economic indicators for comparison.

Contents & Origin of Statistics	Tables per issue: 6. Government statistics 100%. Supporting text 75%

Currency	Varies
Response	1983
Availability	General
Cost	Free
Address	Sandyford House, Newcastle upon Tyne NE2 1ED
Telephone	0632 816144
Contact	R.N. Meachen, Senior Research Officer

960

Originator	TYNE AND WEAR COUNTY COUNCIL

Title	FACT CARD, quarterly
Coverage	Covers wide range of activities and services, such as councillors, finance, population, fire services, waste disposal, police, transport, shipping, parking, employment, house and car ownerships.

Contents & Origin of Statistics	Tables per issue: 17. Government statistics 10%, Unstated 90%.

Currency	Varies
Response	1983
Availability	General
Cost	Free
Address	Sandyford House, Newcastle-upon-Tyne NE2 1ED
Telephone	0632 816144
Contact	R.N. Meachen, Senior Research Officer

961

Originator	ULSTER TELEVISION

Title	MARKETING GUIDE TO NORTHERN IRELAND, bi-annual
Coverage	Sections on population, television audience, economy, agriculture, consumer expenditure, motor vehicles, sport, leisure and tourism, research and production facilities, retail and wholesale trade, transport and communications.

Contents & Origin of Statistics	Tables per issue: 30. Non official source 40%, Government statistics 60%. Supporting text 20%.

Currency	Varies
Response	1983
Availability	General
Cost	£5
Address	Havelock House, Ormeau Rd, Belfast BT7 1EB

Telephone	0232 28122; Telex: 74654
Contact	R. Kennedy, Information Officer

962

Originator	UNION OF SHOP, DISTRIBUTIVE AND ALLIED WORKERS
Title	UNTITLED, irregular
Coverage	Internal statistics collected on wage conditions.
Response	1983
Availability	Internal
Address	188 Wilmslow Rd, Manchester M14 6LJ
Telephone	061 224 2804
Contact	Above address

963

Originator	UNIT FOR RETAIL PLANNING INFORMATION LTD
Title	CONSUMER RETAIL EXPENDITURE ESTIMATES FOR SMALL AREAS, continuous
Coverage	Expenditure by goods type categories for local authority areas or other geographically defined areas.
Comments	URPI can produce various statistical packages relating to retail and consumer trends including shopping surveys, demographic profiles, floorspace figures etc.
Response	1984
Availability	General
Cost	Varies according to information required. Basic price from £120.
Address	26 Queen Victoria St, Reading, RG1 1TG
Telephone	0734 588181
Contact	Bryan Wade

964

Originator	UNIT TRUST ASSOCIATION
Title	MONTHLY UNIT TRUST SALES STATISTICS, monthly
Coverage	Sales of unit trusts and the value of the industry overall.
Contents & Origin of Statistics	Tables per issue: 1. Own research 100%. Supporting text 50%
Currency	2-3 weeks
Response	1984
Availability	Financial groups
Cost	Free
Address	Park House, 16 Finsbury Circus, London EC2M 7JP

| Telephone | 01 628 0871/0431 |
| Contact | Tony Smith, Secretary |

965

Originator	UNIT TRUST ASSOCIATION
Title	QUARTERLY UNIT TRUST PERFORMANCE STATISTICS, quarterly
Coverage	Performance over 5, 10 and 15 years of the median fund of the different unit trust sectors, compared with building society accounts, bank deposit accounts and National Savings. (Offer to bid basis, net income reinvested)
Contents & Origin of Statistics	Tables per issue: 3. Own research 100%. Supporting text 50%
Comments	These quarterly figures include the monthly figures in January, April, July and October.
Currency	3 weeks
Response	1984
Availability	General
Cost	Free
Address	Park House, 16 Finsbury Circus, London EC2M 7JP
Telephone	01 628 0871/0431
Contact	Tony Smith, Secretary

966

Originator	UNITED KINGDOM AGRICULTURAL SUPPLY TRADE ASSOCIATION (UKASTA) LTD
Title	FEED FACTS, annual
Coverage	Livestock numbers, output of compounds, compound production on a regional basis, usage of raw materials, expansion of UK food production, hosehold consumption, prices. Also some EEC data.
Contents & Origin of Statistics	Tables per issue: 11. Non official source 10%, Government statistics 40%, Unstated 50%.
Response	1984
Availability	General
Cost	Free
Address	3 Whitehall Court, London SW1A 2EQ
Telephone	01 930 3611; Telex: 917868
Contact	Mr Roger Dean, Deputy Director General

967

Originator	UNITED KINGDOM IRON AND STEEL STATISTICS BUREAU
Title	UK IRON AND STEEL INDUSTRY: ANNUAL STATISTICS, annual
Coverage	Figures on production, trade, and prices of iron and steel products. Also details of raw materials consumed, cokemaking, iron foundries, and manpower. Historical figures given in most tables.
Contents & Origin of Statistics	Tables per issue: 50. Own research 60%, Other non official source 2%, Government statistics 38%.
Comments	Also publish 'International Steel Statistics' annually consisting of individual volumes for each country - includes a UK volume and a summary volume.
Currency	4-6 months
Response	1984
Availability	General
Cost	£40
Address	P.O. Box 230, NLA Tower, 12 Addiscombe Rd, Croydon CR9 6BS
Telephone	01 686 9050; Telex: 946372
Contact	Avril Kovacs, Statistical Publications

968

Originator	UNITED KINGDOM PARTICLEBOARD ASSOCIATION
Title	MARKET SHARES OF IMPORTED AND DOMESTICALLY PRODUCED WOOD CHIPBOARD, monthly (approx)
Coverage	Domestic and international trade in wood-based panels.
Contents & Origin of Statistics	Tables per issue: Own research 50%, Government statistics 50%
Response	1983
Availability	Members
Address	4th Floor, East Wing, 29 St. James's St, London SW1A 1HL
Telephone	01 839 2822
Contact	David Duke-Evans

969

Originator	UNITED KINGDOM PROVISION TRADE ASSOCIATION
Title	OFFICIAL MARKET REPORTS, weekly
Coverage	Market reports for butter, cheese, lard, bacon giving commodity prices.

Contents & Origin of Statistics	Tables per issue: 1. Own research 100%

Response	1983
Availability	Members
Address	1 London Bridge, London SE1 9SZ
Telephone	01 407 1093
Contact	A. Chandler, Secretary General

970

Originator	UNITED KINGDOM PROVISION TRADE ASSOCIATION
Title	UK IMPORTS, weekly
Coverage	Import figures for various commodities such as bacon, lard, butter fruits and other canned products.
Contents & Origin of Statistics	Tables per issue: 1. Government statistics 100%
Response	1983
Availability	Members
Address	1 London Bridge, London SE1 9SZ
Telephone	01 407 1093
Contact	A. Chandler, Secretary General

971

Originator	UNIVERSITIES CENTRAL COUNCIL ON ADMISSIONS (UCCA)
Title	STATISTICAL SUPPLEMENT, annual. 1966-
Coverage	Detailed figures on university admissions and applicants by age, subject, sex, type of school, A-levels, parental occupation, region, social class etc.
Contents & Origin of Statistics	Tables per issue: 22. Own research 100%.
Currency	6 months
Response	1984
Availability	General
Cost	£2.50
ISBN	0 900 95148 6
Address	P.O. Box 28, Cheltenham, Gloucestershire GL5O 1HY
Telephone	0242 519091; Telex: 43662
Contact	M.J. Hiscock, Head of UAS Group

972

Originator	UNIVERSITIES CENTRAL COUNCIL ON ADMMISSIONS (UCCA)
Title	ANNUAL REPORT, annual. 1964-
Coverage	Includes statistics on total university applications, acceptances and admissions within the UCCA scheme. Also breakdown by subject category.
Contents & Origin of Statistics	Tables per issue: 9. Own research 100%. Supporting text 25%.
Currency	6 months
Response	1984
Availability	General
Cost	£1.50
ISBN	0 900 95146 X
Address	P.O. Box 28, Cheltenham, Gloucestershire GL50 1HY
Telephone	0242 519091; Telex: 43662
Contact	Mr. J. Hiscock, Head of UAS Group

973

Originator	UNIVERSITIES CENTRAL COUNCIL ON ADMISSIONS (UCCA)
Title	UNIVERSITY APPLICATIONS FOR 19-ENTRY, 5 issues per year.
Coverage	Press release giving number of university applications by sex and UK/overseas distribution.
Contents & Origin of Statistics	Tables per issue: 1. Own research 100%. Supporting text 80%
Currency	1 month
Response	1984
Availability	General
Cost	Free
Address	P.O. Box 28, Cheltenham, Gloucestershire GL50 1HY
Telephone	0242 519091; Telex: 43662
Contact	Mr J. Hiscock, Head of UAS Group

974

Originator	UNIVERSITY COLLEGE OF WALES
Title	FARM MANAGEMENT SURVEY IN WALES: STATISTICAL RESULTS, annual. 1982-

Coverage	Results of a survey of a sample of 500 farms, classified by farm type and subclassified by farm size (European size units).
Contents & **Origin of** **Statistics**	Tables per issue: 31. Own research 100%. Supporting text 10%
Comments	In addition produce 'Welsh studies in agricultural economics', which contains articles on the work of the Dept. and a summary of the farm management survey.
Currency	6 months
Response	1984
Availability	General
Cost	£3
Address	Dept. of Agricultural Economics, Penglais, Aberystwyth, Wales SY23 3DD
Telephone	0970 3111 ; Telex: 35181
Contact	Dr D.A.G. Green, Senior Lecturer in Agricultural Economics

975

Originator	UNIVERSITY OF ABDERDEEN, NORTH OF SCOTLAND COLLEGE OF AGRICULTURE
Title	CEREAL FUTURES CHARTS, weekly
Coverage	Wheat and barley prices.
Contents & **Origin of** **Statistics**	Tables per issue: 9. Own research 100%.
Currency	2 months
Response	1983
Availability	General
Cost	Free
Address	Agricultural Economics Division, School of Agriculture Building, Aberdeen AB9 1UD
Telephone	0224 40291
Contact	Garth Entwistle

976

Originator	UNIVERSITY OF ABERDEEN, NORTH OF SCOTLAND COLLEGE OF AGRICULTURE
Title	POTATO FUTURES CHARTS, weekly
Coverage	Potato prices.
Contents & **Origin of** **Statistics**	Tables per issue: 5. Own research 100%
Currency	2 months

Response	1983
Availability	General
Cost	Free
Address	Agricultural Economics Division, School of Agricultural Building, Aberdeen, AB9 1UD
Telephone	0224 40291
Contact	Garth Entwistle

977

Originator	UNIVERSITY OF ABERDEEN, NORTH OF SCOTLAND COLLEGE OF AGRICULTURE
Title	SCOTTISH CEREAL EXPORTS, monthly
Coverage	Exports of barley and wheat.
Contents & Origin of Statistics	Tables per issue: 1. Own research 100%.
Response	1983
Availability	General
Cost	Free
Address	Agricultural Economics Division, School of Agriculture Building, Aberdeen AB9 1UD
Telephone	0224 40291
Contact	Garth Entwistle

978

Originator	UNIVERSITY OF ABERDEEN, NORTH OF SCOTLAND COLLEGE OF AGRICULTURE
Title	U.K. CEREAL EXPORTS, monthly
Coverage	Exports of barley and wheat.
Contents & Origin of Statistics	Tables per issue: 2. Own research 50%, Government statistics 50%.
Response	1983
Availability	General
Cost	Free
Address	Agricultural Economics Division, School of Agricultural Building, Aberdeen AB9 1UD
Telephone	0224 40291
Contact	Garth Entwistle

979

Originator	UNIVERSITY OF CAMBRIDGE, AGRICULTURAL ECON-OMICS UNIT
Title	ECONOMIC RESULTS, annual. 1966-
Coverage	Income and cost data for glasshouse, vegetable, dessert apple and miscellaneous fruit farms.
Contents & Origin of Statistics	Tables per issue: 20. Own research 90%, Government statistics 10%. Supporting text 15%
Currency	6 months
Response	1984
Availability	General
Cost	£3.50
Address	Dept. of Land Economy, 19 Silver St, Cambridge CB3 9EP
Telephone	0223 355262
Contact	W.L. Hinton, Assistant Director of Research

980

Originator	UNIVERSITY OF CAMBRIDGE, AGRICULTURAL ECON-OMICS UNIT
Title	FARMING IN THE EASTERN COUNTIES OF ENGLAND, annual. 1978-
Coverage	Farm incomes data, costs, investment.
Contents & Origin of Statistics	Tables per issue: 150. Own research 90%, Government statistics 10%. Supporting text 50%
Currency	6 months
Response	1984
Availability	General
Cost	£5.50
Address	Dept. of Land Economy, 19 Silver St, Cambridge CB3 9EP
Telephone	0223 355262
Contact	M.C. Murphy, Technical Officer

981

Originator	UNIVERSITY OF CAMBRIDGE, AGRICULTURAL ECON-OMICS UNIT
Title	PIG MANAGEMENT SCHEME RESULTS, annual. 1936-
Coverage	Economics of pig production by degree of end product.

Contents & Origin of Statistics	Tables per issue: 40. Own research 90%, Government statistics 10%. Supporting text 5%
Currency	3 months
Response	1984
Availability	General
Cost	£2
Address	Dept. of Land Economy, 19 Silver St, Cambridge CB3 9EP
Telephone	0223 355262
Contact	R.P. Ridgeon, Technical Officer

982

Originator	UNIVERSITY OF DUNDEE
Title	D.10 ANNUAL SERIES FOR AVERAGE GROSS WEEKLY EARNINGS IN SCOTLAND FOR 1959 - AT SIC ORDER, annual
Coverage	Data on each SIC order for male and females and for manual and non- manual workers. One of a series of 12 'Green Books' produced regularly.
Contents & Origin of Statistics	Tables per issue: Government statistics 100%
Comments	The report is produced by photocopying and there are plans to make available the data on computer printout.
Response	1984
Availability	General
Cost	Free, but there may be photocopying charges
Address	Dundee Scottish Economic Modelling Group, Dundee DD1 4HN
Telephone	0382 23181, ext 369
Contact	Charlotte Lythe

983

Originator	UNIVERSITY OF DUNDEE
Title	D.11 INCOME IN SCOTLAND 1960-, annual
Coverage	Data on Scottish GDP, personal income and personal disposable income. The figures are further disaggregated into types of income. One of a series of 12 'Green Books' produced on a regular basis.
Contents & Origin of Statistics	Tables per issue: Government statistics 100%
Comments	The report is produced by photocopying and there are plans to make available the data on computer printout.
Response	1984
Availability	General

Cost	Free, but there may be photocopying charges
Address	Dundee Scottish Economic Modelling Group, Dundee DD1 4HN
Telephone	0382 23181, ext 369
Contact	Charlotte Lythe

984

Originator	UNIVERSITY OF DUNDEE
Title	D.12 OUTPUT IN SCOTLAND 1958-, annual
Coverage	Data on Scottish domestic product by industry at current and constant prices. One of a series of 12 'Green Books' produced on a regular basis.
Contents & Origin of Statistics	Tables per issue: Government statistics 100%
Comments	The report is produced by photocopying and there are plans to make available the data on computer printout.
Response	1984
Availability	General
Cost	Free, but there may be charges for photocopying
Address	Dundee Scottish Economic Modelling Group, Dundee DD1 4HN
Telephone	0382 23181, ext 369
Contact	Charlotte Lythe

985

Originator	UNIVERSITY OF DUNDEE
Title	D.2 UNEMPLOYMENT IN SCOTLAND 1959-, annual
Coverage	One of a series of 12 'Green Books' covering unemployment in Scotland by industrial order. It also gives the percentage unemployment rate, percentage seasonally adjusted unemployment rate and comparative Scotland and UK unemployment trends.
Contents & Origin of Statistics	Tables per issue: Government statistics 100%
Comments	The document is produced by photocopying and there are plans to make available a computer printout of the data.
Response	1984
Availability	General
Cost	Free, but there may be photocopying charges
Address	Dundee Scottish Economic Modelling Group, Dundee DD1 4HN
Telephone	0382 23181, ext 369
Contact	Charlotte Lythe

986

Originator	UNIVERSITY OF DUNDEE
Title	D.3 SELF EMPLOYMENT (INCLUDING EMPLOYEES) IN SCOTLAND 1951-, annual
Coverage	Total self employment in Scotland and disaggregated by SIC order. One of a series of 12 'Green Books' published regularly.
Contents & Origin of Statistics	Tables per issue: Government statistics 100%
Comments	The report is produced by photocopying and there are plans to make available a computer printout of the data.
Response	1984
Availability	General
Cost	Free, but there may be photocopying charges
Address	Dundee Scottish Economic Modelling Group, Dundee DD1 4HN
Telephone	0382 23181, ext 369
Contact	Charlotte Lythe

987

Originator	UNIVERSITY OF DUNDEE
Title	D.4 CONSUMERS' EXPENDITURE IN SCOTLAND 1961-, annual
Coverage	Consumer expenditure aggregates consistent with the CSO National Income and Expenditure Blue Book. Series given for food, drink and tobacco, housing and fuel, durable goods and vehicles, others at current and constant prices. These categories are further disaggregated. One of a series of 12 'Green Books' regularly produced.
Contents & Origin of Statistics	Tables per issue: Government statistics 100%
Comments	The report is produced by photocopying and there are plans to make available the data on computer printout.
Response	1984
Availability	General
Cost	Free, but there may be photocopying charges
Address	Dundee Scottish Economic Modelling Group, Dundee DD1 4HN
Telephone	0382 23181, ext 369
Contact	Charlotte Lythe

988

Originator	UNIVERSITY OF DUNDEE
Title	D.5 TAXES ON EXPENDITURE AND SUBSIDIES IN SCOT-LAND 1961-, annual
Coverage	Taxes and subsidies at current and constant (1975) prices. One of a series of 12 'Green Books' produced regularly.
Contents & Origin of Statistics	Tables per issue: Government statistics 100%
Comments	The report is produced by photocopying and there are plans to make available the data on computer printout.
Response	1984
Availability	General
Cost	Free, but there may be photocopying charges
Address	Dundee Scottish Economic Modelling Group, Dundee DD1 4HN
Telephone	0382 23181, ext 369
Contact	Charlotte Lythe

989

Originator	UNIVERSITY OF DUNDEE
Title	D.6 INVESTMENT IN SCOTLAND 1961-, annual
Coverage	Data on Scottish Gross Domestic Fixed Capital Formation by industry at current and constant prices for all assets. One of a series of 12 'Green Books' produced regularly
Contents & Origin of Statistics	Tables per issue: Government statistics 100%
Comments	The report is produced by photocopying and there are plans to make available the data on computer printout.
Response	1984
Availability	General
Cost	Free, but there may be a charge for photocopying
Address	Dundee Scottish Economic Modelling Group, Dundee DD1 4HN
Telephone	0382 23181, ext 369
Contact	Charlotte Lythe

990

Originator	UNIVERSITY OF DUNDEE
Title	D.7 CAPITAL STOCK AND CAPACITY UTILISATION IN SCOTTISH MANUFACTURING INDUSTRIES 1951-, annual

Coverage	Data on the derivation of Scottish gross capital stock in manufacturing giving annual gross investment, annual retirements and annual gross capital stock. There is also an index of industrial production by industry group, Scottish current price output and manufacturing output with the Wharton School capacity index. One of a series of 12 'Green Books' produced regularly.
Contents & Origin of Statistics	Tables per issue: 5. Government statistics 100%
Comments	The report is produced by photocopying and there are plans to make available the data on computer printout.
Response	1984
Availability	General
Cost	Free, but there may be charges for photocopying
Address	Dundee Scottish Economic Modelling Group, Dundee DD1 4HN
Telephone	0382 23181, ext 369
Contact	Charlotte Lythe

991

Originator	UNIVERSITY OF DUNDEE
Title	D.8 VALUE OF PHYSICAL INCREASE IN STOCKS AND WORK IN PROGRESS BY INDUSTRY GROUP FOR SCOTLAND, annual
Coverage	Value of increase in stocks at current and constant (1975) prices. One of a series of 12 'Green Books' produced regularly.
Contents & Origin of Statistics	Tables per issue: 18. Government statistics 100%
Comments	The report is produced by photocopying and there are plans to make available the data on computer printout.
Response	1984
Availability	General
Cost	Free, but there may be photocopying charges
Address	Dundee Scottish Economic Modelling Group, Dundee DD1 4HN
Telephone	0382 23181, ext 369
Contact	Charlotte Lythe

992

Originator	UNIVERSITY OF DUNDEE
Title	D.9 LOCAL AUTHORITY AND CENTRAL GOVERNMEN' CURRENT EXPENDITURE ON GOODS AND SERVICES I? SCOTLAND 1961-, annual
Coverage	Central and local government expenditure. One of a series of 1 'Green Books' produced regularly.

Contents & Origin of Statistics	Tables per issue: 15. Government statistics 100%
Comments	The report is produced by photocopying and there are plans to make available the data on computer printout.
Response	1984
Availability	General
Cost	Free, but there may be photocopying charges
Address	Dundee Scottish Economic Modelling Group, Dundee DD1 4HN
Telephone	0382 23181, ext 369
Contact	Charlotte Lythe

993

Originator	UNIVERSITY OF DUNDEE
Title	D1. MANUAL/NON-MANUAL DIVISION OF EMPLOYEES IN EMPLOYMENT BY SEX AND INDUSTRIAL ORDER (SIC) SCOTLAND 1959-, annual
Coverage	One of a series of 12 regularly produced 'Green Books' covering trends in employment by SIC in Scotland.
Contents & Origin of Statistics	Tables per issue: 4. Government statistics 100%
Comments	The document is published by photocopying and there are plans to make the data available on a computer printout.
Response	1984
Availability	General
Cost	Free, but may be photocopying charges
Address	Dundee Scottish Economic Modelling Group, Dundee DD1 4HN
Telephone	0382 23181, ext 369
Contact	Charlotte Lythe

994

Originator	UNIVERSITY OF EXETER, AGRICULTURAL ECONOMICS UNIT
Title	FARM INCOMES IN SOUTH WEST ENGLAND, annual. 1940s-
Coverage	Changes in outputs, inputs and income, net cash flows and changes in credit use and trends in incomes, capital and borrowing. Aggregated by type of farming.
Contents & Origin of Statistics	Tables per issue: 49. Own research 100%. Supporting text 40%
Comments	Sample of over 300 farms
Currency	c.9 months

Response	1984
Availability	General
Cost	£2.50
ISSN	0306 8277
Address	Lafrowda House, St German's Rd, Exeter EX4 6TL
Telephone	0392 73025; Telex: 42894
Contact	Professor J. P. McInerney, Director of Unit

995

Originator	UNIVERSITY OF EXETER, AGRICULTURAL ECONOMICS UNIT
Title	FARM MANAGEMENT HANDBOOK, annual. 1976-
Coverage	Farm results - financial and physical standards by type-of-farming group, gross margins - crop and livestock enterprises, tenants' capital, assets and liabilities. Covers South West England.
Contents & Origin of Statistics	Tables per issue: c.70. Own research 90%, Other non official source 5%, Government statistics 5%. Supporting text 15%
Currency	c.9 months
Response	1984
Availability	General
Cost	£3
Address	Lafrowda House, St German's Rd, Exeter EX4 6Tl
Telephone	0392 73025; Telex: 42894
Contact	Professor J. P. McInerney, Director of the Unit

996

Originator	UNIVERSITY OF EXETER, AGRICULTURAL ECONOMICS UNIT
Title	PIG PRODUCTION IN SOUTH WEST ENGLAND, annual. 1940s-
Coverage	Costs of production, herds by size, performance factors, prices and financial data.
Contents & Origin of Statistics	Tables per issue: 30. Own research 100%. Supporting text 30%
Response	1984
Availability	General
Cost	£2.50
ISSN	0306 8900
Address	Lafrowda House, St German's Rd, Exeter EX4 6TL

Telephone	0392 73025; Telex: 42894
Contact	Professor J. P. McInerney, Director of the Unit

997

Originator	UNIVERSITY OF LIVERPOOL, MARINE TRANSPORT CENTRE
Title	INLAND WATERWAY FREIGHT STATISTICS, annual. 1982-
Coverage	Commercial usage of inland waterways, including definition, classification, full inventory. Covers goods lifted and moved by commodity, by regions, vessels.
Contents & Origin of Statistics	Tables per issue: 59. Own research 70%, Other non official source 10%, Government statistics 20%. Supporting text 30%
Comments	Only one completed so far. Project funded by SERC and the Department of Transport.
Response	1984
Availability	General
Cost	£10
Address	P.O. Box 147, Liverpool L69 3BX
Telephone	051 709 6002; Telex: 627095
Contact	Mrs M. Brash, Secretary

998

Originator	UNIVERSITY OF LIVERPOOL, MARINE TRANSPORT CENTRE
Title	WATERBOURNE FREIGHT STATISTICS FOR THE UK, annual. 1980-
Coverage	Trends over 10 years, covering inland waterway traffic, coastwise shipping and special traffic. Commodities covered with origin and destination by region.
Contents & Origin of Statistics	Tables per issue: 23. Own research 40%, Other non official source 10%, Government statistics 50%. Supporting text 20%
Comments	Edition with 1983 data available late 1984.
Currency	1 year
Response	1984
Availability	General
Cost	£10
Address	P.O. Box 147, Liverpool L69 3BX
Telephone	051 709 6002; Telex: 627095
Contact	Mrs M. Brash, Secretary

999

Originator	UNIVERSITY OF LONDON, WYE COLLEGE
Title	FARM BUSINESS STATISTICS FOR SOUTH-EAST ENG-LAND, annual.
Coverage	Financial and physical data on farms, which are divided by size and type into 18 groups. Survey of approximately 200 farms.
Contents & Origin of Statistics	Tables per issue: 29. Own research 100%. Supporting text 10%
Response	1984
Availability	General
Cost	£2.50
ISBN	0 86266 005 X
Address	Farm Business Unit, Department of Agricultural Economics, Wye, Ashford, Kent
Telephone	0233 812401; Telex 96118
Contact	Publications Office

1000

Originator	UNIVERSITY OF LONDON, WYE COLLEGE
Title	FARM MANAGEMENT POCKETBOOK, annual
Coverage	Gross margin data for a range of crops and livestock, labour, machinery and miscellaneous data.
Contents & Origin of Statistics	Tables per issue: c130. Non official source 5%, Government statistics 5%, Unstated 90%. Supporting text 30%
Response	1984
Availability	General
Cost	£33.25
ISBN	0 86266 003 3
Address	Farm Business Unit, Department of Agricultural Economics, Wye, Ashford, Kent
Telephone	0233 812401; Telex: 96118
Contact	Publications Office

1001

Originator	UNIVERSITY OF MANCHESTER
Title	FARM MANAGEMENT SURVEY, annual
Coverage	Survey of sample (164) of farms in the North West over 3 year period for comparison. Covers arable, lowland dairy and upland farms, physical and trading characteristics, assets and liabilities.

Contents & Origin of Statistics	Tables per issue: 102. Own research 100%. Supporting text 5%
Currency	1 year
Response	1983
Availability	General
Cost	£3.50
Address	Department of Agricultural Economics, Manchester M13 9PL
Telephone	061 273 7121/6888
Contact	Librarian

1002

Originator	UNIVERSITY OF NEWCASTLE-UPON-TYNE, DEPT. OF AGRICULTURAL ECONOMICS
Title	FARM INCOMES IN THE NORTH OF ENGLAND, annual. c1958-
Coverage	Income changes for a sample of farms in the North of England. Physical and financial data relate to farm size, type, output, input and capital structure.
Contents & Origin of Statistics	Tables per issue: 42. Own research 95%, Government statistics 5%. Supporting text 15%
Currency	6 months
Response	1984
Availability	General
Cost	£2.50
Address	Newcastle-upon-Tyne, NE1 7RU
Telephone	0632 328511
Contact	Mr D.C. Johnson, Senior Investigation Officer

1003

Originator	UNIVERSITY OF NOTTINGHAM, DEPARTMENT OF AGRICULTURE AND HORTICULTURE
Title	FARMING IN THE EAST MIDLANDS, annual
Coverage	Farm outputs, inputs and incomes.
Contents & Origin of Statistics	Tables per issue: 70pgs. Own research 100%. Supporting text 10%
Currency	8 months
Response	1984
Availability	General
Cost	£2.50
Address	School of Agriculture, Sutton Bonington, Loughborough LE12 5RD

Telephone	0602 506101
Contact	H.W.T. Ken, Senior Lecturer

1004

Originator	UNIVERSITY OF READING
Title	FARM BUSINESS DATA, annual
Coverage	In 3 parts: whole-farm data based on Farm Management Survey fc the area; summary of recently completed surveys of individua enterprises and research reports; forward planning.
Contents & Origin of Statistics	Tables per issue: 29 (in Part 1)
Comments	Gives detail of sampling used.
Currency	2 years
Response	1984
Availability	General
Cost	£2
ISBN	0 7049 0088 2
Address	Dept of Agricultural Economics and Management, 4 Earley Gat Whiteknights Rd, Reading, RG6 2AR
Telephone	0734 875123; Telex: 847813
Contact	Mrs. C. Searle, Publications Secretary

1005

Originator	UNIVERSITY OF READING
Title	FINANCIAL RESULTS OF HORTICULTURAL HOLDING\$ annual
Coverage	Results given for 3 groups - glasshouse holdings, vegetable and mixe horticultural holdings and fruit holdings. Level of total costs, tot revenue and net income.
Contents & Origin of Statistics	Tables per issue: 15. Own research 85%, Government statistics 15% Supporting text 30%
Comments	Part of 'National Farm Management Survey'. Gives sampling detai
Currency	2 years
Response	1984
Availability	General
Cost	£31.50
ISBN	0 7049 0809 3
Address	Dept of Agricultural Economics and Management, 4 Earley Gat Whiteknights Rd, Reading RG6 2AR

Telephone	0734 875123; Telex: 847813
Contact	Mrs. C. Searle, Publications Secretary

1006

Originator	UNIVERSITY OF SUSSEX, INSTITUTE OF MANPOWER STUDIES
Title	LABOUR MARKET INFORMATION BRIEFS, irregular
Coverage	Topics ranging from forecasts of graduate output and availability to employment effects of technological change. Includes data on education, employment, earnings, trade union membership, as well as general statistics on population and the economy.
Contents & Origin of Statistics	Tables per issue: 77. Non official source 45%. Government statistics 50%, Unstated 5%. Supporting text 50%
Comments	Briefs intended to update and complement IMS publications: UK Labour Market and Education and Employment
Currency	Varies
Response	1983
Availability	General
Cost	£20 set, nos. 1-9 £3 each, nos. 10-28 £2 each
Address	Mantell Building, Falmer, Brighton BN1 9RF
Telephone	0273 686751
Contact	Above address

1007

Originator	UNIVERSITY OF WARWICK, INSTITUTE FOR EMPLOY-MENT RESEARCH
Title	REVIEW OF THE ECONOMY AND EMPLOYMENT, every 1-2 years
Coverage	Forecasts of employment by industry and by region with a commentary on the structure of employment and a review of recent economic developments and the medium term economic outlook.
Contents & Origin of Statistics	Tables per issue: 43. Own research 85%, Government statistics 15%. Supporting text 60%
Comments	Also publish various other reports.
Response	1984
Availability	General
Cost	£3.50
Address	Gibbett Hill Rd, Coventry CV4 7AL
Telephone	0203 24011, ext 2503
Contact	R.M. Lindley, Director

1008

Originator	VERIFIED FREE DISTRIBUTION LTD
Title	VFD DISTRIBUTION REVIEW, bi-annual. 1982-
Coverage	Distribution of over 600 free publications, includes newspapers, magazines, local directories. Also average pagination and advertising contents percentages.
Contents & Origin of Statistics	Tables per issue: 24pgs. Own research 100%.
Comments	This company is a subsidiary of Audit Bureau of Circulations. The data is currently being computerised.
Currency	3 months
Response	1984
Availability	Members
Cost	Free
Address	13 Wimpole St, London W1M 7AB
Telephone	01 631 1343 ; Telex: 25247G
Contact	Dennis Bruce, General Manager

1009

Originator	VICKERS DA COSTA (UK) LTD
Title	LEISURE REVIEW, quarterly
Coverage	3 sections covering financial trends and sector charts, industry monitors by leisure sector and company information.
Contents & Origin of Statistics	Tables per issue: 44
Comments	Various other reports published on oil and mining, electronics, food, property and construction but most of these have an international coverage.
Response	1984
Availability	Primarily for clients but available to others on request
Cost	On application
Address	Regis House, King William St, London EC4R 9AR
Telephone	01 623 2494; Telex: 886004
Contact	Jan Wills

1010

Originator	VODKA TRADE ASSOCIATION
Title	RETURNS FOR THE FOUR HALF YEARS ENDED 31 DECEMBER, annual

Coverage	Gives production, home trade sales, export trade sales to EEC countries and non-EEC countries for last 4 six month periods.
Contents & Origin of Statistics	Tables per issue: 1. Own research 100%
Currency	2 months
Response	1983
Availability	General
Cost	Free
Address	37 Waterford House, 110 Kensington Park Rd, London W11 2PJ
Telephone	01 229 9222
Contact	Above address

1011

Originator	WALES TOURIST BOARD
Title	ANNUAL REPORT, annual
Coverage	Apart from accounts, includes general data over a 5 year period in an appendix. Covers visitors to tourist attractions, number of passenger journeys and revenue from tourism.
Contents & Origin of Statistics	Tables per issue: 6. Own research 50%, Government statistics 50%
Response	1983
Availability	General
Cost	£3.00
Address	Brunel House, 2 Fitzalan Rd, Cardiff CF2 1UY
Telephone	0222 499909
Contact	Stephen Webb, Senior Planning and Research Officer

1012

Originator	WALES TOURIST BOARD
Title	HOTEL OCCUPANCY IN WALES, annual
Coverage	Analysis of trends in hotel demand, by county and size of hotel. Data for a 6 year period.
Contents & Origin of Statistics	Tables per issue: 12. Own research 100%
Comments	Data also compiled monthly and distributed to participants and trade associations. Also more detailed information available on request.
Response	1983
Availability	General
Cost	£1
Address	Brunel House, 2 Fitzalan Rd, Cardiff CF2 1UY

| Telephone | 0222 499909 |
| Contact | Stephen Webb, Senior Planning and Research Officer |

1013

Originator	WALES TOURIST BOARD
Title	VISITORS TO TOURIST ATTRACTIONS, annual
Coverage	Visitors to tourist attractions in Wales over a 5 year period. Includes data on number of journeys on light railways.
Contents & Origin of Statistics	Tables per issue: 2. Own research 100%
Response	1983
Availability	General
Cost	Free
Address	Brunel House, 2 Fitzalan Rd, Cardiff CF2 1UY
Telephone	0222 499909
Contact	Stephen Webb, Senior Planning and Research Officer

1014

Originator	WALSALL CHAMBER OF COMMERCE AND INDUSTRY
Title	ECONOMIC SURVEY, quarterly. 1978-
Coverage	Survey of 100 local manufacturing companies to determine industrial trends, eg. deliveries, production stocks, cash-flow, labour, investment, confidence, etc.
Contents & Origin of Statistics	Tables per issue: 8. Own research 100%.
Currency	2 weeks
Response	1984
Availability	General
Cost	Free
Address	Chamber of Commerce House, Ward St, Walsall, West Midlands W51 2AG
Telephone	0922 647209; Telex: 338212
Contact	David Frott

1015

Originator	WARWICK STATISTICS SERVICE
Title	THE COUNTIES AND REGIONS OF THE UNITED KINGDOM, every 3 years. 1983-

Coverage	Statistical and economic data on individual counties in England and Wales, regional and island authorities in Scotland and Northern Ireland. Data on population, main towns, age structure, employment, unemployment, earnings, industrial floorspace, housing and industrial structure.
Contents & Origin of Statistics	Tables per issue: 70. Non official source 30%,Government statistics 70%. Supporting text 50%
Currency	Varies
Response	1984
Availability	General
Cost	£30
ISBN	0 903220 15 6
Address	University of Warwick Library, Gibbett Hill Rd, Coventry CV4 7AL
Telephone	0203 418938; Telex: 31406
Contact	David Mort

1016

Originator	WARWICKSHIRE COUNTY COUNCIL
Title	INDUSTRIAL LAND AVAILABILITY STATISTICS, bi-annual. 1980-
Coverage	Amount of industrial land and planning status by districts and areas withindistricts. Individual sheets for each district.
Contents & Origin of Statistics	Tables per issue: 1pg.
Comments	Also publish 'Structure Plan Information Report' with some statistics bi-annually.
Response	1984
Availability	General
Cost	£2, per district
Address	County Planning Department, P.O. Box 43, Shire Hall, Warwick CV34 4SX
Telephone	0926 493431; Telex: 311419
Contact	Jenny Coles, Principal Officer, Planning

1017

Originator	WARWICKSHIRE COUNTY COUNCIL
Title	RESIDENTIAL LAND AVAILABILITY STATISTICS, bi-annual. 1975-
Coverage	Planning status of residential land by district and areas within districts. Individual sheets for each district.

Contents & Origin of Statistics	Tables per issue: 1pg.
Comments	Also publish 'Structure Plan Information Report' with some statistics bi-annually.
Response	1984
Availability	General
Cost	£1-3, depending on district selected
Address	County Planning Department, P.O. Box 43, Shire Hall, Warwick CV34 4SX
Telephone	0926 493431, ext 2534; Telex: 311419
Contact	Jenny Coles, Principal Officer, Planning

1018

Originator	WATER SERVICES
Title	WATER SERVICES YEARBOOK, annual published separately from monthly journal
Coverage	Statistical data on rivers, water supply, sewage and sewage treatment, waterworks, statistics, water consumption etc.
Contents & Origin of Statistics	Tables per issue: Own research + other non official source 100%
Response	1984
Availability	General
Cost	£19.50
Address	Industrial and Marine Publications Ltd, Queensway House, 2 Queensway, Redhill RH1 1QS
Telephone	0737 68611; Telex: 948669
Contact	Mark Corliss

1019

Originator	WELSH DEVELOPMENT AGENCY
Title	ANNUAL REPORT AND ACCOUNTS, annual. 1977-
Coverage	General and financial information. Advance factory projects, factory building, investments by size and source of funding and location, land reclamation, key economic statistics.
Contents & Origin of Statistics	Tables per issue: 9. Own research 90%, Government statistics 10%. Supporting text 80%
Response	1984
Availability	General
Cost	Free
ISSN	0264 9284
Address	Pearl House, Greyfriars Rd, Cardiff CF1 3XX

| Telephone | 0222 32955; Telex: 497513 |
| Contact | Calvin Pugsley, Controller Promotion |

1020

Originator	WELSH WATER AUTHORITY
Title	ABSTRACT OF STATISTICS, occasional
Coverage	Water resources and supply, sewage treatment and disposal, land drainage, water quality and pollution, recreation and fisheries, manpower, charges, finance and social and economic data.
Contents & Origin of Statistics	Tables per issue: c.45. Unstated 100%. Supporting text 40%
Comments	Only two editions to date, 1979 and 1984.
Currency	3 months
Response	1984
Availability	General
Cost	£3
ISBN	0 860 97051 5
Address	Cambrian Way, Brecon, Powys, LD3 7HP.
Telephone	0874 3181 ; Telex: 497428
Contact	Mr C.W. Head, Principal Data Officer

1021

Originator	WESSEX (ELECTRONIC) PUBLISHING LTD
Title	COMPREHENSIVE BUILDING PRICE BOOK, annual. 1983-
Coverage	Prices and costs for materials, work and labour.
Contents & Origin of Statistics	Tables per issue: 500. Own research + other non official source 100%
Response	1984
Availability	General
Cost	£29, plus £2.50 p+p
ISSN	0265 2056
Address	Beaminster, Dorset, DT8 3BJ
Telephone	0308 862314
Contact	Above address

1022

| Originator | WESSEX WATER AUTHORITY |
| Title | DATA, annual. 1979- |

Coverage	Area, population, rainfall, soil moisture density, river flows, public water supply consumption and sewage flows.
Contents & Origin of Statistics	Tables per issue: 9. Own research 100%.
Currency	3 months
Response	1984
Availability	Internal
Address	Wessex House, Passage St, Bristol BS2 OJQ
Telephone	0272 290611
Contact	Judy Hayes, Regional Planning Group

1023

Originator	WEST MIDLAND PASSENGER TRANSPORT EXECUTIVE
Title	ANNUAL REPORT AND ACCOUNTS, annual. 1969-
Coverage	Includes some data on operations, eg number of passengers, times of travel, age of vehicles etc.
Contents & Origin of Statistics	Tables per issue: 40pgs. Own research 100%. Supporting text 80%
Currency	4-6 months
Response	1984
Availability	General
Address	16 Summer Lane, Birmingham B19 3SD
Telephone	021 622 5151; Telex: 336231
Contact	Ken Longmore, Press and Publicity Officer

1024

Originator	WEST MIDLAND PASSENGER TRANSPORT EXECUTIVE
Title	ANNUAL STATISTICAL REPORT, annual
Coverage	Passenger transport data covering West Midlands County Council area plus fringe areas in Staffordshire, Warwickshire and Hereford and Worcester. Data covers own bus operations, local BR operation, and NBC and independent bus operations.
Contents & Origin of Statistics	Tables per issue: 28-30. Own research 99%, Other non official source less than 1%, Government statistics less than 1%. Supporting text 33%
Currency	4-6 months
Response	1984
Availability	General
Cost	Cost: £2
Address	16 Summer Lane, Birmingham, West Midlands B19 3SD

Telephone	021 622 5151; Telex: 336231
Contact	Ernest Godward, Market Research Officer

1025

Originator	WEST MIDLANDS COUNTY COUNCIL
Title	STATISTICS FACT CARD, annual. 1979-
Coverage	Summary information taken from annual publication 'Statistics 19..'(see next entry).
Contents & Origin of Statistics	Tables per issue: 1.
Currency	6-12 months
Response	1984
Availability	General
Cost	Free
Address	CSIRU, Planning Department, County Hall, 1 Lancaster Circus, Queensway, Birmingham B4 7DJ
Telephone	021 300 6022
Contact	Jackie Sumner, Research Assistant, Planning Department

1026

Originator	WEST MIDLANDS COUNTY COUNCIL
Title	STATISTICS 19.., annual. 1976-
Coverage	General and political, demographic, housing, employment and industry, communications, public services, public finance. Data by district.
Contents & Origin of Statistics	Tables per issue: 115. Own research 30%, Other non official source 20%, Government statistics 50%. Supporting text 10%
Comments	More up to date figures may be available on request.
Currency	6-12 months
Response	1984
Availability	General
Cost	£5
ISSN	0265 4733
Address	CSIRU, Planning Dept, County Hall, 1 Lancaster Circus, Queensway, Birmingham B4 7DJ
Telephone	021 300 6022
Contact	Jackie Sumner, Research Assistant, Planning Department

1027

Originator	WEST MIDLANDS FORUM OF COUNTY COUNCILS
Title	INDUSTRIAL LAND AVAILABILITY IN THE WEST MID-LANDS REGION, annual
Coverage	Data for a number of years, on industrial land stocks, land ownership, land availability and planning permissions by county.
Contents & Origin of Statistics	Tables per issue: 10. Own research 100%. Supporting text 50%
Comments	Most data in graph form. Report prepared by Warwickshire County Council on behalf of the West Midlands Forum
Currency	3-4 months
Response	1984
Availability	General
Cost	£1
Address	West Midlands Regional Study, Stanier House, 1st Floor, 10 Holliday St, Birmingham B1 1TH
Telephone	021 235 4198
Contact	David Miller, Principal Officer

1028

Originator	WEST MIDLANDS FORUM OF COUNTY COUNCILS
Title	RESIDENTIAL LAND AVAILABILITY IN THE WEST MID-LANDS REGION, annual. 1983-
Coverage	Data for a number of years on stocks of land, housing completions and progress towards structure plan targets by county.
Contents & Origin of Statistics	Tables per issue: 9. Own research 100%. Supporting text 50%
Comments	Most figures presented in the form of graphs. Report prepared by Warwickshire County Council on behalf of the West Midlands Forum.
Currency	3-4 months
Response	1984
Availability	General
Cost	£1
Address	West Midlands Regional Study, Stanier House, 1st Floor, 10 Holliday St, Birmingham B1 1TH
Telephone	021 235 4198
Contact	David Miller, Principal Officer

1029

Originator	WEST SUSSEX COUNTY COUNCIL
Title	ANNUAL MONITORING REPORT, annual. 1979-
Coverage	Examination of trends and events of significance to the structure plan and presentation of new estimates and forecasts of population, housing and employment.
Contents & Origin of Statistics	Tables per issue: 50. Own research 65%, Other non official source 10%, Government statistics 25%. Supporting text 50%
Comments	Issue 'Population projections' leaflet containing extracts from the above, which is free.
Currency	2 months
Response	1984
Availability	General
Cost	£5
ISBN	0 86260 076 6
Address	County Planning Dept, County Hall, Chichester, West Sussex PO19 1RL.
Telephone	0243 777100; Telex: 86279
Contact	A.C. Blackman, Planning

1030

Originator	WEST SUSSEX COUNTY COUNCIL
Title	COMMERCIAL AND INDUSTRIAL DEVELOPMENT SURVEY, annual. 1975-
Coverage	Survey of land and floorspace available for industry, offices, shops and storage with examination of changes to committment.
Contents & Origin of Statistics	Tables per issue: 70. Own research 100%. Supporting text 10%
Currency	6 months
Response	1984
Availability	General
Cost	£8
ISBN	0 86260 053 7
Address	County Planning Dept, County Hall, Chichester, West Sussex PO19 1RL
Telephone	0243 777100; Telex: 86279
Contact	A.C. Blackman, Planning

1031

Originator	WEST SUSSEX COUNTY COUNCIL
Title	HOUSING LAND SUPPLY IN WEST SUSSEX, annual. 1980-
Coverage	Results of survey and compares with structure plan housing provision.
Contents & Origin of Statistics	Tables per issue: 40. Own research 100%. Supporting text 10%
Comments	Issue print out of survey as 'Residential Land Availability Survey', which is incorporated into the above.
Currency	5 months
Response	1984
Availability	General
Cost	£6.50
ISBN	0 86260 650 0
Address	County Planning Dept, County Hall, Chichester, West Sussex PO19 1RL
Telephone	0243 777100; Telex: 86279
Contact	A.C. Blackman, Planning

1032

Originator	WEST YORKSHIRE METROPOLITAN COUNTY COUNCIL
Title	ECONOMIC BULLETIN, monthly. Oct 1983-
Coverage	General summary of economic conditions and events.
Contents & Origin of Statistics	Tables per issue: 1-2. Supporting text 90%
Currency	1 month
Response	1984
Availability	General
Cost	Free
Address	Economic Development Group, Department of Planning, Cliff Hill House, Sandy Walk, Wakefield, West Yorkshire WF1 2DJ
Telephone	0924 367111, ext 4321; Telex: 556122
Contact	S. Taylor, Group Planner

1033

Originator	WEST YORKSHIRE METROPOLITAN COUNTY COUNCIL
Title	ECONOMIC TRENDS, quarterly. 1976-
Coverage	Sections on manpower, employment and unemployment, European affairs, regional and industrial issues and a local developments summary. A statistical appendix gives job changes by district.

Contents &	Tables per issue: 15. Own research 20%, Government statistics 80%.
Origin of	Supporting text 70%
Statistics	
Currency	Varies
Response	1984
Availability	General
Cost	Free
Address	Economic Development Group, Department of Planning, Cliff Hill House, Sandy Walk, Wakefield, West Yorkshire WF1 2DJ
Telephone	0924 367111, ext 4321; Telex: 556122
Contact	S. Taylor, Group Planner

1034

Originator	WEST YORKSHIRE PASSENGER TRANSPORT EXECU-TIVE
Title	ANNUAL REPORT AND ACCOUNTS, annual
Coverage	Apart from financial statistics, includes state carriage operating statistics, weekly Metrobus direct operations, manpower levels, training. Also includes section on inter P.T.E. comparisons, services operation levels.
Contents &	Tables per issue: 18. Own research 100%
Origin of	
Statistics	
Response	1983
Availability	General
Cost	£1
Address	Metro House, West Parade, Wakefield WF1 1NS
Telephone	0924 378234
Contact	Terry Grant, Public Relations Officer

1035

Originator	WEST YORKSHIRE PASSENGER TRANSPORT EXECU-TIVE
Title	INTER P.T.E. COMPARISONS, annual
Coverage	Produced by Passenger Transport Executive Group, formed from the Yorkshire P.T.E.s. Largely financial information. Also includes service operation levels for direct operations, statistical indicators for direct operations, co-ordinated operations for bus and rail and fares matrix.
Contents &	Tables per issue: 13. Own research 100%
Origin of	
Statistics	
Response	1983
Availability	Internal

Address	Metro House, West Parade, Wakefield WF1 1NS
Telephone	0924 378234
Contact	Terry Grant, Public Relations Officer

1036

Originator	WEST YORKSHIRE PASSENGER TRANSPORT EXECU- TIVE
Title	METRO - NATIONAL ANNUAL REPORT AND ACCOUNTS, annual
Coverage	Includes statistical information section covering numbers of vehicles, miles and depots in Yorkshire divisions of NBC and operations, staff and assets of West Yorkshire county.
Contents & Origin of Statistics	Tables per issue: 4. Own research 100%
Response	1983
Availability	General, but limited number
Cost	£1
Address	Metro House, West Parade, Wakefield, WF1 1NS
Telephone	0924 378234
Contact	Terry Grant, Public Relations Officer

1037

Originator	WESTLAKE AND CO
Title	WEST COUNTRY SHARES, weekly
Coverage	Includes quoted prices, movements, dividend yields, and dividend paid dates.
Contents & Origin of Statistics	Tables per issue: Non official source 100%
Response	1983
Availability	General
Cost	£520
Address	Princes House, Eastlake Walk, Plymouth PL1 1HG
Telephone	0752 20971
Contact	Above address

1038

Originator	WHITE OILS ASSOCIATION
Title	QUANTITY RETURNS, monthly

Coverage	Sales of white oils, petroleum jellies and transformer oils, UK and exports.
Contents & Origin of Statistics	Tables per issue: 1. Non official source 100%
Response	1983
Availability	Members
Address	1 Puddle Dock, Blackfriars, London EC4V 3PD
Telephone	01 236 8000
Contact	Above address

1039

Originator	WIGAN RICHARDSON INTERNATIONAL LTD
Title	HOP REPORT, annual. 1952-
Coverage	Production, growing areas, prices, market demand and trade for hops and hop products.
Contents & Origin of Statistics	Tables per issue: 20pgs. Own research 30%, Government statistics 70%. Supporting text 50%
Currency	6 months
Response	1984
Availability	Trade only
Cost	Free
Address	3 Church Rd, Paddock Wood, Tonbridge, Kent TN12 6ES
Telephone	089 2832235 ; Telex: 957022
Contact	David N. Richardson, Director

1040

Originator	WILTSHIRE ASSOCIATION OF FINANCIAL OFFICERS
Title	WILTSHIRE STATISTICS, annual
Coverage	Mainly financial information, also housing and manpower.
Contents & Origin of Statistics	Tables per issue: 20. Unstated 100%. Supporting text 25%
Currency	6 months
Response	1984
Availability	General
Cost	£2
Address	County Treasurer, County Hall, Trowbridge, Wiltshire
Telephone	02214 3641, ext 2668
Contact	Hon. Sec. M. Collier, Research and Technical Officer

1041

Originator	WINE AND SPIRIT ASSOCIATION OF GREAT BRITAIN AND NORTHERN IRELAND
Title	SURVEY OF COUNTRIES OF ORIGIN OF WINES CLEARED TO HOME USE, monthly
Coverage	Survey of countries of origin of wines imported for home use.
Contents & Origin of Statistics	Tables per issue: 5. Government statistics 100%
Response	1983
Availability	General
Cost	£90, minimum 2 year subscription
Address	Five Kings House, Kennet Wharf Lane, London EC4V 3BH
Telephone	01 248 5377
Contact	Above address

1042

Originator	WOOD MACKENZIE & CO
Title	ECONOMIC MONITOR, monthly
Coverage	Economic and financial data for the month with a commentary. A section also gives international data.
Contents & Origin of Statistics	Tables per issue: 61.
Currency	Varies
Response	1984
Availability	Mainly clients but available to others by negotiation.
Cost	Unstated
Address	Erskine House, 68-73 Queen St, Edinburgh EH2 4NS
Telephone	031 225 8525
Contact	Above address

1043

Originator	WOOD MACKENZIE & CO
Title	EQUITY MARKET ANALYSIS, monthly
Coverage	Data presented in 5 sections: a market view and summary, UK corporate sector, equity market evaluation, sector and stock evaluation, international perspective.
Contents & Origin of Statistics	Tables per issue: 49. Unstated 80%

Response	1984
Availability	Mainly clients but available to others by negotiation
Cost	By negotiation
Address	Erskine House, 68-73 Queen St, Edinburgh EH2 4NS
Telephone	031 225 8525
Contact	Above address

1044

Originator	WOOD MACKENZIE & CO
Title	FOCUS ON BREWERS AND DISTILLERS, annual
Coverage	Company data and general figures on the industry including beer production, whisky market, duties on wines and soft drinks consumption.
Contents & Origin of Statistics	Tables per issue: 38.
Response	1984
Availability	Mainly clients but available to others by negotiation
Cost	By negotiation
Address	Erskine House, 68-73 Queen St, Edinburgh EH2 4NS
Telephone	031 225 8525
Contact	Above address

1045

Originator	WOOD MACKENZIE & CO
Title	FOCUS ON FOOD MANUFACTURING, monthly
Coverage	Appendix contains data on biscuit deliveries by type, despatches of chocolate confectionery and sugar confectionery, household food expenditure and food manufacturing production and prices. Appendix also contains a company information section.
Contents & Origin of Statistics	Tables per issue: 5. Unstated 100%
Response	1984
Availability	Mainly clients but available to others by negotiation
Cost	By negotiation
Address	Erskine House, 68-73 Queen St, Edinburgh EH2 4NS
Telephone	031 225 8525
Contact	Above address

1046

Originator	WOOD MACKENZIE & CO
Title	FOCUS ON LEISURE, monthly
Coverage	Mainly company information on the sector but also includes general data on the leisure sector, e.g. cinema admissions and receipts, retail sales of leisure products, room occupancy trends, TV ratings.
Contents & Origin of Statistics	Tables per issue: 26.
Response	1984
Availability	Mainly clients but available to others by negotiation
Cost	By negotiation
Address	Erskine House, 68-73 Queen St, Edinburgh EH2 4NS
Telephone	031 225 8525
Contact	Above address

1047

Originator	WOOD MACKENZIE & CO
Title	NORTH SEA SERVICE, monthly
Coverage	Regular reports with figures on reserves, cash flow, pricing and supply and production etc.
Contents & Origin of Statistics	Tables per issue: Own research 90%, Non official statistics + government statistics 10%. Supporting text 60%
Response	1984
Availability	General
Cost	£1,150
Address	Erskine House, 68-73 Queen St, Edinburgh EH2 4NS
Telephone	031 225 8525
Contact	T.D. Morgan

1048

Originator	WOOD MACKENZIE & CO
Title	UK WINE AND SPIRITS INDUSTRY, monthly. March 1983-
Coverage	Financial and market data on the industry.
Response	1984
Availability	General
Cost	£650
Address	Erskine House, 68-73 Queen St, Edinburgh EH2 4NS

Telephone	031 225 8525
Contact	Tony Mackintosh

1049

Originator	WOOL INDUSTRY BUREAU OF STATISTICS

Title	MONTHLY BULLETIN OF STATISTICS, monthly
Coverage	UK wool textile production, deliveries, consumption, and stock. Also data on machinery and personnel.
Contents & Origin of Statistics	Tables per issue: 15. Unstated 100%
Currency	1 month
Response	1984
Availability	General
Cost	£28 (Free to Members)
Address	60 Toller Lane, Bradford BD8 9BZ
Telephone	0274 491241
Contact	M.A. Smith

1050

Originator	WOOL INDUSTRY BUREAU OF STATISTICS

Title	QUARTERLY REVIEW OF UK TRADE STATISTICS, quarterly
Coverage	UK wool textile imports and exports by country and region.
Contents & Origin of Statistics	Tables per issue: 50-60. Government statistics 100%
Currency	1 month
Response	1984
Availability	General
Cost	£6 (Free to Members)
Address	60 Toller Lane, Bradford BD8 9BZ
Telephone	0274 491241
Contact	M.A. Smith

1051

Originator	WOOLWICH EQUITABLE BUILDING SOCIETY

Title	WOOLWICH REVIEW, 3-4 times a year. 1981-
Coverage	House price guide by age and type of property and by area.

Contents & Origin of Statistics	Tables per issue: 1. Own research 100%. Supporting text 75%

Currency	2 months
Response	1984
Availability	General
Cost	Free
Address	Equitable House, Woolwich, London SE18 6AB
Telephone	01 854 2400
Contact	S. Gowans, Public Relations

1052

Originator	WREKIN DISTRICT COUNCIL
Title	WARD POPULATION PROFILES, annual. 1982-
Coverage	Population, household and social statistics.
Contents & Origin of Statistics	Tables per issue: 136. Own research 100%.
Currency	1 year
Response	1984
Availability	General
Address	PO Box 213, Malinslee House, Telford TF3 4LD
Telephone	0952 52267
Contact	Les Worrall, Policy Unit

1053

Originator	WREN, JONATHAN AND CO LTD
Title	GUIDE TO CURRENT SALARIES IN BANKING, bi-annual. 1978-
Coverage	Average salary figures, based on London salaries, for 140 job titles in banking at all levels. For each job title, 3 types of salary information are given - applicants' salaries, vacancy salaries registered by companies and salaries on appointment.
Contents & Origin of Statistics	Tables per issue: 140. Own research 100%.
Currency	6 months
Response	1984
Availability	Financial corporates
Cost	£100 + VAT
Address	170 Bishopgate, London EC2M 4LX

Telephone	01 623 1266 ; Telex: 8954673
Contact	Mr R.J. Meredith, Consultant

1054

Originator	WYATT COMPANY (UK) LTD
Title	SURVEY OF POOLED PENSION FUNDS, quarterly
Coverage	Investment performance of tax-exempt unitised funds restricted to UK pension funds.
Contents & Origin of Statistics	Tables per issue: Own research 100%
Response	1983
Availability	General
Cost	£300
Address	30 Queen Anne's Gate, London SW1H 9AW
Telephone	01 222 8033
Contact	Above address

1055

Originator	WYMAN-HARRIS RESEARCH LTD
Title	LICENSED TRADE MONITOR, quarterly. 1972-
Coverage	Product sales, brand shares, prices and distribution in GB public houses and registered clubs. In addition, demographic, round buying, mixing and ordering terminology data. Effect of outlet characteristics, for example size, catering facilities, day/time and traffic.
Contents & Origin of Statistics	Tables per issue: 100. Own research 100%.
Comments	Available in machine-readable formats.
Currency	3 weeks
Response	1984
Availability	General
Cost	From £25000
Address	8 Lansdown Place, Cheltenham, Glos GL50 2HU
Telephone	0242 519371
Contact	C.J. Nutt, Marketing Director

1056

Originator	WYMAN-HARRIS RESEARCH LTD
Title	SURVEY OF REGULAR DRINKERS, quarterly. 1983-

Coverage	Comprehensive behavioural data regarding alcoholic drink consumption. Includes media volumetrics.
Contents & Origin of Statistics	Tables per issue: 100. Own research 100%.
Comments	Aims to achieve 95% coverage. Available in machine-readable formats.
Currency	5 weeks
Response	1984
Availability	General
Cost	from £13000
Address	8 Lansdown Place, Cheltenham, Glos GL50 2HU
Telephone	0242 519371
Contact	C.J. Nutt, Marketing Director

1057

Originator	YORKSHIRE WATER AUTHORITY
Title	SUMMARY OF STATISTICS, annual. 1977-
Coverage	General statistics on the Authority, including water supply, sewage disposal, pollution, fishing licences etc.
Contents & Origin of Statistics	Tables per issue: 25pgs. Own research 100%.
Comments	Available to researchers at the Authority's library.
Currency	Varies
Response	1984
Availability	Internal
Cost	Free
Address	67 Albion St, Leeds LS1 5AA
Telephone	0532 448201
Contact	Paul Foxcroft, Librarian

1058

Originator	ZINC DEVELOPMENT ASSOCIATION
Title	MARKETS FOR ZINC DIE CASTINGS IN THE UNITED KINGDOM IN 19--, annual. 1973-
Coverage	Data on the end-uses of die castings, and prices, plus a commentary on the industry structure and general consumption of die castings. Historical figures are also given for the last few years.
Contents & Origin of Statistics	Tables per issue: 15. Own research 100%. Supporting text 40%

Comments	Association estimate that the figures are based on a survey covering 90% of the consumption of die castings.
Currency	Latest year
Response	1984
Availability	Primarily members but older reports available generally on specific request.
Cost	Free
Address	34 Berkeley Square, London W1X 6AJ
Telephone	01 499 6636; Telex: 261286
Contact	F.C. Porter

1059

Originator	ZINC DEVELOPMENT ASSOCIATION
Title	TRENDS IN GENERAL GALVANIZED PRODUCTS IN THE UNITED KINGDOM 19-- TO 19--, annual. 1974-
Coverage	Data on the production of galvanized steel and end-use markets for galvanized steel products. Historical figures for the last few years given in most tables.
Contents & Origin of Statistics	Tables per issue: 17. Own research 100%. Supporting text 35%.
Currency	Latest year
Response	1984
Availability	Primarily members but older reports available generally on specific request.
Cost	Free
Address	34 Berkeley Square, London W1X 6AJ
Telephone	01 499 6636; Telex: 261286
Contact	F.C. Porter

Part II

Index

Note

Indexing terms such as 'Agriculture – Specific crops', 'Wages and Salaries – Specific sectors', 'Motor Vehicles – Specific types', 'Marketing – Local areas', etc, bring together all the sources that relate to specific products, sectors, areas, etc. To trace sources on a particular product, sector or local area, however, please look for that product, sector or local area by name in the index.